THE COMPLETE BOOK ON CHILDBIRTH

THE COMPLETE BOOK ON

Childbirth

by DEBRA EVANS

Tyndale House Publishers, Inc.
Wheaton, Illinois

All Scripture references are taken from the *Holy Bible,
New International Version,* unless otherwise noted.
Library of Congress Catalog Card Number 85-51568
ISBN 0-8423-0407-X
95 94 93 92 91 90
 9 8 7 6 5 4 3 2

In loving memory of Pastor Theodore Mosies, the "little Dutchman" who was a spiritual giant to those who knew him, for teaching me to put my trust in the Lord, no matter what the circumstances.

"Not by might nor by power, but by my spirit," says the Lord *Almighty.* ZECHARIAH 4:6

CONTENTS

Foreword	9
Preface	11
Acknowledgments	13
Introduction	15

ONE
Childbirth from the Beginning of Time — 17

TWO
Childbirth Today — 21

THREE
God's Design for Childbirth — 29

FOUR
Preparing Your Inner Self — 37

FIVE
Preparing Your Life-style — 43

SIX
Preparing Your Body — 53

SEVEN
Planning Your Baby's Birth Day — 63

EIGHT
Learning to Labor Together — 71

NINE
Coping with Pain in Labor — 77

TEN
Once Labor Begins: What to Expect and Do — 99

ELEVEN
God Works for Good in All Things — 121

TWELVE
Preparing for a Cesarean Birth — 129

THIRTEEN
A Baby Learns about Love — 137

FOURTEEN
Feeding Your Baby — 143

FIFTEEN
*The Fifth Stage of Labor: A Word to Fathers
and Labor Companions* — 163

SIXTEEN
Sharing the Same Love   167

APPENDIX A
Family Nutrition Guide   171

APPENDIX B
Cardiovascular Fitness   181

APPENDIX C
Summary of Obstetric Procedures and
Medications   187

APPENDIX D
What to Ask, Take, and Know   197

APPENDIX E
Scripture References   201

Bibliography   203
Recommended Reading   207
Glossary   209
Endnotes   213
Index   215

FOREWORD

*I*n this book, Debra Evans, educator and mother of four, has worked diligently to consolidate in a clear and personal manner what she has learned about childbirth. I feel that she has created a balance between the biblical perspectives on childbearing and the scientific techniques. Her aim is to help pregnant women, as well as those close to them, to experience childbirth with joy and dignity.

She exposes the reader to choices that must be made, not only in the who, wheres, and hows of delivery, but also in the adjustments that must be made as new parents and friends of the newly born. She explains the "babymoon," when rest and patience are essential, and she elaborates on the pros and cons of breast-feeding and bottle-feeding as well as the importance of nurturing.

Not only does Evans help the reader through the stages of a "normal" birth, but she also thoroughly describes cesarean birth, a technique too frequently used and therefore not to be ignored. She deals professionally with what to expect during a cesarean birth and covers other possible complications to birth and the remedial steps.

Debra Evans has succeeded both from a practical perspective and a deeply Christian point of view to give a preparation for childbirth that is comforting and realistic. May her book, through its clear presentation, help many to know that bringing new life into the world can be one of the most rewarding experiences of our lives.

—Ingrid Trobisch

PREFACE

About This Man Jesus

Either he was a raving lunatic of an unusually abominable type, or else he was, and is, precisely what he said. If the records make the first hypothesis unacceptable, you must submit to the second. And if you do that, all else that is claimed by Christians becomes credible— that this Man, having been killed, was yet alive, and that this death, in some manner incomprehensible to human thought, has effected a real change in our relations to One "awful" and "righteous" Lord, and a change in our favor. C.S. LEWIS, *The Problem of Pain*

*T*his book is based on the belief that Jesus was, in fact, who he said he was when he walked among us nearly two thousand years ago. The life of Jesus Christ has had a greater impact on world history than the life of any other man. The prophet Isaiah foresaw the coming of the Son of God in the eighth century before his birth. This is what he said, in Isaiah 53, about the "Servant of the Lord" who was to come:

Who has believed our message and to whom has the arm of the Lord been revealed? He grew up before him like a tender shoot, and like a root out of dry ground. He had no beauty or majesty to attract us to him, nothing in his appearance that we should desire him. He was despised and rejected by men, a man of sorrows, and familiar with suffering. Like one from whom men hide their faces he was despised, and we esteemed him not.

Surely he took up our infirmities and carried our sorrows, yet we considered him stricken by God, smitten by him, and afflicted. But he was pierced for our transgressions, he was crushed for

our iniquities; the punishment that brought us peace was upon him, and by his wounds we are healed. We all, like sheep, have gone astray, each of us has turned to his own way; and the Lord has laid on him the iniquity of us all.

He was oppressed and afflicted, yet he did not open his mouth; he was led like a lamb to the slaughter, and as a sheep before her shearers is silent, so he did not open his mouth. By oppression and judgment, he was taken away. And who can speak of his descendants? For he was cut off from the land of the living; for the transgression of my people he was stricken. He was assigned a grave with the wicked, and with the rich in his death, though he had done no violence, nor was any deceit in his mouth.

Yet it was the Lord's will to crush him and cause him to suffer, and though the Lord makes his life a guilt offering, he will see his offspring and prolong his days, and the will of the Lord will prosper in his hand. After the suffering of his soul, he will see the light of life and be satisfied; by his knowledge my righteous servant will justify many, and he will bear their iniquities. Therefore I will give him a portion among the great, and he will divide the spoils with the strong, because he poured out his life unto death, and was numbered with the transgressors. For he bore the sin of many, and made intercession for the transgressors.

Parents who prepare to give birth with the Lord's help find that childbearing provides them with an opportunity to rely more completely on their heavenly Father. As their trust in him grows, their fears subside and they discover the Lord's peace, which "transcends all understanding" (Philippians 4:7). Through God's Word, the forgiveness in Christ, and the comfort of the Holy Spirit, Christians learn that they do not travel alone; Jesus lives today in each of us.

Following Jesus makes a tremendous impact on the way we conduct our lives. We find, as believers in Christ over the centuries have found, that the call of our Savior and King is a radical one, pointing us to Christ's kingdom first; to love not the world, but to love our neighbor as we love our own selves.

If you do not know this man Jesus, or have left his calling behind, this book may seem strange and "religious." If you wish to know Christ better, and glorify him in all you do and are, you will find that becoming parents allows you to partake in a miracle beyond description: the joy of sharing in the unfolding of God's creation. Parenthood also will require you to trust the Lord in new and challenging areas.

Jesus died to reconcile all to God, so that we all may receive God's blessings. His call is the same today as it was when he spoke to those fishermen back in Galilee: "Follow me."

This is really what this book is all about.

ACKNOWLEDGMENTS

*T*hough I cannot thank them individually, I am indebted to the many expectant parents I have worked with over the past twelve years. Their sincere questioning, search for quality in childbirth education, and desire to find out what birth is *really* like have caused me to grow in my own understanding of human life.

Martha Hutchens and Cathy Newhouse were instrumental in assisting me with the original Parents Preparing in Christ program. Phyl Kenney, R.N., has been a joy to work with due to her continuing support through St. Elizabeth's Hospital.

Deb Klopping, Trina Sollars, and Cinda Childers provided typing skills and demonstrated how one part of the body of Christ can serve another that is lacking in practical ways. (In this case, you were the fingers!)

My friend and pastor, Dave Argue, gave opinions regarding my use of Scripture—and also concerning my grammar! His smile, and his wife Rogene's sparkling eyes, nourished my soul.

Dr. Sam Fuenning, M.D., director of Athletic Medicine at the University of Nebraska, conveyed the affirming power of Christ's love through his example and encouragement.

Dr. Roger Bruce, M.D., family physician and pioneer in his practice of Christ-centered medicine, read and critiqued the manuscript with special attention to the medical and emotional aspects of childbearing. Meg Bruce, R.P.T., provided additional help as she reviewed many chapters along with her husband.

Carol Newsom provided me with vital prayer support. Members of my small group—Janet and Fred Smith, Rich and Susie Newcomer, Mick and Cheryl Martin, Scott and Di Keller, and Tom Eggert—supported me through many weeks of Wednesday night updates. Sally Herman, Barb O'Malley, Barb Woodhead, and Lori Marcuson were always willing to provide well-timed expressions of encouragement.

Dr. Wendell Hawley and Lucille Leonard, my initial contacts at Tyndale House, and Karen Ball, my editor (who polished the manuscript and made all the pieces fit together in the process), all have portrayed a warm, personal, and efficient professionalism.

Sue Beckwith, my sister-in-law, inspired me with her fit life-style, and Betty Gorman, my mother-in-law, courageously battled leukemia throughout the months I approached the issue of pain theoretically. You are both very dear to me.

Mom and Dad . . . I'm glad you used Lamaze first when you had Nancy in '63, so that I could go a step further when my turn came. Kerry—Jesus loves you!

Finally, there are five people who truly understand the daily costs of the writing of this book: my daughters, Joanna and Katherine; my sons, David and Jonathan; and my "hub," Dave. Thank you, family, for the hot tea, back rubs, mopped floors, and dinners at Amigo's. Your gifts allowed me to use a few of my own when it would have been easier for all of us to save our talents rather than invest them (Matthew 25:14-30). How blessed I am to be a member of such a fine family!

To all of these dear brothers and sisters, I extend my deepest gratitude. Through you all I gained what I lacked on my own: the confidence to see this project through to its completion.

INTRODUCTION

"He tends his flock like a shepherd: He gathers the lambs in his arms and carries them close to his heart; he gently leads those that have young." ISAIAH 40:11

*T*his beautiful word picture was painted by God to reassure us of his never-ending love, to describe how he personally cares for those who draw near to him for help. During the childbearing process, you as expectant parents are faced with many decisions, questions, challenges, and issues. It is easy to feel anxious or fearful concerning the outcome of your pregnancy; to wonder about the health of your baby, how the labor will go, and what impact an infant will have on your lives. The transition from being a couple to becoming parents is both exciting and demanding, perhaps more so than any other change you will face. Yet the Lord reminds us that he carries our young close to his heart, and will lead us through this time gently.

This book was written to encourage you to look to the Lord and his Word, increasing your confidence in his ability to protect and lead you. When you become more familiar with God's design for childbearing, it becomes easier to understand the special needs of pregnancy and the stress of childbirth. If you are pregnant or planning to have a baby, put your trust in the Lord; he will strengthen and uphold you.

As you read through these pages, glorify God for the new life that he has caused to grow within your body. Also, realize that what this book offers you is a biblical perspective of childbirth in addition to practical advice for dealing with the physical and emotional changes of childbearing. You will learn a method of childbirth preparation that is both comforting and realistic.
In his love,

Debra Evans

Debra Evans

Praise be to the God and Father of our Lord, Jesus Christ, the Father of compassion and the God of all comfort, who comforts us in all our troubles, so that we can comfort those in any trouble with the comfort we ourselves have received from God (2 Corinthians 1:3, 4).

CHAPTER ONE
Childbirth from the Beginning of Time

The powerful images of creation, life, pain, work, and birth presented in the first three chapters of Genesis are familiar to Christians everywhere. Although many different interpretations exist about the impact of these events, I feel that it is useful to reflect upon them.

I would like to share with you a few ideas that have come from my personal experience as a Christian wife and mother, and as a childbirth educator who has taught thousands of expectant parents and learned a great deal from them.

The first passages of Genesis explain that when man and woman were created, the Lord desired them to "be fruitful and increase in number; fill the earth and subdue it" (Genesis 1:28). The Creator of the first two human beings created them in a much different way than babies are conceived and birthed today; the man was formed out of the ground, and the woman was brought forth out of the flesh and bone of man's side (Genesis 3:19; 2:22). They were born fully grown and ready to be joined together.

At some later point, the crafty serpent asked the woman if the Lord really had commanded her not to eat from any tree in the garden. ("Crafty" is a good description of the serpent, who knew that the woman had not yet been created when the Lord had spoken to the man about which fruit was forbidden!) This serpent then convinced the woman to partake of the fruit that "was good for food and pleasing to the eye, and also desirable for gaining wisdom" (Genesis 3:6).

In what appears to be just a brief moment of history, the future of the human race was drastically altered. When the man disobeyed his God-given orders "the eyes of both of them were opened" to the realization of their nakedness. It is in this way, we are told by God's Word, that sin entered the world: through the deception of one woman and the disobedience of one man.

What has this to do with childbirth in our time? The impact of the Fall upon the process of childbearing was significant and will continue to be so until the Lord returns. There is no way to know what the Lord had in mind as a design for human reproduction before the Fall, but we are explicitly told that the actions of the serpent, the woman, and the man had consequences that affected all of their descendants (Genesis 3:14-19).

Yet, if we continue to read through the Bible, we are comforted repeatedly by the Lord's compassion for his people. Psalm 145:13 reminds us that "the Lord is faithful to all his promises and loving toward all he has made." His greatest gift of love to us was Jesus, through whom the Lord grants us everlasting life and restores sinners to eternal fellowship with himself. It is a *loving* Lord who decided what the consequences of the Fall would be.

God understood what the effects of sin would be upon the lives of Adam and Eve when they disobeyed him, but he did not forsake them. In determining the consequences of their transgression, the Bible tells us that the Lord chose to make these activities physically stressful. I believe that God did not arbitrarily mete out punishment in anger, but that he acted in accordance with his divine character. If we believe in God's love for his creation, we can view his response to Adam and Eve as one motivated by love and a desire to cause his children to continue to look to him for protection and sustenance after they had left the Garden of Eden.

In the fourth chapter of Genesis, the effect of childbirth on Eve shows, perhaps, what the Lord had hoped for: "Adam lay with his wife Eve, and she conceived and gave birth to Cain. She said, 'With the help of the Lord, I have brought forth a man'" (Genesis 4:1). It appears that giving birth through painful toil turned Eve toward the Lord for help, and it was to him that she gave thanks for the safe delivery of her son.

As women giving birth today, we should acknowledge the biblical basis of labor pain and its role in drawing us closer to the Lord. Painful toil can draw our eyes heavenward and cause us to admit that we are not "as gods," sufficient unto ourselves and able to exert complete control over our lives. In James 4:8, 10 we are given the promise that if we draw near to God, he will draw near to us; that if we humble ourselves before him, he will lift us up. We can openly declare our shortcomings and sin before the Lord, for he has been with us from the beginning and has promised that he will never forsake us.

As Christians we are able to approach our Creator with assurance and confidence. Christ's sacrifice on Calvary opened up a way to defeat sin and death once and for all. We cannot alter Adam's and Eve's actions, but we can walk in the newness of life God gives through Jesus Christ.

The childbirth preparation method presented in this book is unique because it incorporates into its curriculum a biblical and moral view that labor pain is not evil. This book will provide you with information that will help you eliminate unnecessary sources of discomfort that result from not understanding how your body functions during labor. It will also show you how it is possible to bear the amount of pain experienced during childbirth if you cooperate with the process of labor, rather than fighting it, and draw close to the Lord in prayer.

PRAYER AND SCRIPTURE

Since this book is based on a Christian world view, it contains encouraging passages from Scripture that I hope you can adapt into your own walk with the Lord. However, this is not meant to be a substitute for Bible study. Rather, it is meant to *stimulate* a meaningful, independent study of God's Word.

The value of personal, family, and corporate prayer is emphasized. In classes, participants and I frequently read from the Psalms during relaxation practices and labor rehearsals. My goal in both my teaching and in my writing is to help motivate and challenge other believers to look to the Lord through the use of prayer, fellowship, and Bible study. This way, they can gain everything they need to be enriched by this major life event.

ACKNOWLEDGING GOD AS CREATOR

Describing the anatomy and physiology of childbirth by saying, "Nature intends . . ." or "The organism determines . . ." or in similar terms seems to me to label the process of childbearing a biological accident or evolutionary feat. In our program, credit is given where credit is due. We recognize the Lord as our Maker, the One who designed the entire universe and created everything in it! Knowing that God is behind everything is tremendously reassuring and comforting.

ACKNOWLEDGING GOD AS SOVEREIGN

Another aspect of this method is the belief that our Lord is sovereign. In basing our concept of human dignity on the truth of holy Scripture, we know that every child conceived is valued by the Lord. The Christian view of human life places a high regard on the worth of all individuals, regardless of their age, sex, race, or ability.

The belief that our heavenly Father's love is unconditional also is incorporated into all aspects of this childbirth preparation program. We recognize the truths of such Scriptures as Psalm 139:15, 16 in which David remarks, "My frame was not hidden from you when I was made in the secret place. When I was woven together in the depths of the earth, your eyes saw my unformed body. All the days ordained for me were written in your book before one of them came to be," and Job 10:8: "Your hands shaped me and made me. Will you now turn and destroy me?"

Also, through years of studying, discovering, teaching, and living out the principles shared in this book, some practical helps for relief of emotional and physical pain have been developed. By combining the God-given resources of the Bible, the knowledge of the human body, and medical science, I have worked to create a balance between a biblical perspective on childbearing and on scientific techniques. As our Western culture has become increasingly influenced by Eastern philosophies and socialism, this balance has become even more important.

For many, the difference between preparing in Christ to give birth and preparing from a secular point of view has had quite a remarkable impact. I have seen expectant mothers give their fears to God, drawing strength from him to cope with the challenges they faced during their pregnancies, labors, and months afterward. Reluctant fathers-to-be have opened up in prayer on behalf of their wives and babies, assuming the responsibilities of protecting and providing for them.

These men and women, who have truly turned to God, have not come away empty. Every cup has been filled beyond measure. It is my hope that you, also, will find your lives enriched through these principles; that you will draw ever nearer to our almighty Father, through his Son, Jesus Christ.

"We wait in hope for the Lord; he is our help and our shield. In him our hearts rejoice, for we trust in his holy name. May your unfailing love rest upon us, O Lord, even as we put our hope in you" (Psalm 33:20-22).

CHAPTER TWO
Childbirth Today

"Do not conform any longer to the pattern of this world, but be transformed by the renewing of your mind. Then you will be able to test and approve what God's will is—his good, pleasing and perfect will." ROMANS 12:2

*T*he twentieth century has brought as many changes to childbirth practices as it has to all other aspects of life. Until the discovery of antiseptic techniques and anesthetics in the mid-1800s, childbearing was routinely accomplished without them, and infection was not uncommon. As physicians began to assume greater control over birth practices through childbirth technologies, deliveries took place with greater frequency in hospitals.[1] Medical intervention in the birth process became common practice in the United States, and women sought pain relief in greater numbers with each passing year.

Women expected modern medicine to bring about a higher number of safe deliveries with less pain, but these changes in birthing practices did not satisfy everyone. From the 1930s onward, people began to speak out against this trend toward the medicalization of childbirth, creating a movement that has become popularly accepted and which now encompasses many different views and organizations.

Today, expectant parents often find themselves placed in an awkward position between a physician who provides traditional obstetric care and a childbirth educator who introduces students to a world of controversy concerning traditional birth practices. Physicians and childbirth educators seek to enhance the childbearing experience of the couples they serve by providing professional services that are based upon their personal viewpoints. Yet, the proliferation of books, classes, theories, childbirth methods, and obstetric practices proves that we have yet to arrive at one "right" way of dealing with childbirth.

Thankfully, though, we are living at a time in history when mothers and babies have the greatest chance of surviving childbirth. In the midst of today's controversy in obstetrics, I believe it is possible to give birth with joy and dignity by looking to the Lord for direction in our lives. The number of choices available to us can be a blessing as we pray for discernment in deciding what is best in our own situation. In doing so, it is important to consider the philosophies upon which these methods are based and to think about how the theories behind them compare to biblical truth.

THE LAMAZE METHOD

The Lamaze method currently is the most popular method of preparation for childbirth, yet many are unaware of its origin. Fernand Lamaze, an ardent socialist, based the method named in his honor on techniques he learned while visiting clinics in Russia. Technically, Lamaze's method is called the "Psychoprophylactic method" (the name means "mind [psycho] in favor of [pro] prevention [phylaxis]") or PPM.

As the Communists took control of Russia following the Revolution, the government developed from Pavlov's studies the PPM as the solution to the age-old problem of childbirth pain.[2] In the thirties, a massive propaganda campaign was conducted to convince Russian women that they could deliver their babies painlessly by using this method.

Through this form of mind control, the propaganda stated, women could rid themselves of the effects of the Fall (viewed as an archaic religious doctrine) and the "curse" of childbirth pain.[3]

By the time Lamaze visited the Soviet Union, this program was in full swing. To his amazement, he saw that pain expression among laboring women in Russia was noticeably absent. Lamaze carried his discovery back to the socialist clinic where he worked in France and developed a program to teach women the method he had learned in Russia.

He emphatically believed that childbirth pain is created in women's minds through the influence of their socialization and culture. His intense training program involved using prenatal education to "correct" the notions his students had acquired while growing up. By replacing these ideas with information based on "scientific knowledge," Lamaze believed that childbirth pain could be erased completely.

Yet, pain expression and pain experience are two very different things.[4] With the repression of personal and religious freedom in the Soviet Union following the advent of communism, few women would have chosen to refute government propaganda or give birth in a way other than what the "experts" recommended. Medical bills were no longer a consideration, and the majority of women were probably very grateful to be receiving care. *I believe women felt labor pain while using PPM but chose not to express it.*

As with others who have studied human labor and birth in various cultures, Lamaze confused the lack of pain expression with a lack of pain experience. Current anthropological research suggests that one's culture defines what types of pain experiences are acceptable,[5,6] with different groups of people expressing pain in different ways. These studies also claim that labor pain seems to be universal among all peoples and that our former belief that more "primitive" women give birth painlessly is a myth.

By the late seventies, few Lamaze instructors were teaching the "pure Lamaze" method of childbirth because it proved to be unrealistic.[7] A diluted version of Lamaze's beliefs has been adopted over the years and Lamaze's book, *Painless Childbirth,* is no longer widely read or recommended to Lamaze class members.

When I trained to be a Lamaze instructor in 1973, I did not see the contradictions between this method and my Christian beliefs. Yet, as I began studying the subject of labor pain for academic reasons, a closer scrutiny of Lamaze's original statements revealed great discrepancies between his beliefs and my own. Many Christians have been involved as students or instructors of Lamaze theory over the years without being aware of its atheistic orientation and dismissal of biblical truth.

Lamaze's disciples originally believed that childbirth could be completely painless if the PPM was used. Recent research has denied this. Dr. Ronald Melzack conducted an important study in Montreal on the use of the Lamaze method and its effect on labor pain. In an article by Melzack published in the *Canadian Medical Association Journal* in 1981, he concluded that even after Lamaze training, labor is still painful.[8] What is especially significant about Melzack's study is that he is one of the most respected authorities on the subject of pain in the world. He is the developer, along with Patrick Wall, of the gate-control theory of pain,[9] which has revolutionized the field of pain research over the past fifteen years.

Lamaze instructors have realized for at least as long as I've been involved in childbirth education that what Melzack has stated is true. Very few Lamaze teachers inform participants that labor can be painless.

It is ironic that these classes are named after a man whose beliefs are no longer held by those who teach in his name. The reason for this may be that the name "Lamaze" is often synonymous with childbirth education. Even though Lamaze classes no longer teach much of Lamaze's own philosophy, his name alone sells the product. For Christians who participate in Lamaze classes, it may be helpful to understand this change while remembering that not all aspects of Lamaze's theory are compatible with a biblical view of childbirth.

ASPECTS OF LAMAZE'S THEORY IN CONFLICT WITH A BIBLICAL VIEW:

● The concept that only words and thoughts create labor pain.
● The belief that labor pain is nothing more than the product of the fear of childbirth and, consequently, is psychological rather than physical in origin.
● The view that this fear of childbirth originates in "ancient" religious teachings and that there is no truth in religious teachings concerning labor pain.

ASPECTS OF LAMAZE'S THEORY COMPATIBLE WITH A BIBLICAL VIEW:

● The desire to help women adapt to the process of childbearing.
● The value of noninvasive pain relief measures to decrease suffering during labor.
● The importance of understanding the physical events of childbirth.

THE DICK-READ METHOD

Another currently used method of childbirth was introduced by Grantly Dick-Read in his book *Childbirth without Fear,* published in 1942.[10] Dick-Read advocated a spiritualized view of childbirth that essentially states that a loving Creator could not have intended childbirth to be painful. Instead, he believed that true, natural childbirth allows a woman to joyfully participate in giving birth the way God intended.

About 10 percent of all labors are relatively painless and uncomplicated, taking place fairly quickly and with a minimum of physical effort on the mother's part. On the other hand, another 10 percent are unusually long, complicated, or difficult. This leaves about 80 percent that involve a moderate amount of pain at various times, depending on the different factors present.

For the 10 percent of the women who experience "easy" labors, childbirth is understandably perceived to be more enjoyable and more gratifying than for the remaining 90 percent. That's 1 in 10 women who may say afterward, "It was easy," or "I was only in labor a couple hours, then pushed a few times. I'd do it again tomorrow," or "I thought I had a mild case of the flu, but fortunately I decided to go to the hospital to be checked and had the baby twenty minutes later."

These women seem ideally suited to the childbearing function of their bodies. I sincerely doubt that their ease in childbirth has anything to do with their choice of method, or how well they applied their breathing and relaxation techniques. Instead, I would imagine that they have anatomical and physiological traits that allow them to go through labor and birth with a minimum of disturbance.

An "easy" birth is not necessarily a reflection of a close walk with the Lord. Some of the most fervently Christian women I know have had far less than ideal birth experiences. And longer or more complicated labors are not necessarily God's way of judging us for any wrongdoing we have done! *Childbirth pain is present to varying degrees in most labors and certainly is not the result of a lack of faith or the wrath of God.*

It may have been a woman belonging to the uncomplicated 10 percent that caused Dick-Read to wonder why labor is not always a gratifying experience. In response to his consideration of the matter, Dick-Read developed a theory that fear creates labor pain. He believed that in the absence of fear, pain experience could be substantially reduced or eliminated altogether.

Once again, I would like to point out that the source of labor pain is *not* only fear, but, instead, can be traced to the Fall. Dick-Read mistakenly believed that in cultures around the world in which women are not taught to fear childbirth, labor pain is not prevalent. In fact, the mental picture held by many of us of the Third World women who labor in the fields, squat to have the baby, and then return to work, is a simplistic and naive estimation of childbearing behavior.

Brigitte Jordan described pain in her book *Birth in Four Cultures* as an expected part of the childbirth process. Maintaining the belief that nowhere in the world is birth purely a "natural" event, Jordan builds a convincing argument that birth practices are culturally produced, created by groups of people according to the values and beliefs shared by their tribe or group or community.[11] To believe that birth takes place somewhere in the world without pain and free of cultural expectations is to believe in a fantasy about how "less civilized" humans act during childbirth.

Proponents of Dick-Read's method teach that labor pain can only be the result of physical, functional, emotional, or medical interferences in the natural process of human labor and birth.[12] Labor pain is viewed as an abnormality or ab-erration of childbirth—an indication that something is wrong. However, Dick-Read instructors do not clearly say what percentage of all labors are free of any abnormalities. If only the minority of all women experience little or no labor pain, they are the exception instead of the norm!

It is inaccurate and irresponsible to tell a woman that pain in childbirth is due only to fear, or because of an abnormality. Rather, the reverse is true: It is pain that creates fear. Fear may then magnify painful sensations and/or stimulate adrenaline secretion.

ASPECTS OF DICK-READ'S THEORY IN CONFLICT WITH A BIBLICAL VIEW:

- The belief that the experience of pain is incongruent with a loving Creator's design for childbirth.
- The concept that fear creates bodily tension which produces rather than intensifies labor pain.
- The idea that labor pain can be the product of only abnormal physical, functional, and/or emotional processes, or technical intervention in labor.
- The view that pain in childbirth is an evil that mars this experience.

ASPECTS OF DICK-READ'S THEORY COMPATIBLE WITH A BIBLICAL VIEW:

- The belief that God is motivated by love.
- The theory that fear and tension can interfere with the process of labor.
- The importance of physical fitness through prenatal exercise.
- The value of learning how to relax during childbirth.

THE BRADLEY METHOD

While the methods of Robert Bradley (the initiator of husband-coached childbirth) are based on the same theories as the Lamaze and Dick-Read methods, they are animalistic rather than atheistic or naturalistic.[13] Bradley suggests that animals such as sheep do not seem to experience pain during normal labors because they instinctively "know" how to cope with the childbearing process. He concludes from this that if human females would imitate sheep, they, too, would find labor relatively painless.

What Bradley fails to acknowledge is that the human mind makes the experience of pain something quite different than that of animals. We assign meanings and comparative significance to the sensations we feel. We are able to store our own history of painful experiences in our minds, and we can remember what we've been told about pain.[14] (See diagram on page 27.)

We have the capacity to worry about future events and imagine all sorts of outcomes to situations. We are capable of an almost unbelievable range of emotions and feeling expressions: embarrassment, pride, guilt, courage, crying, laughing, moaning, speaking, yelling, whispering, smiling, and grimacing. For a woman in labor, these are just a few of the possible modes of expression. While behavioral psychologists would disagree, I believe free will differentiates our species from other species more than any other trait.

Just as we wouldn't wish to imitate other aspects of animal sexuality (no birth control, poor mate selection, etc.) it makes little sense to compare human labor and birth too closely with that of the animals. This would deny that we are created in the image of God, that the value of human life differs from that of animal life or that the Fall affected us in specific ways.

ASPECTS OF BRADLEY'S METHOD IN CONFLICT WITH A BIBLICAL VIEW:
- The belief that human pain experience can be exactly equated with the pain experience of animals.
- The view that labor pain is an unnatural phenomenon.
- The denial of the many differences between humans and animals.

ASPECTS OF BRADLEY'S METHOD COMPATIBLE WITH A BIBLICAL VIEW:
- The concept that husbands and wives benefit from going through labor together. (See chapters 8 and 9.)
- The idea that husbands are capable of providing help and direction for their wives during pregnancy and childbirth.
- The emphasis placed upon the importance of allowing the body to function as it should in labor.
- The promotion of relaxation as a means to allow the body to adapt to the birth process.

NEW AGE METHODS OF CHILDBIRTH

Though the methods of Lamaze, Dick-Read, and Bradley all contain fallacies of their own, a more subtle trend in childbirth is developing, which has introduced perspectives that are blatantly anti-Christian.

Within our Western world a new movement is gaining momentum. Marilyn Ferguson has named this movement "The Aquarian Conspiracy" in her book of the same title.[15] Also called the New Age Movement, this trend incorporates people from all professions and backgrounds in a united effort to "bring about world peace and a heightened spirituality" that is based on an eclectic blend of Eastern religions. Within this movement, the Judeo-Christian concepts of sin and atonement are completely replaced by a philosophy of self-perfection. While several books have been written about the possible implications of this movement upon Christianity as a whole, its specific impact upon methods of childbirth may be summarized briefly.

Before I was born again in 1971, I explored Hinduism and Yoga, practicing dietary restrictions as well as breathing, relaxation, and meditation techniques. What especially appealed to me about Eastern mysticism was its lack of condemnation of sinners and the inclusion of evil into good. I was taught that the ultimate state that the Hindu or Buddhist strives to obtain through cycles of life and death, taking place during repeated "reincarnations," is one of "Nirvana," or nothingness. This nihilistic view, as I found out after becoming a Christian, contradicts the biblical concept of heaven and hell and the sacredness of each human life before the Lord.[16]

Because of my personal background, I am particularly sensitive to the childbirth books that have been appearing in the popular market that are saturated with Eastern mysticism in its various guises. Paul's words in Colossians 2:8 seem especially applicable to the kind of thinking represented in these books:

See to it that no one takes you captive through hollow and deceptive philosophy, which depends on human tradition and the basic principles of this world rather than on Christ.

Frederic Leboyer's *Birth without Violence,* Claudia Panuthos's *Transformation through Birth,* Elizabeth Noble's *Childbirth with Insight,* Ina May Gaskin's *Spiritual Midwifery,* and *Birth* by Catherine Milinaire, are just a few of the books that include mystical viewpoints. The information they present is not spiritually neutral. Rather, it can bring occult influence to bear on Christians who accept their messages.

Certain words and phrases have become a part of the language of those influenced by Eastern mysticism. (See figure 1.) The use of these words may serve to alert Christians of the philosophy behind the advocate and enable them to listen more carefully to the world view of a particular author or speaker.

Christians cannot be united to nonbelievers however much it may appeal to them to have world peace and harmony among all peoples.[17] Jesus tells us in Matthew 16:24 and 10:34 to "love not the world," and that he came not to bring peace, but a sword that would separate his followers from those "of the world." Just as light cannot have fellowship with darkness, so we as Christians should be sensitive to any influence exerted upon us that would confuse biblical truths with current self-oriented trends.

In Psalm 131, David's words direct us to the only true source of strength and guidance: "My heart is not proud, O Lord, my eyes are not haughty; I do not concern myself with great matters or things too wonderful for me. But I have stilled and quieted my soul; like a weaned child with its mother, like a weaned child is my soul within me. O Israel, put your hope in the Lord both now and forevermore."

There are some things we must trust to God alone. Some spiritual knowledge is beyond our comprehension.[18] We must recognize God as our portion and provider, and realize that self-help and self-perfection techniques based on Eastern mysticism are incompatible with the calling of Christ. In John 12:24, 25, Christ bids us to die to ourselves, that we might live more fully in him. Salvation comes only through the atoning sacrifice of Christ on Calvary; it cannot be earned. This cannot be more clear than as stated by Christ himself in John 14:6, "'I am the way and the truth and the life. No one comes to the Father except through me.'"

SUMMARY

When a method of childbirth denies labor pain, labeling it people-created or evil, that method also denies the truth of Scripture. The effects of the Lord's judicious wisdom as to the consequences of the Fall are carried in our bodies, and in nature. They serve as a reminder for us to seek God's help and protection, especially during the experience of childbirth.

Some may consider this cruel, yet Jesus' death on the cross doesn't make much sense either, according to worldly logic. The first chapter of Paul's letter to the church at Corinth reassures us that "the message of the cross is foolishness to those who are perishing" (1 Corinthians 1:18), and "the foolishness of God is wiser than man's wisdom, and the weakness of God is stronger than man's strength" (1:25).

Even more, we are told, "But God chose the foolish things of the world to shame the wise; God chose the weak things of the world to shame the strong. He chose the lowly things of this world and the despised things—and the things that are not—to nullify the things that are, so that no one may boast before him. It is because of him that you are in Christ Jesus, who has become for us wisdom from God—that is, our righteousness, holiness and redemption. Therefore, as it is written: 'Let him who boasts boast in the Lord'" (1 Corinthians 1:27-31).

It is indeed the God of Abraham, Isaac, and Jacob who is able to lift us up. Parents who are preparing in Christ to give birth know that it is the Lord's strength, not their own, that enables them to face childbearing with peace and joy.

Doctors Lamaze, Dick-Read, and Bradley have each contributed to our knowledge of childbirth. They have contributed greatly to returning childbirth to the family and counteracting the impact of routine hospitalization upon those at the center of the childbearing experience: the mother, the father, their infant, and other family members. Yet, none of their theories has ever been sufficiently proven through research, and the issue of labor pain remains.

We are living at a time when we can give birth in relative safety and select the conditions under which we will have our babies. Through prudent planning and preparation for childbirth from a biblical view of creation, bringing new life into the world can be one of the most rewarding experiences of our lives, drawing us even closer to the Lord as we look to him to lead us. How very blessed we are!

DIAGRAM OF HUMAN PAIN EXPERIENCE

Diagram 2.1

adapted from H. K. Beecher

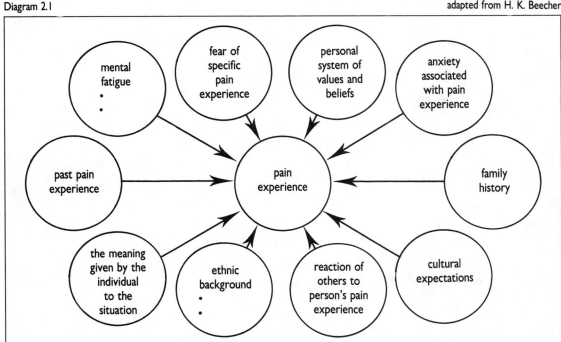

NEW AGE TERMINOLOGY
Figure 1

altered states of
consciousness
aquarian age
astral planes
at-one-ment (three
words as opposed
to atonement)
auras
autogenic (self-
source) training
bioenergetics
birth traumas or
arias/chants
body imaging

centering
christed hands
cosmic system
creative energy
creative spirituality
guided imagery
haptonomic therapy
human potential
movement
inner voice
life force
limbic system
mind power
networking

out of body
experience
primal pain
psychology of being
re-birthing
reflexology
right/left brain
spirit breathing
telepathy/telepathic
transcendence
transformation
through birth
universal energy/mind
visualization

CHAPTER THREE
God's Design for Childbirth

"They will not toil in vain or bear children doomed to misfortune; for they will be a people blessed by the Lord." ISAIAH 65:23

*G*iving birth is truly a labor of love! As your body works to bring forth new life, you can draw close to the Lord and gain strength. Every step of the way, he will accompany you and your child through the hours and minutes of labor. In the safety of his gaze you will attend to your body and allow it to press your baby out of your womb and into the world.

The physical events of late pregnancy are designed to ready your body for birth. Although medical science has learned many things about the process of human labor and birth, it still is not known what actually initiates labor. But with each new discovery, the amazing design of the human reproductive system becomes more apparent. Imbalances rarely occur; the majority of all births require little, if any, intervention.

It is important to keep in mind that your pregnancy is not a disease or an illness, but rather a physiological state that often is wonderfully "normal!" In spite of how complicated this entire process seems to us, the Lord's design is not geared for frequent technical complications. As a functioning model of balanced activity, our bodies are capable of accomplishing amazing tasks, especially if we take care of ourselves wisely.

OUR BODIES ARE DESIGNED TO WORK

One of the newest sports to hit the public eye is called the "triathlon." I recently spent an hour watching this event on television, and could not believe my eyes: nearly one thousand men and women traveled all the way to Hawaii to compete in a race that required them to swim 2½ miles in the Pacific Ocean (that's two hundred lengths in an Olympic-sized pool), then run out of the water to change and cycle 112 miles on a bike, only to return back to the starting point, change again, and run a 26-mile marathon. Titled "The Ironman" championship, its challenge to all those competitors was to accomplish what seemed impossible. Yet, for well over seven hundred of those people, it *was* possible!

Can you imagine it? What a testimony to the strength and endurance of the human body! Yet, many women worry about their bodies giving birth to a baby, a function for which we were specifically designed! Both the triathlon and giving birth can be painful "toil," but when our goal is to serve God by pleasing him rather than seeking our own comfort, toil can become rewarding. And what a reward awaits us!

Being in labor is not unlike running a race. In response to changes in circulating hormone levels within the blood stream and substances secreted by the baby and the placenta, the muscles of the uterus (fundus) begin to contract and retract. Across the top of the womb lie three thick layers of muscle which press down upon the baby intermittently. Each contraction of these muscles moves the baby down against the opening of the uterus, called the cervix. During pregnancy, the cervix must remain closed to prevent an untimely birth.

When the time nears for your baby to be born, the cervical area will soften and become more elastic. As a result, when the muscles in the upper part of the uterus press down, the part of the baby lying closest to the cervix stretches it open. About 96 percent of the time it is the baby's head that presses down on the cervix and about 3 percent of the time the baby's buttocks lie at the opening to the uterus. If the presenting part is the head, it is termed a vertex presentation; if it is the baby's buttocks, it is said that the presentation is breech. It is possible to have the baby present shoulder, face, or forehead first, but these presentations make up a minority of all births. Most of the time, the crown of the baby's head finds its way to the cervix, opening the cervix much the same as when you pull a turtleneck sweater over your head.

Try to picture putting on a sweater. Its opening for your head is thickly knitted and not very large, though you know your head will be able to pass through. With both hands, you begin to pull it flat down over the top, but find that it is more difficult this way. You tilt your head forward, sliding your chin down onto your chest for additional leverage. Then, while pulling the sweater over the crown, your head presses through the neck of the sweater quite smoothly until it is almost all the way through. You discover that this last bit of stretching requires extra effort and a more determined tug. Finally, the sweater is over your head and you finish putting it on. The uterus works in much the same way as this during childbirth.

The Latin word for cervix is *neck*. The cervix reacts similarly to the pull of the muscles of the uterus as the force of the fundus presses the baby's head through the cervix and into the birth canal. It is a dual action of stretching in response to pressing. This activity is called the First Stage of labor.

Contractions of the uterus usually increase in strength and length as the cervix opens and "thins out." Each contraction, or period of work done by the uterus, is followed by a period of rest. As the first stage of labor progresses, the rest periods become increasingly shorter since the uterus must work more actively, in a sustained effort, to open the cervix all the way. Once it is open to ten centimeters, or about four and a half inches, the cervix is said to be completely effaced and dilated. It is at this point that the mother may begin to use her abdominal muscles to help the uterus push the baby down through the birth canal so that the baby may be born.

The pushing phase is called the Second Stage of labor. Contractions are fairly long, but usually not as close together as during the final stretching of the cervix in the first stage of labor. Since the cervix is totally opened, all of the work done by the uterus comes from the thick muscle bundles at the fundus, which press down firmly on the baby in a coordinated fashion. As the baby's head moves onto the pelvic floor, the muscles must open and allow for the passage of the baby.

When the head passes under the mother's pubic bone, or pubis, the head is said to be crowning and is visible both during and between contractions. With crowning, the mother feels a stretching and burning sensation around the vaginal outlet, similar to what the mouth feels like when stretched.

When the head crowns, the mother's health care provider advises her to push only at certain times, since continuous pushing might stretch the tissues in the pelvic floor too suddenly. Many physicians in this country make an incision in the perineum between the mother's vaginal opening and the rectum. Called an episiotomy, this procedure is believed to allow for an easier delivery of the baby with less resulting injury to the mother's pelvic floor structure. (See appendix C.)

Through this series of contractions, the baby is pressed from the mother's body and into the world. As the head is released from the mother's pelvic floor, a sensation of relief is experienced. The shoulders of the baby may immediately follow the birth of the head, or may be delivered with the next contraction after a few moment's rest. When the shoulders come through, there is no longer any resistance exerted by the rest of the body. In a sudden rush, the baby slides out in one tremendous, exhilarating moment. The mother feels the smooth skin of her child's back as he slips into sight.

In this instant, the baby must take his first breath and adjust to an atmosphere of oxygen. Having lived within a fluid-filled environment for about nine months, the newborn infant must switch over to breathing air and living in much cooler surroundings. The Lord has designed the first breath so that it closes off the duct that allowed the baby to bypass respiration while in the uterus. With one breath a flap shuts, and the outside air begins to circulate through the baby's lungs.

Within several minutes of birth, the umbilical cord through which the baby was nourished stops pulsating, signaling the end of the placenta's provision for the growing baby. The cord is clamped and cut, and shortly thereafter the placenta detaches from the wall of the uterus and slips down and out of the mother's body. Ac-companied by a certain amount of blood, the placenta is delivered usually within fifteen minutes after the baby's birth. This is called the Third Stage of labor.

Meanwhile, the baby is checked and may begin to nurse at his mother's breast. The suckling of the infant stimulates the uterus to contract, diminishing the flow of blood from the open vessels where the placenta had previously been attached. Breast-feeding is a marvelous feat of engineering! There need be no lapse in the infant's source of nutrition. The substances that nurtured the baby *in utero* now become a highly select combination of nutrients and antibodies designed to sustain life outside the mother's womb.

During the Fourth Stage of labor, the mother's body begins to recover its "steady state." With the delivery of the placenta (which had supplied high levels of progesterone and estrogen to maintain the pregnancy) a rapid and immediate drop in hormone levels takes place. This decrease triggers the onset of lactation, although milk usually is not produced for thirty-six to seventy-two hours.

The fourth stage lasts two hours, during which time the mother should be closely attended. A nurse routinely checks the new mother's blood pressure, pulse, and uterus, which is palpated by pressing on the fundus through the abdominal wall. If the uterus is not contracting well, the nurse will massage the fundus firmly. This helps to diminish bleeding. The flow of lochia is checked every so often to be sure that it is not heavier than it should be.

The Fifth Stage of labor often is the most neglected stage. Because it lasts six full weeks, many women tend to think that once the birth is over they should feel "normal" again. It is important to understand that after nine full months of tremendous metabolic, hormonal, and anatomical changes one does not immediately revert back to a pre-pregnant state! Instead, the mother's body readjusts itself over a forty-two-day span of time, during which she is likely to be spending a great deal of time nurturing her baby at the breast.

In many cultures around the world, newly delivered mothers are tended to by family members who provide them with complete respite from routine tasks.[1,2] This is a wise practice, since it gives a woman the attention she deserves and allows her ample time to know her newborn baby.

Labor requires stamina and a willingness to work toward a goal without stopping every few minutes to exclaim, "This is hard!" Giving birth requires nothing less than your complete attention; it involves your whole being in a way unlike any other activity. You gain a better perspective of the value of life through this process. A baby newly born from his mother's womb is a wonderful reward for the effort of childbirth. Jesus understood this well when he said, "A woman giving birth to a child has pain because her time has come; but when her baby is born she forgets the anguish because of her joy that a child is born into the world" (John 16:21).

STAGES OF LABOR

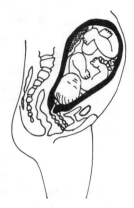

1. Before Labor.

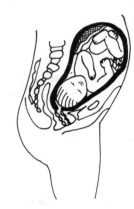

2. Cervix Effaced.

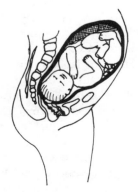

3. Early First Stage.

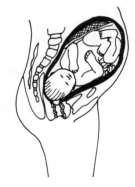

4. Late First Stage.

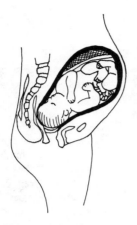

5. Early Second Stage.

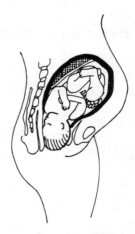

6. Late Second Stage.

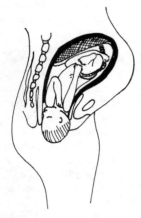

7. Birth of the Head.

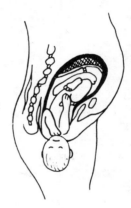

8. Birth of the Shoulders.

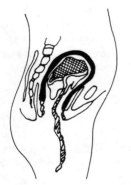

9. The Third Stage of Labor (birth of placenta, membranes, and cord).

10. The Fourth Stage of Labor.

AN OVERVIEW OF THE PROCESS OF CHILDBIRTH

PRELABOR:
- The body prepares itself to give birth
- Increased frequency of Braxton-Hicks contractions
- Increased vaginal discharge
- Changes in the cervix—softening, thinning, possible dilation
- Relaxation of pelvic joints and ligaments
- Beginning descent of the baby into the pelvis engagement
- Rectal pressure, backache
- Diarrhea
- Restlessness; emotional readiness to have the pregnancy over with

FIRST STAGE:
- With cervical dilatation, uterine contractions typically become longer, stronger, closer together, more like menstrual cramps, and have associated backache
- These contractions thin and open the cervix to ten centimeters, as well as press the baby deeper into the pelvis
- The first stage of labor is divided into three phases:

(1) Early—1 to 3 centimeters;
(2) Active—4 to 6 centimeters; and
(3) Transition—7 to 10 centimeters

SECOND STAGE:
- This stage begins when the cervix is completely dilated to ten centimeters
- Following the completion of dilatation, uterine contractions typically become less crampy, more powerful in the area of the fundus, and farther apart, with two- to five-minute intervals between
- The bag of waters, or amniotic sac, is likely to break during this stage if it has not done so earlier
- The baby moves through the pelvis and into the birth canal, finally stretching open the pelvic floor muscles and entering the world

THIRD STAGE:
- The placental structure detaches from the lining of the uterus and is delivered
- The baby is checked and reunited with the mother to begin breast-feeding, if possible

- The process of lactation is initiated as hormone levels drop

FOURTH STAGE:
- This is a two-hour period during which the mother, father, and baby begin to adjust to post-pregnant life
- The uterus continues to contract, which typically feels menstruallike, prevents excessive bleeding, and begins the process of involution (or the return of the uterus to its normal size)

FIFTH STAGE:
- During this forty-two-day period following childbirth: the uterus completes the process of involution; incisions associated with the pelvic floor or cesarean birth heal; the lining of the uterus is sloughed away through a discharge called lochia, which persists for two to six weeks; breast-feeding is established, or suppressed if found undesirable to the mother; the family adjusts to the new baby; and the baby's neuromuscular system, digestive tract, and sensory capabilities mature considerably

FACTORS INFLUENCING THE PROCESS OF LABOR

Chapter 2 discusses several of the theories upon which many of today's methods of childbirth preparation are based. If you were to visit your local library or a nearby bookstore and browse through a variety of books on childbirth you would discover that none of them present a thorough description of the factors that cause pain in labor. It is a rude awakening for women who enter labor after reading these books or taking classes that often avoid teaching women about the reality of pain in giving birth.

There most definitely are very real physical sources of pain in labor. The pain is not "culturally induced" nor is it only the result of fear.[3] Although pain perception may be influenced by many factors, including one's socialization and emotions, the process of childbirth involves the stimulation of pain fibers in the pelvic area that is unmistakably physical, rather than psychological, in origin.[4]

It is important to gain an understanding of the basic process of labor and birth as it normally takes place before introducing a time frame, environmental factors, or conditions that make one labor different from another. Then, after gaining an understanding of the basics, one should consider the many variations in the process of birth. Each labor has its own unique character and is influenced by maternal, fetal/placental, cultural, environmental, and technological factors.

MATERNAL FACTORS

Maternal factors involved in labor are those associated with the mother and include the mother's state of health, age, and physical condition; number of previous pregnancies; number of babies carried to full term; size and shape of pelvis; pain relief measures used during labor; pain threshold or ability to tolerate pain; attitudes, knowledge, and beliefs; body's reaction to labor; structure of the uterus; elasticity of perineum, pelvic floor muscles; inherited traits; stamina or ability to cope with stress; hormonal factors; effort expended; choices in birth arrangements (who, what, where, and when); type of birth (vaginal or cesarean) and types of previous births; and prenatal care.

FETAL/PLACENTAL FACTORS

Fetal/placental factors are those associated with the baby, placenta, umbilical cord, and amniotic sac. These include the baby's size (genetic inheritance); age in weeks (gestational age); position; physical condition; the number of babies in the uterus; when the amniotic sac, or "bag of waters," breaks; and the condition and location of both the placenta and the umbilical cord.

CULTURAL FACTORS

Cultural factors are practices associated with childbirth. They include the birth attendant's identity, training, beliefs, and skills; the other people present (including family members, nursing staff, and friends) and their training, beliefs, and skills; cultural beliefs about pain and childbirth (view of pregnancy as a state of illness vs. wellness); and the behavioral expectations of the mother, her birth attendant, and others present.

ENVIRONMENTAL FACTORS

Environmental factors are those associated with where the birth takes place and include the place of birth; positions used by the mother during labor and birth; cleanliness of the mother's surroundings; the routines used; the staff present; and the physical setting and layout.

TECHNOLOGICAL FACTORS

Technological factors are the tools, drugs, and techniques used to facilitate the birth. They include what drugs are used; the obstetrical interventions employed; the monitoring of the baby's condition; and the cost factors.

As you can see, many different things combine to influence a woman's labor. It is not so simplistic a picture after all. Though childbirth is a natural, basic, biological function, it also is much more than that. It is a reflection of the culture in which we live, and the means through which families perpetuate themselves. It also is the manner in which the Lord expands his creation.

Commonly, expectant parents desire that things go well. Whether aware of it or not, they make choices that have a significant impact on their birth experiences. Each of the previously mentioned factors interacts with all of the others to determine the course of labor, the baby's condition, and the mother's experience of childbirth. If one aspect is emphasized more than another, it is likely that an equally important factor will be neglected. Because of the interaction of all the things that influence childbirth and its outcome, it is easy to understand why no two births are alike. No one can predict what will take place.

Yet, one vital factor is missing from those previously discussed, and that is the Lord, who not only determines the course of our lives, but in whose hands all these other factors lie. Our heavenly Father takes everything into consideration; our lives are conducted under his watchful eye. Can you trust him to accomplish what he desires to do in your life? To act in your best interest? Or are you afraid of what he will do, viewing your Creator as One who forever threatens, punishes, takes away, withholds, and judges harshly?

This is not the Father revealed to us in Jesus Christ and who, through Jesus, forgave all our sins. Our God is a God of love and compassion, as Paul explains so clearly in Romans 5:1-11.

There can be no fear in God's love once we grasp the beauty of his involvement in our lives and the wisdom of his ways. When we are free of fear, we can honestly pray, "Thy will be done," without qualifying this statement with our limited vision and a list of "ifs." David, a man close to the heart of God, tells us, "The Lord is gracious and compassionate, slow to anger and rich in love. The Lord is good to all; he has compassion on all he has made" (Psalm 145:8, 9). And, in 1 Timothy 2:15, we find the promise that "women will be kept safe through childbirth, if they continue in faith, love and holiness with propriety."

Does this mean that "bad" things can't happen to a good Christian woman? Or is it something more—that the Lord will preserve us no matter what the circumstances? Theologians disagree as to the answer to these questions, but the words are there, as a promise that stands forever.

God is with us. He will not forsake us. We can trust him and commit our lives to him. Regardless of the outcome, the Lord "directs our paths" and will not allow our feet to slip.

CHAPTER FOUR

Preparing Your Inner Self

"Trust in the Lord with all your heart and lean not on your own understanding; in all your ways acknowledge him and he will make your paths straight." PROVERBS 3:5, 6

*S*omething marvelous occurred the day you were conceived! Within your mother's body, a single sperm cell penetrated the outer covering of the egg produced by her ovary. This ovum had been waiting to be released since it was created while your mother was in *her* mother's womb. For some reason, that one sperm cell—out of the millions upon millions your father had previously produced—and that particular egg were the ones the Lord caused to become you. It did not happen by chance. David tells us in Psalm 139:13-16:

> *For you created my inmost being; you knit me together in my mother's womb. I praise you because I am fearfully and wonderfully made; your works are wonderful, I know that full well. My frame was not hidden from you when I was made in the secret place. When I was woven together in the depths of the earth, your eyes saw my unformed body. All the days ordained for me were written in your book before one of them came to be.*

Before these two cells joined, God had ordained "all the days" of your life. He saw you before anyone else even knew you existed. This high view of the special nature of each individual to the Lord should encourage and delight us. How very loved we are!

As the Lord watched over the merging cells, a beautiful radiance called the *corona radiata* surrounded you. A biologist once told me that he had watched this phenomenon under the magnification of a microscope in a laboratory using animal cells. His face broke into a smile as he described what he had seen: "It was so colorful! One of the most beautiful things I've ever seen!" He viewed conception as a moment to be celebrated, even on a microscopic level.

Your life began with the joining of two half cells, since sex cells contain only half the number of chromosomes found in all other cells in the human body. Once fused together, they became a single complete cell that contained all of the genetic information necessary for your development. Like a scripted code, your genes helped to direct each phase of your growth, step by step, as the cells divided at an incredibly rapid pace, differentiating into the structures that became your skin, eyes, nose, ears, and heart. Bit by bit you were "knit together" within your mother's body. She finally could feel you kicking sometime around the twentieth week of her pregnancy.

Until she felt your first motion, you may have been more of a nuisance than anything else. All sorts of changes took place within her body as you, and then your placenta, secreted the various hormones that enabled her body to nurture you. Perhaps she was tired and nauseated and her breasts grew tender as they began to prepare for nursing. She may have planned for you or perhaps you were a real surprise—a factor that changed her life as nothing else could.

Your father only knew what your mother told him about your presence; his physical participation in your development was limited to one brief moment in time. Their relationship may have been sweet, steady, strained, or stagnant; but they were your parents just the same.

The Lord brought you forth from your mother's womb as David expresses in Psalm 22:9. Whatever the circumstances of your birth and throughout all the years that followed, the Lord has loved, protected, and guarded you. Your experiences, coupled with your God-given talents, personality, and genetic traits, all have fit together to shape you into the unique person you are.

Your individuality is expressed in many different ways. Yet, regardless of your financial, physical, or emotional circumstances, the Lord knows what motivates you, quiets you, disheartens you. He has been with you through every day of your life. Consider Psalm 139:1-6:

O Lord, you have searched me and you know me. You know when I sit and when I rise; you perceive my thoughts from afar. You discern my going out and my lying down; you are familiar with all my ways. Before a word is on my tongue you know it completely, O Lord. You hem me in, behind and before; you have laid your hand upon me. Such knowledge is too wonderful for me, too lofty for me to attain.

If you are expecting a child of your own, the poignancy of your own beginnings and the Lord's careful tending of your life can serve to encourage you. By relating your own experience to that of your growing baby's, you may discover a greater depth of the Lord's love for you. Each of us needs to recognize the constancy of God's love for us; to appreciate our individuality and be satisfied with the life God has given to us.

PREPARING FAMILY RELATIONSHIPS

I will never forget the day I was having dinner with my husband's mother and sister. They were reminiscing, which brought to mind the many hurts of my own life; a less-than-ideal relationship with my mother as an adolescent. I mused aloud to my mother-in-law: "Sometimes I wish you had been my mother."

My sister-in-law smiled and jokingly replied, "Then you would have been me!"

At that moment I saw, more clearly than ever before, that all the experiences in my life made me who I am. The trials, sad times, and heartaches I've experienced have produced a depth for which I can now be thankful.

We each need to learn to thank God for the *entire* life he has given us. When we say this sincerely, then we will find it much easier to love and forgive those whom we feel have wronged us, or not lived up to our expectations.

One of the most important things you can do to prepare for your baby's arrival is to make peace within your family, forgiving those you feel have hurt you. Realize that, without forgiveness, love cannot be given or received fully. Reflect on the fatherly nature of God's love. He is able to heal your hurts and restore relationships that may be distressing to you. Pray for his strength and wis-

1. What was your reaction to the description given in this chapter of your conception? As you relate this to your own baby's existence, what is your reaction?
2. Is it easy or difficult for you to relate to your parents? Are there things for which you need to forgive them? Pray with one another, or with a friend, that the Lord will enable you to forgive, and that he will begin to heal any hurts in your relationships.
3. Consider writing a note to your mother or father, a grandparent, sister or brother ... someone who has known you throughout your life and to whom you can return some encouragement. Use this time, while your baby is waiting to become a part of your family, to "clean house."

dom, through the power of the Holy Spirit, to enable you to forgive, thereby creating a loving atmosphere within your home. Know that there are no "perfect" families and no "perfect" people. As your baby grows and prepares for birth, learn to say "I'm sorry" and "I forgive you." This will help you prevent the conflicts that can tear families apart and cause them to stray from God.

PREPARING YOUR HEART

The Lord's design for human growth and childbearing is very intricate, woven together in the most beautiful way through many minute details. The physiological aspects of pregnancy—the various changes your body goes through from the moment of your baby's conception—are amazing. They can give you confidence in God's design for your life. The emotional ups and downs, however, are far less predictable. Still, *you can choose what feelings to create and how to cope with them.*

Adam and Eve were not created as robots, but were formed in the image of God. Within their God-created bodies, their Maker placed minds that differed from all other animals. Man was created to think and feel by *choice*, rather than by instinct.

During pregnancy, Christian expectant parents can turn to the same Father who made the first man and woman so long ago. It is possible to learn to conform your lives to God's will, and draw near to him for strength and sustenance as you face this new and exciting part of your lives.

THE CHRISTIAN'S SOURCE OF SELF-ESTEEM

A basic concept in health education classes is that self-esteem promotes a healthy life-style. When a person hurts emotionally or places a low value on his life, poor health often results due to inadequate rest, nutrients, and exercise. Total wellness can begin only in a heart at peace with God: a heart that accepts his love and forgiveness completely.

Overeating, undereating, alcohol and drug abuse, sexually transmitted diseases ... the list of prevalent health problems in the eighties goes on and on. Many of them can be directly related to life-styles that correspond to one's self-concept.

Do you long to look like the people you see in advertisements and on TV? As a Christian, you are not called to strive to obtain a glamorous appearance or the latest status symbol. You must determine what the Lord wants you to be.

Can you recognize the special talents and gifts God has bestowed on you? Is your heart at peace, or do you find yourself striving for worldly approval, success, or achievement? What is it that the Lord requires you to be? Consider Deuteronomy 10:12: "What does the Lord your God ask of you but to fear the Lord your God, to walk in all his ways, to love him, to serve the Lord your God with all your heart and with all your soul."

God created you to be able to *choose* to love and serve him. As you prepare your life for your baby's arrival, there may be times you feel weak, fatigued, frightened, tempted, or confused. You may feel pulled in many different directions. There is reassurance to be found in the Bible for these times. Learning about your identity in Christ will lead you to form a self-concept that conforms to God's Word rather than to the present culture's standards.

It will be much easier for you to care for yourself and for your unborn child if you will "seek peace and pursue it" by keeping close to the Lord. As he reassures you of his love through his Word, you will be strengthened and renewed daily. Positive changes in your life-style will be less difficult to make and you will be creating an atmosphere within your home in which family relationships can be nurtured and made fruitful. This doesn't mean your experiences won't be difficult and frustrating at times, it just means your foundation, which is in Christ, will never crumble.

HEARTFELT PEACE

A heart at peace comes from knowing and reflecting on who you are in relationship to the Lord. For starters, you are—

- A precious child of your heavenly Father (Matthew 7:11)
- A coheir with Christ (Romans 8:17)
- A person granted the protection of angels (Psalm 91:11)
- God's slave, not the world's (Romans 6:22)
- A temple of the living God (2 Corinthians 6:16).

You also are redeemed, justified, cleansed, guarded, forgiven, blessed, saved from condemnation, and loved beyond measure! The source of your self-esteem is the Lord, and, as you learn to see yourself the way he sees you, you will find peace.

"Thou will keep him in perfect peace, whose mind is stayed on thee" (Isaiah 26:3, KJV).

EXERCISES

1. Read Romans 8 together and discuss how the concepts in the following verses apply to you. Verses 1, 2, 3-16, 17 & 18, 19-23, 24 & 25, 26 & 27, 28, 29 & 30, 31, 32-34, 35-38, and 37.
2. Make a list of conclusions you reached from this study of Romans 8. For instance, you might start your list with: "I am in Christ Jesus (v. 1), I am free from the law of sin and death (v. 2)," and so on. Place the list in a prominent place until you have it memorized.
3. In the following weeks, make an effort to put some of your conclusions into practice. Encourage others to live "according to the Spirit" rather than according to the flesh. Be positive and supportive. Avoid comparing yourself to others. Instead, turn frequently to the Lord in prayer.

Make cards with the following Scripture verses on them, memorizing each passage to use when needed:

Isaiah 43:1-2	Hebrews 12:2, 3
John 14:1	James 4:7, 8
Philippians 4:13	1 Peter 5:7

SCRIPTURAL INSTRUCTIONS FOR WORRY

PREPARING YOUR MIND

There are many passages in Scripture that encourage us to trust in the Lord's protection. Because childbearing is a great responsibility filled with many unknown factors, it is normal to wonder what sex your baby will be and if he will be "normal."

Think for a moment about the differences between worry, anxiety, and fear. How would you define these words? Are you fairly prone to any of these emotional states?

Being human makes it easy to hug our concerns close to ourselves, pondering over them. Learning to trust the Lord takes effort; we must walk with him day by day, getting to know him better. Pregnancy, childbirth, and parenthood will provide you with ample opportunities to experience firsthand the Lord's ability to take care of your needs. You will become increasingly aware that his Word is true.

PUTTING GOD'S WORD INTO ACTION

During a difficult time in my life, I found that by breaking down Philippians 4:4-9 and meditating on each portion of the verses, I could put into practice what I now believe is one of the Lord's prescriptions for the maintenance of our emotional health. As you read through the following verses from Philippians, consider how you can follow your Counselor's plan for promoting a sound mind, and how you can apply each verse in your own life.

Rejoice in the Lord always. I will say it again:
Rejoice!
Let your gentleness be evident to all.
The Lord is near.
Do not be anxious about anything,
but in everything,
by prayer
and petition,
with thanksgiving,
present your requests to God.
And the peace of God, which transcends all under-
standing,
will guard your hearts and your minds in
Christ Jesus.
Finally, brothers, whatever is true,
whatever is noble,
whatever is right,
whatever is pure,
whatever is lovely,
whatever is admirable—
if anything is excellent or praiseworthy—
think about such things.
Whatever you have learned or received
or heard from me, or seen in me—
put it into practice.
And the God of peace will be with you.

Write down what these words bring to mind. How can you change your thought patterns for the better? The Lord is able to strengthen us, but we must be willing to do our part. It may help to copy this passage down and display it as a reminder.

We make the choice of what we will or won't think about. When we experience worry, fear, doubt, or anxiety, it is by choice. In turning our thoughts to the Lord, we can spare ourselves a tremendous amount of grief. True, it takes self-control and discipline, but these are qualities the Lord wants to develop more fully in us.

The Lord's part in your pregnancy and birth experience can't be known fully, but we can say that he knows this baby and he knows you. Tell him your fears, share your worries with him. Believe in his ability to bless you throughout your life and to direct your paths, even while you may not understand why certain things happen.

Maria Von Trapp is famous for saying, "God's will hath no why." If your pregnancy or birth is difficult, if your baby isn't what you expected, if your life plans must change—even if what in your opinion is "the worst" happens—realize that the Lord's grace *is* sufficient for you. You cannot be separated from his unfailing love and goodness.

Never forget Romans 8:28: "And we know that in all things God works for the good of those who love him, who have been called according to his purpose."

EXERCISES

1. Write down any specific concerns, worries, or fears you may have. Discuss these with your spouse or labor partner. Consider the following questions:

   a. Are your concerns realistic—based on real, possible, or probable concerns? If they *are* realistic, to what extent are they likely to happen?

   b. What steps will you take together to diminish any anxiety you have, encourage each other, and build your confidence in God's provision?

   c. What other scriptural passages offer solutions or promises dealing with worry, anxiety, or fear?

CHAPTER FIVE
Preparing Your Life-style

When we want something other than the thing God wants us to be, we must be wanting what, in fact, will not make us happy.
C. S. LEWIS

*C*hildbearing requires an adjustment of priorities. Adequate rest, regular meals, suitable working hours, and safe exercise become important ingredients in promoting your health and the growth of the child within you. The quality of your pregnancy can be improved by eating and drinking that which will provide your baby with the nutrients needed for optimal development, and by easing the strains you may have previously placed on your body (overworking, skipping meals, smoking cigarettes, etc.).

It is best if you can discuss with your husband the changes you need to make and learn about the special needs of pregnancy together. In this way, he can help you to take care of yourself, encourage you to stick to whatever plan you adopt, and protect you from undue stress and overwork. Hopefully, the changes you make during your pregnancy will be fairly permanent so that your child will learn sound habits by your example as he grows older.

The following life-style evaluation consists of three corresponding sections: questions about your life-style as it is now; information that will help you to know what changes to make to improve the quality of your pregnancy; and suggested ways to make these changes together.

PART 1:
YOUR CURRENT LIFE-STYLE

Couples should answer these questions separately. After completing the evaluation, you may proceed to Part 2.

1. How many days a week do you usually eat breakfast?
2. Do you normally eat balanced meals consisting of the "Basic Four" (breads and cereals, fruits and vegetables, dairy products, and high protein foods)?
3. How much water and other beverages do you drink per day?
4. How many hours of sleep do you usually get per night?
5. Are you taking any prescribed or over-the-counter medication on a regular basis? List any medications you currently take and why you are taking them. Make sure also to in-

clude vitamins, aspirin, and simple cold remedies.

6. What is your current weight?

7. Are you working outside the home or are you in school? How many hours a week does your job/school demand, including side trips, business-related activities, take-home work, etc.?

8. Do you participate in a fitness program or exercise regularly? What activities do you enjoy and how long have you been doing them?

9. Have you moved recently or do you plan to move within the next twelve months?

10. List any traumatic events that have occurred within your family or closest friendships during the past year (e.g., deaths, major illnesses, financial crises, etc.). Describe what effect, if any, the event(s) you listed have had upon you.

11. Do either of you plan to quit your job, switch employment, stop or begin school, or otherwise change your financial picture within the next year? What impact will this have on your life-style?

12. List any illnesses or injuries you have had during the past year, as well as ongoing health concerns (such as high blood pressure, anemia, obesity, or diabetes).

13. What is your health insurance coverage?

14. Do you smoke cigarettes or drink alcoholic beverages? If so, how often? Do you plan to continue to do so while you are pregnant (or while your wife is pregnant)?

15. How many previous pregnancies have you had? How many were carried full term?

16. Have you ever had a sexually transmitted disease?

17. Do you regularly wear seat belts?

18. Are you fairly calm, stable, and even-tempered, or are you more tense, moody, and sometimes temperamental?

19. Do you find it easy or difficult to fully relax, other than when sleeping?

20. Are you satisfied with the sexual relationship you have with your spouse? If so, why? If not, how would you change it?

21. What is your current level of involvement in volunteer work?

22. How active would you say you are in your church or fellowship?

23. How often do you have a regular quiet time with the Lord? With your spouse? How often do you pray together, other than at meals?

24. How do you view this pregnancy? Is it a nuisance, a blessing, or a challenge? Do you see it as an illness or as a healthy event?

25. How satisfied are you with your marriage?

PART 2: IDEAS FOR PROMOTION OF FAMILY WELLNESS

After discussing your responses to the evaluation, read through the following recommendations for a healthy life-style. Discuss how these ideas coincide or conflict with your answers; then proceed to Part 3.

1. A balanced breakfast is still considered to be the single most important meal of the day and should be a regular part of your daily schedule.

2,3. The following is the recommended daily food intake (see appendix A for serving sizes and suggestions) for women during pregnancy and while breast-feeding.

Dairy products: 4 servings
Eggs: 1–2 (may be incorporated into meals/ beverages)
Meats and meat substitutes: 6–8
Fresh, green vegetables: 2
Whole grain foods: 5
Foods high in vitamin C: 2
Fats: 3–5
Food high in vitamin A: 1
Water: 6–8 glasses, more while nursing

Restrict your intake of foods and beverages that are high in calories, fats (especially saturated fats), salt, caffeine, alcohol, additives, sugars, artificial sweeteners, and preservatives. Many of these substances have been shown to increase symptoms of stress and to lower pain tolerance.

4. In spite of the opinions of various people, eight hours of sleep is still the recommended amount. During late pregnancy, two or three twenty-minute rest periods per day while lying on your left side will help your circulation and metabolism. In addition, you may find that you need more than eight hours of sleep at night while you are pregnant and several naps per day while your baby has you up at night.

5. Discuss all medications you take while you are pregnant and during lactation, even vitamins (if taken in large doses), with your health care provider.

6. See appendix A for weight chart.

7. There are no specific time-management guidelines for pregnant women as long as things are going well. Certain jobs, however, are inappropriate for pregnant women. If environmental hazards are part of your work, you will need to consider what effect they will have on your developing baby. During the last four to six weeks of pregnancy, a job that demands heavy exertion or too much time on your feet is not advisable. My suggestion is that you and your husband pray for the Lord's direction.

8. Generally, it is not advisable to begin any type of strenuous fitness program, or engage in any new physical activity that might be harmful while you are pregnant. Fitness experts recommend participating in a program suited to the special needs of pregnancy, which protects the lower back and abdominal and pelvic floor muscles from strain. With your doctor's approval, walking, swimming, cycling, modified aerobic dance, and running activities can promote cardiovascular endurance, while certain stretching and strengthening exercises will enable your body to adapt more easily and recover more readily from the stresses exerted upon it during childbearing. (Walking and swimming are preferable if you are not currently engaged in any of the other activities listed. See appendix B for specific suggestions.)

9. It doesn't take an expert to tell you that moving is stressful. Times to avoid it for expectant and new parents: the last two months of pregnancy and the first three months of your baby's life.

10. Regardless of what brought about any of the events you listed, their impact on your life is inescapable. Healing of the body or the mind takes time. Staying busy may only exhaust you, if that is how you are coping. On the other hand, withdrawal and inactivity can bring about stagnation, or even self-destructive behavior. The Lord wants you whole again; be patient with his way of bringing it about. Remember that "the one who calls you is faithful . . ." (1 Thessalonians 5:24) and he will take care of you.

11. Money and sex are the two most significant sources of conflict within marriage, as you may already know. Finances become an even greater concern with the advent of parenthood due to the responsibility of caring for your child. However, many expenses in our culture are exaggerated, if not unnecessary. There are basic needs, and then there are wants. Matthew 6 reassures us that our Father knows our needs, and teaches us how we ought to pray. He warns us not to worry because "each day has enough trouble of its own." Perhaps this is a time in your life when the Lord would have you simplify your life-style and learn to trust him more fully.

12. Since childbearing aggravates many conditions that could be harmful to your health

and that of the baby, it is vital for someone qualified to attend to your health concerns now and throughout your pregnancy. Prenatal care plays an important role in the outcome of any pregnancy, whether it is complicated or not.

13. Be sure you understand what expenses your health insurance covers. It is easier to plan possible ways to pay for the costs not covered by your insurance if you know what they are early in the pregnancy. Also, most hospitals will allow you to bring in things to help you save money, such as disposable diapers, sanitary napkins, and similar items. Check all your options. Generally, birthing centers are much less expensive than hospitals for maternity care, as they are based on an outpatient model and do not require the same type of staff and equipment use as hospitals do.

14. Cigarette smoking and inhaling the smoke of others is to be avoided during pregnancy. If you smoke now, it is worth it to your baby to quit because:
    - blood flow to the baby is restricted if the mother is a smoker, impairing the ability of the placenta to nourish the baby and often resulting in premature birth and/or a low-birthweight baby;
    - children of smokers have a higher incidence of upper respiratory infections;
    - parents set the example for their children, who love to imitate their parents' behavior.

    The Lord can set you free from this addiction if you sincerely want to quit.

    Alcohol consumption during pregnancy should be discontinued altogether. Though recent research suggests that fetal alcohol syndrome is dependent on genetic factors rather than on the level of alcohol intake, why take a chance?

15. Make sure your health care provider has your complete medical history recorded correctly. This is an important tool used for planning the medical management of your pregnancy. A history of miscarriage may suggest certain precautions at different times during your pregnancy.

16. This is another important area of concern for your physician or midwife. You will most likely be tested for both gonorrhea and syphilis at your first prenatal visit. Herpes Simplex II (genital herpes) is of concern as well. If an active case of herpes is present at the onset of labor, it would be harmful or even fatal to your baby if you were to have a vaginal birth. A cesarean delivery would be indicated.

17. It has been estimated that only about 14 percent of the adult population in the U.S. wears seat belts regularly. Many states now require that children be placed in a safety restraint until the age of four. Again, your child will learn by example.

18,19. Pregnancy is an ideal time to seek the Lord's will for your life together and pursue a closer walk with him. Many passages in the New Testament make it clear what "fruit" the Lord expects us to bear. While you are nurturing your unborn baby, the Lord wants to show you how to become more productive in him. In becoming parents, we can learn to be less self-centered through being directly responsible for the needs of another human being who is dependent upon us for protection, sustenance, and love.

If you are struggling with anger, depression, guilt, covetousness, ambition, or any aspect of your life from which the Lord desires to set you free, don't be surprised! It's by God's grace we are saved, not by our worth or virtues. As parents preparing in Christ for parenthood, your call is to learn to be less anxious as a result of drawing closer to the Lord. Your Father in heaven meant it when he said, "My grace is sufficient for you, for my power is made perfect in weakness" (2 Corinthians 12:9). Then you will be able to say sincerely the same words Paul said: "I can do everything through him who gives me strength" (Philippians 4:13). All who choose to look to God in humility rather than use worldly techniques to achieve self-control and freedom from stress find solutions to life's many challenges.

20. As mentioned earlier, money and sex are not always easy subjects of discussion for husbands and wives. Communication, "speaking the truth in love," and a willingness to learn how to be sensitive to one another's needs are important for every couple.

Be honest about what you would change if you could, and discuss this together. Keep an open mind that allows you to really "hear" what your partner is saying. The Lord created men and women with different, sometimes fluctuating, sexual drives. While masculine reproductive function involves one primary aspect, a woman has five expressions within her body's design. In addition to the act of intercourse, these are ovulation, menstruation, pregnancy, and breast-feeding. Each of these expressions of female sexuality are uniquely controlled by a variety of combinations and levels of hormones. A sexual relationship within marriage ideally allows men and women to appreciate the differences that our Creator designed into our bodies. We must seek to understand the whole picture rather than just a one-dimensional view of human sexuality.

21,22,23.   Many believers spend little time with their families. This should not be the case, except for specific and limited periods of time. As a wife and a mother of four, I'm just beginning to scratch the surface of what it means to serve my family in love. Love takes time, time spent together. The time spent with the Lord in his Word and in prayer (both individually and together as a family) will yield a lasting harvest. You must weigh the needs of your family and yourself against your other involvements. The church can always find another volunteer. Your family cannot replace you as easily!

24. An important question, don't you agree? Not all babies are completely planned or wanted by both partners. Even when they are, the whole process can be exasperating at times, making you wonder if it's worth it or not. In my own life, I've found that being a mother has required me to make more changes in myself and in my life than any other role that I fill.

Children may be viewed as a liability by some in our society, but we read in Psalm 127:3(KJV) that "children are an heritage of the Lord: and the fruit of the womb is his reward." Jesus, on his way to the cross, stopped to speak to some women who "mourned and wailed for him." His response? "Daughters of Jerusalem, do not weep for me; weep for yourselves and for your children. For the time will come when you will say, 'Blessed are the barren women, the wombs that never bore and the breasts that never nursed'" (Luke 23:28, 29). To a woman of Jesus' time, this must have sounded absolutely incredible. Barrenness a blessing? They must have thought to themselves, *May it never be!*

Yet today sterilization is rapidly becoming our nation's most popular method of birth control, with many women being made infertile before ever having borne or nursed a child. Abortion destroys millions of lives. Our society has placed a comparative value on human life, the afflicted and genetically different becoming objects of fear rather than people who deserve compassion and understanding.

Your life came into being under God's

watchful eye. Because your parents did not prevent your conception, you possess a life that is everlasting. If you are pregnant, praise God for the life you carry in your womb! The Lord has blessed you and your child with life. If you view the value of this event from an eternal perspective, you will feel true satisfaction in participating together in the Lord's plan for your child's life.

25. Marriage relationships are diverse and challenging. The variety of today's teachings on marriage only reflects the variety of relationships. As you consider the following "one anothers" of the New Testament, reflect on how they are being expressed in your marriage, and keep in mind that one thing never changes: the truth of God's Word.

- *Have peace one with another (Mark 9:50, KJV).*
- *Love one another (John 13:34).*
- *Be devoted to one another (Romans 12:10).*
- *Be likeminded one toward another (Romans 15:5, KJV).*
- *Instruct one another (Romans 15:14).*
- *Greet one another (Romans 16:16).*
- *Serve one another (Galatians 5:13).*
- *Be patient, bearing with one another (Ephesians 4:2).*
- *Be kind to one another, forgiving each other (Ephesians 4:32).*
- *Submit to one another (Ephesians 5:21).*
- *Lie not one to another (Colossians 3:9, KJV).*
- *Admonish one another (Colossians 3:16).*
- *Abound in love one toward another (1 Thessalonians 3:12, KJV).*

Also consider the "one anothers" found in the following Scripture references:

1 Thessalonians 4:18; 5:11; Hebrews 3:13; 10:24; James 4:11, 12; 5:9, 16; 1 Peter 1:22; 3:8; 4:10; 5:5; and 1 John 1:7.

Each of these guidelines needs to be practiced within the Christian home. The Golden Rule of "do unto others" ideally begins with our closest neighbor, our spouse. Encourage one another to work toward having the marriage the Lord desires for you. Your baby, too, will harvest what is sown in your home. Wouldn't it be great if that harvest contained a minimum of "tares"?

PART 3: DEVELOP A PLAN

Now that you have read through the previous suggestions for a healthy life-style during and after pregnancy, you may wish to use the next section for ideas in developing a plan of action in making your life-style healthier and more enjoyable.

1, 2, 3. Suggestions for improved eating habits:

- Keep track of your food intake and try to stay close to the Daily Food Guide and suggestions in appendix A.
- Make menus that appeal to you and shop only for items for which you have planned ahead.
- Clean out your cupboards. Remove all inappropriate foodstuffs.
- Don't condemn yourself if you slip and eat a hot fudge sundae rather than a cup of cottage cheese! The Lord loves you and will help you to improve your eating habits. Just seek his guidance next time.

4. Changes I can make to get sufficient rest (ways that I can help my wife to get the rest she needs):

5. List of drugs and vitamins I've taken so far during my pregnancy (show this to your

physician if you haven't discussed this yet):

6. Refer to 1–3.
7. Plans for work or school activity during pregnancy and afterward (what we will continue and what we can eliminate):

HOUSEHOLD TASKS
Who will:
Vacuum_____
Make the bed/change linens_____
Wash dishes_____
Cook (which meals?)_____
Clean the bathroom(s)_____
Take out the garbage_____
Wash the floor(s)_____
Mow the lawn_____
Do grocery shopping_____
Pay the bills_____
Do laundry_____
Take care of the pet(s)_____

Four questions to ask about all household tasks: Can this task (a) be eliminated? (b) be done less often? (c) be done at the same time as another task or activity? (d) be done by another household member?
8. Our current level of physical activity:

Type of fitness program we will participate in with our doctor's approval:

9. We can make moving easier by:

10. The events that still bother me (husband and wife should each answer):

My plan for coping:

Scriptural references to help put these events in perspective:

11. Additional scriptural references concerning money:

Debts that can be avoided or eliminated before the baby is born or within the next six months:

Expenses associated with this pregnancy and early infancy (minimum):

Worries we have about meeting expenses:

Reassurances from God's Word about his provision for us:

12. Current health care plan regarding existing health concerns:

13. Our plan for reducing health care expenses if our coverage is not sufficient:

14. What I desire to change about smoking or drinking during pregnancy and afterward:

    Plan for support:

15. Special recommendations to follow:

16. Our health care provider's suggestions concerning any of these conditions:

17. Plan for changing seat belt wearing or driving habits:

18,19. Two areas of our life in which we desire the Lord's help:

Plan of action (such as prayer, regular fellowship, quiet time with the Lord, etc.):

20. Ways we can improve our communication and our sexual relationship during pregnancy so that we can be relatively free of resentment, frustration, and guilt in this area:

21. Current volunteer activity involvement that can be reduced, phased out, or eliminated before the baby is born:

22. Current church involvements (committees, Bible studies, small group meetings, ministries, etc.) that can be phased out until our child is older, or that can be entirely eliminated (seek guidance from the Lord and your pastor, remembering that your decision needs to be based on what's best for you and your family):

23. Changes we can make in our prayer and Bible study habits:

24. Scriptural references on the value of children:

25. A list of five "one anothers" we want to put into practice in our marriage now:

Encouragement from God's Word

Some of the changes that you decide to make in your life-style may take time, while others need to begin as soon as possible for the sake of promoting the mother's and baby's well-beings. Prioritize the changes you desire to make. Remember, you need not depend on your own willpower or strength alone to change; the Lord is your shepherd and will give you the things you ask for.

Consider the following verses as you begin preparing your life-style for your new baby: Psalms 121:1, 2; 18:31, 32; Proverbs 3:5, 6; Isaiah 40:30-31; and Colossians 3:23, 24.

CHAPTER SIX
Preparing Your Body

"The fruit of your womb will be blessed." DEUTERONOMY 28:4

As you prepare your body for its birth-giving role, an important element in late pregnancy will be your willingness to let God be sovereign in your life. This chapter will present ideas that will help your body adapt to late pregnancy and prepare for harvesttime as the fruit of your womb "ripens."

The physical discomforts of late pregnancy can be divided into four major categories: musculo-skeletal, circulatory, digestive, and breast changes. Learning how your body prepares itself to give birth will help you understand the sensations and inconveniences during the last three months of your pregnancy.

YOUR MUSCULO-SKELETAL SYSTEM

Until the fifth or sixth month of pregnancy you may have felt minimal changes taking place within the muscles and bones that surround your baby. But, as your baby grows, a variety of muscles must stretch to a greater degree to accommodate the growth of your unborn child. Many muscles that are attached to your skeletal system must bear the extra weight. The bones in your lower back and pelvis shift from their usual placement, due to hormonal influences on the ligaments which maintain your posture and the framework of your bone structure.

The Lord designed your body for these changes. There may be days when you wonder what his plan was, but if you are willing to temporarily change certain habits and movements, you may find that it is not so unbearable after all.

YOUR ABDOMINAL MUSCLES

Your abdominal muscles may have come to your mind first when I said that some muscles need to stretch as your baby grows. The corset-like structure which comprises your abdominal wall may be strengthened in a variety of ways.

The best exercises protect your lower back while at the same time providing your abdominal muscles the opportunity to do some work, helping them become stronger and more supportive. Before you begin, learn how each exercise is to be done and check the condition of your abdominal wall.

Abdominal Muscle Evaluation. Lie on your back with your knees bent and your feet flat on the floor, about hip-width apart. While placing one hand on the floor for stability, lift your head up until you feel your abdominal muscles tighten. Keep your head lifted forward until the check is completed.

With your free hand, feel down the midline of your abdomen with two fingers, from your breastbone to your navel. You should feel an indentation that can be less than half an inch to over an inch wide. On either side of this indentation, you will feel two firm ridges of muscle. These vertical bands are called your recti muscles. Measure the size of the indentation between the recti muscles by the number of fingertip widths you can place between them. Then relax your head, and place it back on the floor.

If the gap between the muscles is one fingertip wide or less, you should do variation A of the following exercise. If the gap is wider, or bulges up like a long bubble when you lift your head, do variation B. The wider gap simply means that your recti muscles have become separated to a degree. This is especially likely if you have been doing sit-ups or have been pregnant before. Don't worry . . . just protect this weakened area when you exercise and avoid activities that cause you to bear down excessively with these muscles.

Modified Sit-ups. Variation A: Lie on your back, with your head supported by the floor. Your knees should be up, with your feet flat on the floor about hip-width apart. Press your lower back onto the floor (this helps to protect your back). Inhale through your nose. As you exhale slowly through your mouth, lift your head and reach forward with your arms toward your thighs. Lift only enough to curl your shoulders forward. Notice how the muscles of your abdomen press together and tighten. Hold for

three counts, then relax back as you inhale. Repeat. Begin with a sequence of five, increasing to ten or fifteen daily.

Variation B: Before beginning the exercise described above, cross your arms over your abdomen and support both sides of it. This is done by gently pressing your hands against your recti muscles, instead of reaching forward with your arms, as you lift your head up.

Abdominal Breathing. This exercise is easy to do at various times throughout your day and is a simple way to strengthen these muscles. It is particularly good to do this exercise after a cesarean birth (while gently supporting the incision) as a means of relieving gas buildup. Start in a sitting, standing, or reclining position. Take a deep breath in through your nose, placing one of your hands over your lower abdomen, just beneath your navel, and expand your abdomen out toward your hand as you inhale. Exhale through your mouth slowly, pulling your abdominal muscles in firmly. Feel them move and become tighter underneath your hand. Repeat three to five times at least once daily.

Pelvic Tilt. This basic exercise helps to strengthen lower back and abdominal muscles while easing tension and pain. (See figure 1.) There are three variations of this exercise:

Variation A: Back Press—Lie on your back with knees up and feet flat on the floor, about hip-width apart. Place your arms on the floor on either side of your body for stability. As you breathe in through your nose, note the curve of your lower back. Mentally determine how far this part of your back is off the floor. Exhale slowly through your nose, pressing your back against the floor firmly and erasing the space that was there when you were relaxed. (Notice that when you tilt your pelvis back firmly your abdominal muscles tighten and your buttocks move slightly upward.) Hold three to five seconds. Inhale as you relax back into your original position, making sure not to exaggerate the curve and space (this could cause strain to your back). Repeat five times, building up to fifteen times at least once daily, or whenever your back aches.

Variation B: Feline Stretch—Get into a hands-and-knees position, as if you were imitating a cat. Keep your back flat between tilts; don't let it sag down. Inhale, feeling the normal curve of your spine; exhale and tilt your pelvis by pulling down with your buttock muscles and up with your abdominal muscles. Imagine that your pelvis is connected by a hinge at the level of the back of your waist. Tilt down from this point; hold three to five seconds. Inhale and relax, but don't become swaybacked. Repeat five times, building up to fifteen daily.

Variation C: Passive Pelvic Tilt—While lying on your left side with your knees bent and a pillow under your head, have your husband support your pelvis by placing his right hand on your hip and left hand against the back of your pelvis, pointing toward your tailbone. As you tilt your pelvis, he presses down on your lower back and back on your hip. This movement may ease lower back pain during labor as well as during late pregnancy.

FIGURE I
Pelvic Tilt

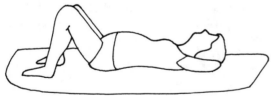

1. At rest.

2. Pelvis is tilted as back is pressed onto the mat. Dots represent position when at rest.

PELVIC FLOOR

During pregnancy the muscles that form the "floor" of your pelvis serve several functions. They must: support the contents of your abdominal cavity (including your baby), the enlarged uterus, fluid surrounding the baby, and the placenta; withstand pressures exerted against the pelvic floor muscles caused by laughing or coughing; and provide sphincter control of the openings to your bladder and rectum.

In late pregnancy, it is not uncommon to inadvertently leak urine due to the pressure placed upon these supportive muscles. Simple exercises may be done to strengthen the pelvic floor and, as a result, provide greater control of these muscles. You may also strengthen this area of your body so that it will be more elastic during the birth process and aid in the recovery of muscles that have been stretched during the birth of your baby.

Evaluating the Strength of Your Pelvic Floor. Sit comfortably in a cross-legged position. Imagine your pelvic floor muscles as a hammock attached from the front of your pelvis to your pubic bone, in back at your tailbone, and sideways between your thighs within your pelvis. This "hammock" has three openings: your urethra, vagina, and anus. Around these openings are two strong bands of muscle. These are called sphincter muscles. One surrounds your rectum and the other surrounds both the urethra and the vagina. These sphincters are separate muscles that form an integrated structure. As you lift the pelvic floor up, the sphincters are designed to tighten and close firmly. Your buttocks and lower abdominal muscles should remain relaxed while you contract your pelvic floor muscles.

To evaluate the strength of this important area of your body, tighten the pelvic floor by lifting it as "high" as you can while at the same time closing the sphincters. Hold this position. Once the pelvic floor is lifted and the sphincters are tightened, slowly count to ten. As soon as you feel your pelvic floor muscles start to droop, note the number at which these muscles began to relax. Use the following exercise daily to strengthen the pelvic floor so that you can hold this lift for a full ten seconds.

The Kegel Exercise. Dr. Arnold Kegel (Kaygell) has the unique distinction of having these exercises named in his honor because of his research on the effect of exercise on pelvic floor relaxation. Dr. Kegel found that while the vagina has relatively few responsive nerve endings, pelvic floor muscles are sensitive during lovemaking and play a key role in a woman's sexual response. He also discovered that exercising the pelvic floor through a series of fifteen to twenty-five contractions several times daily could correct many cases of pelvic floor relaxation, as well as improve sexual response. This work suggests that *prevention* of pelvic floor dysfunction is even more important than the treatment of problems after they arise.

The Kegel exercise can be done anywhere, with no one being made aware of when you're doing it. It is best not to do Kegels while urinating, because stopping and starting the flow of urine can cause urine that has come into contact with bacteria lower in the urethra to move back up toward the normally sterile contents of your bladder.

As in the pelvic floor evaluation, contract the muscles of the pelvic floor by lifting them upward. At the same time, press the openings closed. You may breathe out as you lift if you find you have a tendency to tense any other areas of your body. Lift slowly and purposefully until you reach the "top" of the level you are able to attain. Hold for counts of three to five. Inhale and lower slowly. Repeat ten times, building up to twenty-five repetitions done at least once daily.

POSTURE AND BODY MECHANICS

The way you move changes during late pregnancy. The tendency is for the curve in your lower back to become greater, so you need to pay special attention to your posture and movements while lifting objects, lying down, rising out of a chair or your bed, and climbing stairs. The following changes in daily habits will help you to prevent lower back strain:

Standing—Slightly tuck under your pelvis by pulling down on your buttock muscles and upward with your abdominal muscles. Try to consciously think of straightening your back when standing. Wear shoes that allow for this posture. Raise your head up and try not to slump your shoulders forward. This will enable you to feel and look better, too!

Sitting—To lower yourself into a chair or to stand up, use your legs more than the central part of your body. Grasp something to hold onto. While sitting, avoid crossing your legs since this impairs your blood circulation. Also, become aware of keeping your back straight and squaring your shoulders as you sit.

Lying Down—Sitting at the edge of your bed, swing your legs onto the bed while stabilizing your upper body with your hands placed on the mattress. Using your arms, lower your body onto the bed into a side-lying position. If you wish to lie on your back, roll over from your side instead of dropping straight backward from a sitting position. Reverse this process to get out of bed.

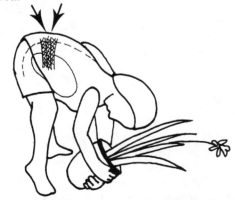

1. Avoid bending at the waist when lifting objects.

2. Instead, kneel and raise yourself and what you are lifting by using your legs.

THE UTERUS AND PELVIS

It is not unusual to feel aching on occasion in your groin on one or both sides just above the pubic bones. This sensation is due to the stretching of the round ligaments that attach the front sides of your uterus to your pelvis. (See figure 2.)

Rubbing firmly with your hand in a slow, circular motion at the point of strain may help to ease the tension.

As further preparation for the birth process, the uterus will contract at regular intervals throughout pregnancy to strengthen itself. These contractions, called Braxton-Hicks contractions after the British physician who "discovered" them, are involuntary. They are more noticeable during and after physical exertion, following orgasm, or when a woman is frightened, fatigued, surprised, or angry. Women who have borne several children generally begin to notice these contractions earlier and more frequently than in previous pregnancies. Since Braxton-Hicks contractions are not associated with changes in the cervix, or with opening of the uterus, they are not true labor contractions.

Also, the joints in your pelvis will become somewhat looser due to the influence of a hormone called *relaxin*. This is the Lord's way of making the bone structure through which your baby passes a bit more flexible.

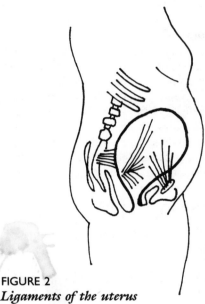

FIGURE 2
Ligaments of the uterus

YOUR CIRCULATORY SYSTEM

By late pregnancy, your total blood volume (which includes that of your baby and placenta) is 30 to 40 percent greater than normal. At this time, it is not unusual to have a lower percentage of iron or hemoglobin in your bloodstream. If that is the case, your health care provider may recommend that you take an iron supplement.

Since hemoglobin carries oxygen to all the cells in your body, it is important that you avoid becoming anemic. Oxygen is consumed in high quantities during labor. This is because the uterus requires oxygen for energy in order to function effectively. Anemia lowers your ability to carry oxygen in your blood. It can also decrease your resistance to infection, make you more prone to fatigue, and increase your sensitivity to pain.

The hormone progesterone relaxes certain muscles within your body. Although its main purpose is to keep the uterus relaxed until the appropriate time for labor to begin, it acts on smooth muscle throughout your entire body. This means that the muscles within the walls of your veins are more relaxed, and varicose veins may result. In your legs, it is more difficult for your blood to return to your heart because it must move "uphill" against gravity. Wearing support hose, walking daily, raising your feet, and doing exercises with your feet all are ways to help the blood get back to your heart more easily, causing less pressure on the walls of your leg veins. Try to get your feet up during the day, and use the following two exercises to help to stimulate leg circulation:

Foot Pumps. While sitting or lying down, pump your feet back and forth as if you were playing an old-fashioned organ. Be careful not to point your toes; you might get a "charley horse."

Foot Circles. While sitting or lying down, circle one or both feet outward and back to the center over and over again. After doing this for a minute or two, reverse the direction and circle inward. Do these frequently, especially if you have been sitting or lying down for a period of time.

Elevated blood pressure and swelling due to fluid retention are not unusual conditions during late pregnancy. By keeping your total protein intake to 100 grams or more per day, restricting the amount of salty foods you eat, and resting on your left side for several hours per day, you may be able to alleviate these conditions.

Some of the sodium-rich food you should limit include:

Pork products: ham,* bacon,* sausage,* hot dogs*

Cheeses: processed cheese, cheese dips, snack spreads

Most canned: meats,* soups, stews,* vegetables

Snacks: pretzels, popcorn, potato chips, many crackers

Seasonings: prepared mustard, catsup, Worcestershire sauce, steak sauce, soy sauce, pickles, relishes, meat tenderizers, many brands of peanut butter

Other: baking soda and most fast-food restaurant items

*These foods also contain high amounts of nitrites.

YOUR DIGESTIVE SYSTEM

Your baby will press against your stomach and intestines as he grows, causing less room for food and difficulties in digestion. The action of progesterone upon smooth muscle in your stomach and intestines also slows down the entire process considerably, sometimes causing heartburn and constipation.

Drinking an adequate amount of water and eating foods high in fiber will place less strain on your bowels. Also, restricting your intake of greasy foods is wise since fat is the most difficult nutrient to digest. The exception to this recommendation is whole or 2 percent butterfat milk, which can help to alleviate heartburn by coating the lining of the stomach.

During the last six to eight weeks of pregnancy it is particularly helpful to eat six smaller meals rather than three large meals per day. (Refer to appendix A for food servings and menu suggestions.) Actually, this eating pattern is probably a more efficient way to eat throughout life. Avoiding spicy foods or eating close to bedtime may promote comfort as well.

Frequency of urination is unavoidable during the last trimester due to the baby's growth and the settling of the baby into your lower pelvis. One of the nicest things about giving birth is that you get your bladder back! It is fairly typical during pregnancy to wake up several times a night to empty your bladder, which is the Lord's way of helping you to prepare for night feedings!

BREAST CHANGES

During late pregnancy your breasts are preparing for their role of nourishing your baby after he is born. Your veins will become more noticeable through your skin as the blood supply to the glands in your breasts increases. The little bumps on your areola (the dark ring around the nipple) become more prominent. These small bumps are called the "glands of Montgomery." They secrete a substance that moisturizes your nipples and kills bacteria. For this reason cleansing your nipples with soap is unnecessary.

The skin color of the areola also darkens, and the breasts themselves become larger as the glandular tissue develops. All of these changes serve to remind you of the special purpose the Lord had in mind when he created this part of your body.

PREPARING YOUR BREASTS FOR LACTATION

Six to eight weeks before your due date is the ideal time to start preparing your breasts for lactation. However, even one or two weeks' worth of preparation will help. Use the following techniques in your preparation:

Breast Massage. During pregnancy, the glands in your breasts become much larger, producing firmer breasts and, occasionally, feelings of heaviness. Massaging your breasts may help to encourage the flow of milk because it stimulates the ducts and glands by improving circulation, and makes the ducts more elastic.

Simply place your hands at the base of the left breast where it is fullest, near the chest. Your hands are positioned with one hand on each side, with your thumbs above the breast and the remaining fingers below. Just slide your hands together gently and firmly in a smooth motion toward the nipple. Repeat this movement several times. Don't forget to massage both breasts in this manner.

Hand Expression of Colostrum. Colostrum is a substance that precedes the production of milk. It is rich in proteins and high in antibodies. To hand express colostrum, position your thumb above and first two fingers below and grasp the area of your left breast where the darkened area (areola) meets the lighter skin. Gently press your fingers and thumb toward your chest, away from the nipple, and then compress them together to squeeze out any fluid which the massage brought down to the collecting ducts located under this area. Rotate your hand clockwise and repeat this compression so that by the time you have finished you have expressed at the twelve, three, six and nine o'clock points.

Don't be concerned if no colostrum appears. It will eventually and this should be considered practice for the hand expression of milk to lessen swelling (engorgement) and to prepare bottles for supplements. There is a belief that the colostrum should be saved for the baby. So far, no adequate research supports this belief. However, you may wish to check with your doctor before doing any hand expression.

TOUGHENING THE SKIN OF THE NIPPLES

Basically, do not overprotect your breasts. Whenever possible, allow your nipples to be exposed to the air. One way this can be done is to wear a nursing bra with the flaps down while at home. In the shower, let the water spray on the nipples. Avoid drying products such as soap or astringents. After bathing or showering, use your dry towel to rub the nipples. During lovemaking, encourage your husband to stimulate your nipples if it is something you both enjoy. Pressure to the skin of the nipples develops *keratin*, or that part of the tissue that produces tougher skin.

Nipple rolling is another method for toughening this area. Grasp your nipple between your thumb and forefinger. Gently pull the nipple outward until you feel a slight discomfort and then slowly rotate the nipple. Continue this for about a minute and repeat on the opposite side.

After toughening the nipples, you may wish to apply a thin layer of pure hydrous lanolin (unless you are allergic to wool), vitamin E oil, or A & D Ointment. These moisturize the skin and counteract the drying effects of bathing.

TREATING INVERTED OR FLAT NIPPLES

If your nipples do not become erect easily, do the nipple rolling more frequently to encourage the shaping of the nipples for breast-feeding. Breast shields are available locally for true inverted nipples. They are worn inside the bra and break down the inner adhesions around the nipples which pull them inward. Many women have found that these double-walled plastic shields help tremendously. If you grasp your nipple, pull it out and let go, you will see the nipple react below the skin if the nipples are inverted. Flat nipples are simply those which do not stay firm and erect for long following this check.

OTHER CHANGES

In addition to the changes already mentioned, there are several other physical and emotional stages of late pregnancy:

- Increased vaginal discharges due to hormonal activity. Try to remember that this prepares your vaginal tissue to become softer and more elastic. Wear breathable, cotton underwear.
- Increased consumption of oxygen and need to breathe due to a greater demand for air in your bloodstream. You don't have to apologize for being out of breath all the time. You really are breathing for two.
- Increased restlessness and decreased ability to sleep soundly. This is due to all the changes mentioned. It also is possibly related to high levels of estrogen circulating throughout your system.
- Decreased ability to concentrate and remember things. I wonder why? Seriously, this is most likely the result of the constant involvement of your body in meeting all the demands of late pregnancy and nurturing your baby.
- Engagement of the baby into the pelvis as labor draws nearer. This can happen up to eight weeks ahead, but two to four weeks prior to labor is the average for a first-time mother. Engagement usually occurs later for a woman who has given birth previously. With the engagement of the baby, the diaphragm can move more freely, making breathing easier. Bladder space, however, is reduced considerably. Backache, rectal pressure, and hip discomfort are common with the additional weight of the baby pressing on the lower pelvis.

By the end of pregnancy your body will have readied itself and your baby for labor. Not surprisingly, you will be thankful when labor finally begins.

COMMON PHYSICAL CONCERNS OF LATE PREGNANCY AND IDEAS FOR COMFORT

COMPLAINT:	REASON:	HOW TO HELP:
Fatigue, restlessness	Your need for rest is interfered with by your ever-growing baby. A decrease in bladder capacity requires frequent urination. Vivid dreams and anxiety can result in lack of rest. It may be difficult to find a comfortable resting position.	Accept the situation as temporary. Your pregnancy won't last much longer. Rest in a semi-sitting or left-side-lying position. Eliminate all activities that are not necessary. Communicate your concerns to share the load. Short, frequent rest periods with music and relaxation techniques after emptying your bladder may help. Pray that the Lord will give you rest.
Constipation	This may be caused by iron supplements and sluggishness in your intestinal tract due to the effects of progesterone, a hormone secreted in high amounts during pregnancy which relaxes smooth muscle.	Avoid caffeine. Drink weak, warm tea upon rising in the morning. Eat plenty of dried fruit, whole grains, and bran. Avoid eating too much cheese or too many bananas. Drink six to eight glasses of water daily.
Breathlessness	As your uterus grows upward it presses against your diaphragm, making lung expansion more difficult. Also, your growing baby needs increasing amounts of oxygen so that the mother's oxygen consumption is 30 to 40 percent above normal.	Slow, deeper breathing helps. Avoid lying flat on your back since the weight of your baby on blood vessels beneath the uterus decreases the availability of oxygen. Stretch your arms overhead, reach with one arm at a time toward the ceiling while doing slow breathing.
Hemorrhoids	A combination of straining and the condition of relaxed walls of rectal veins (due to progesterone) leads to this problem.	Try to solve the constipation problem so that straining can be avoided. Prop feet on stool while sitting on toilet. Tucks pads offer relief of discomfort.
Varicose veins	Also due to the effect of progesterone which relaxes the muscle in leg veins, resulting in decreased resistance to blood flow. The weight of your uterus makes blood flow to your legs sluggish as well.	Foot Pumping and Foot Rotation (see p. 58) as well as walking aid in increasing circulation. Resting with feet propped up makes it easier for blood to return to the heart.
Swelling of ankles, fingers	An alteration in your metabolism.	Increase protein intake. Rest lying on left side for one to three hours, three times per day (!!!). Do not restrict fluids or take "water pills" if at all possible.
Lower back pain	Your enlarged uterus is anchored to your lower back. When the uterus is pulled forward due to poor posture or use of the body without regard for how to properly adjust body mechanics for late pregnancy, pain is more severe.	Use the Pelvic Tilt (see p. 54) to relax the broad ligament supporting your uterus. Rest with knees propped up when lying down. Roll onto side to get up. Lift and stand up with awareness of back and how to utilize posture and legs to decrease strain.

(cont.)

COMPLAINT	REASON	HOW TO HELP
Groin ache	Round ligaments anchor the uterus to the pubic area on both sides. As the uterus grows, your ligaments are stretched.	Rub with heel of hand in a firm, circular motion. Apply warm compresses.
Braxton-Hicks contractions	This is a "warm-up" exercise involuntarily conducted by the uterus to tone and strengthen itself.	Light massage, pubic stroking, slow breathing, and conscious release. Use these contractions to practice relaxation and breathing techniques.
Heartburn	Your enlarged uterus displaces your digestive tract and the relaxing effect of progesterone on the cardiac sphincter of your stomach allows for the seepage of gastric juices into your esophagus.	Avoid large, heavy meals and greasy foods. Rest with your head elevated and try not to eat within four hours of retiring. Eat several smaller meals rather than three large ones.
Itchy skin	Your skin is stretching over the growing breasts and uterus.	Wear non-irritating clothing. Lubricate skin; pure cocoa butter or vitamin E oil works well. Take warm showers.
Vaginal discharge	This can be considered normal unless there is foul odor or an inflamed, itching vulva.	Proper hygiene, mini-pads and cotton-crotch panties help. Avoid feminine deodorants, powders, and bubble baths.
Leaking of urine	The weight of your baby on your pelvic floor weakens the contracting ability of the sphincter around the urethral opening.	Kegel exercises, frequent urination, mini-pads.
Anxiety, apprehension	Major changes are taking place involving shifts in life-style and priorities. The health and condition of the baby is a cause of concern to many expectant parents.	Communication of your concerns, acceptance of how you are feeling. Go to appropriate sources for reassurance, guidance, and information. Review "Preparing Your Inner Self," in chapter 4.
"Charley horses," leg cramps	Excessive potassium or insufficient amounts of calcium in the bloodstream may cause this problem.	Do not massage the cramped muscle. Stretch out cramps by pulling toes up while pressing heel down.

CHAPTER SEVEN
Planning Your Baby's Birth Day

"In his heart a man plans his course, but the Lord determines his steps." PROVERBS 16:9

*I*n our culture today, there is no one "right" way to give birth. Expectant parents usually can choose who will deliver their baby, where their baby will be born, who will accompany the mother through labor, and what things can be done to make their baby's birth special. It is not unlike planning a wedding. A traditional model exists, yet there are many variations.

During pregnancy, there is a waiting period that begins with the pregnancy being confirmed and ends with the onset of labor and the baby's birth. The length of this period is typically seven or eight months long. It is similar to a premarital engagement period. Once the date is known, the preparing and planning begin. Where will the event take place? Who will perform the ceremony? What about guests? What things will be done to make this moment one of a kind? But there is ample time to prepare for the event and to find out the answers to these questions.

CHOOSING YOUR HEALTH CARE PROVIDER

Prenatal care primarily involves three people: the mother, her unborn child, and the mother's health care provider. The baby's father also plays an important role in protecting his wife by helping her adapt her life-style to promote the well-being of herself and their baby. Your choice of a health care provider who will attend the birth in a way that fits your needs will be one of the most important decisions you make. Find out which of the following professionals are available in your community and then determine who can best meet your health care needs.

OBSTETRICIAN

An obstetrician is a medical doctor (M.D.) or doctor of osteopathy (D.O.) who attended medical school for a period of four years and has completed a three-year residency in the area of his or her specialization of obstetrics. This type of physician is usually a practicing gynecologist as well, and therefore a trained surgeon. The ability to treat the complications of pregnancy and childbirth makes an O.B. the most skilled (and therefore the most expensive) maternity health care provider.

If your pregnancy or birth requires expert medical care, you will want to consider an obstetrician. Select an O.B. with whom you feel compatible. If you are against abortion, you may want to find out which O.B.'s perform them in your city and choose not to give them your business.

FAMILY PRACTITIONER

A family practitioner is also either a medical doctor (M.D.) or a doctor of osteopathy (D.O.). Family practice physicians certified since the late sixties have been required to complete a three-year residency program after graduating from medical school. Family practitioners can treat a variety of complications, but are unable to perform cesarean births. For this reason, family practitioners work closely with obstetricians so that an O.B. would be available if necessary.

Many family practice physicians use less routine types of obstetrical intervention and are more conservative about the use of anesthetics during labor. G.P.'s, or general practitioners, are usually doctors who have not completed a three-year residency in family practice or any other specialty, but may provide excellent care due to years of experience.

NURSE-MIDWIFE

Nearly all states provide for the practice of nurse-midwifery and have laws that determine the level of schooling that a nurse-midwife must complete before being allowed to practice professionally. This type of health care provider is a registered nurse who has studied normal gynecology and obstetrics for a one- to two-year period beyond nurse's training.

Nurse-midwives are typically women, whereas many obstetricians and family practitioners are men. Some women consider gender to be an important factor in their selection of a health care provider. Nurse-midwives are qualified to practice normal obstetrics and "well-woman" gynecological care (pap tests, family planning, and regular exams). They must work in conjunction with physicians who serve as their backup if complications arise. A nurse-midwife remains with her client throughout the entire labor, whereas physicians are available only as needed.

TRADITIONAL OR "LAY" MIDWIVES

This profession provided most of the obstetrical care available to childbearing women until the early 1900s. Midwives practice independently, usually attending births in the home, and may or may not be working directly with a physician. Their training varies from having attended relatively few births to being part of a family tradition that extends back through many generations.

A number of midwives practice their art from a spiritual viewpoint; a certain percentage of lay midwives attending home births are Christians, and vary widely in their philosophies. Only a few states have licensure and certification laws which regulate the practice of lay-midwifery, and in some states this practice is considered either illegal or "outside the law."

In considering your health care provider, it is important to think about who is available in your area. Choose whom you are most comfortable with as a couple. Pray together and try to evaluate the skills of the person you are considering by finding out about their training, scope, location and philosophy of practice, availability, and costs. (See figure 1.)

Basically, there are two approaches to providing maternity care. The first approach is the "traditional" approach. With this type of care, the emphasis is on the risk factors; institutionalized settings (labor and birth in separate rooms, centralized nursery, no home support) are used; care is routinized; the economic and legal considerations are from the medical team's view; the education, philosophy, and personal values considered are those of the medical team; beliefs and attitudes are traditional; and there is a lack of involvement from nonmedical disciplines.

The alternative model or approach to maternity care involves an emphasis on pregnancy and birth as normal life processes; a desire for alternative settings (birthing rooms and centers, decentralized nurseries, and home care); individualized care with the economic and legal considerations taken from the consumer's view; the education, philosophy, and personal values of the parents are the determinants; the beliefs and attitudes are not necessarily traditional; and there is multidisciplinary involvement.

Health care is expensive in America. Services differ from place to place and practices vary among health care providers. It is wise to look around before you "buy," especially if your community offers a variety of maternity care services. The numerous options available can be confusing, but they also allow for a greater freedom to choose the type of medical care that is best suited to one's physical needs, life-style, personal values, and budget. Parents can now be more discriminating as to where they spend their health care dollars if they consider the options carefully.

FIGURE I — **POINTS TO PONDER WHEN DECIDING ON A HEALTH CARE PROVIDER**

TRAINING
Certification, place of education, years of experience.

SCOPE OF PRACTICE
Which situations must be referred to a specialist.

PHILOSOPHY OF PRACTICE
Routine recommendations for use of drugs, surgery, and technology during labor; attitudes concerning birth alternatives; view of pregnancy and birth (primarily as inherently dangerous, or normally uncomplicated) and basis of practice (traditional or an alternative approach).

AVAILABILITY
On-call schedule; office hours; length of wait for an appointment or during an office visit; who does the backup if unavailable?

COSTS
Fee; what is included; third party or Medicaid reimbursement; how payment is made (must you pay and wait to be reimbursed through your insurance company?).

LOCATIONS OF PRACTICE
Office location; hospital(s) used (family-centered maternity care, size, neonatal intensive care unit, availability of alternative birth settings such as birthing rooms, birthing chairs, and birthing centers); father's involvement (extent of Dad's involvement during both vaginal and cesarean birth).

OTHER QUESTIONS TO ASK
Is it important to you that your health care provider be a Christian? Do you feel at ease with this person? Does he or she seem responsive to your concerns and able to adequately answer your questions? Does this provider perform abortions or does he or she practice at a hospital where abortions are done? (You may want to consider boycotting any physician or institution that performs abortions as a means of acting on your beliefs . . . but write a letter to explain why to make a greater impact!)

DETERMINING THE PLACE OF BIRTH

When planning where your baby's birth will take place, it is helpful to think about the services available near where you live. In some areas of the country, alternative settings for birth benefit from a degree of medical support that may not be as available in other locations. For a specific comparison of health care options visit the settings that appeal to you and inquire about their policies. It is best not to wait until the seventh or eighth month of pregnancy to do this, since you may find that your health care provider does not utilize the service that suits your needs. If possible, explore all available settings early and then find a health care provider that works at the place you have chosen.

While all of this may seem complicated or just plain unnecessary, remember that there is an incredible freedom to select what is best for your own situation. Living in America provides us with such abundance in all areas of our lives, including maternity care. No one can say what is ultimately going to be the best for you in terms of maternity care. It is between you, your spouse, and the Lord. By being informed, you can utilize the mind God has given to you to make the decisions relative to your care. Compare what's available, then make your plans with the Lord's blessing by committing what you are doing to him. Trust him to direct your steps and be open to changes that may become necessary as the circumstances of your pregnancy and birth unfold.

PICKING YOUR LABOR COMPANIONS

As the time of your baby's birth draws near, thoughts of who will accompany you through labor and birth will increase. This person, or group of people, will be important to you. You will be sharing one of the most important and

IN-HOSPITAL SETTINGS

PROS	CONS
A. HOSPITALS Many types of emergency equipment are readily available; anesthesia for pain relief is available; staff is made up of physicians, nurses, and, where allowed, nurse-midwives; medical personnel are liable for the management of the mother and the baby's health care; recovery is medically supervised for as long as the mother remains in the hospital	Hospital setting can seem foreign and cause apprehension; maternity care is usually routinized; the hospital controls who is present and what roles people play at the birth; unfamiliar bacteria increase the chance of infection; hospitals are the most expensive setting for birth
B. IN-HOSPITAL BIRTHING CENTER The normalcy of birth is emphasized; emergency equipment is available, but is stored out of sight; there are fewer, if any, routine procedures; staff is shared with the hospital labor and delivery unit; liability is assumed by the staff and hospital	Maternity care in this setting may remain fairly routinized and may not be substantially different from the hospital; staff may stipulate who is present and what roles they must assume; unfamiliar bacteria are present; the center may cost the same as a regular hospital birth unless the mother and baby are discharged early

OUT-OF-HOSPITAL SETTINGS

PROS	CONS
A. FREESTANDING MATERNITY CLINIC	
The normalcy of birth is emphasized; it's relatively inexpensive; no routine procedures are used; setting seems friendlier; childbearing families may control who is present at the birth and what roles they assume, through discussion with health care providers; it's usually staffed by nurse- or lay-midwives; early discharge promotes family's responsibility for Mother's and Baby's care	Certain medical conditions may require the mother's or baby's transfer to a hospital; there may be restrictions as to what drugs a woman may take (extensive anesthesia usually not available); liability may vary with the setting
B. HOME BIRTH	
Birth is viewed as a family event; little, if any, intervention in the birth process is used; the family controls who is present; the home provides a familiar setting, with familiar bacteria; parents assume responsibility for the outcome of the birth; home birth is the least expensive option	Emergency treatment is usually not readily available; there is no access to pain-relieving drugs; there may be a lack of medical backup to provide Mother with expert care, if necessary; many health care professionals are vehemently opposed to home birth and may make any necessary care unpleasant

intimate events of your life with whomever is present!

Until the late sixties, fathers were unwelcome at the births of their babies in most hospitals across the United States. With the popularization of prepared childbirth, a movement developed due to the efforts of a large number of parents and other professionals. These people brought about consumer demand for the inclusion of the husband in his wife's labor and birth. Within a relatively brief period of time, most hospitals changed their policies and began allowing father participation throughout the entire process of childbirth.

There are very few hospitals today that do not include fathers in this experience, with the majority actually encouraging the involvement of dads in labor and in the care of the baby after birth. A large number of hospitals do not restrict father participation to just "natural" or vaginal births, but also recognize the value of having the husband present during cesarean birth. The concept of the father's involvement throughout the childbearing cycle is called "family-centered maternity care."

Not every man is comfortable being a labor companion to his wife. In such cases, a woman benefits from choosing a labor companion whom she trusts and knows well, such as a friend or a relative. Actually, it is not a bad idea at all to have two labor companions, since it may be necessary for one to take a break, and they can provide emotional support for one another as well as for the mother during the busiest times of labor.

A labor companion is someone who deeply cares about your well-being and shares your commitment to the Lord; has an ongoing interest in you and your baby; is able to be gentle, aggressive, and straightforward with you; can recognize his or her limitations and is comfortable asking for help and advice; is able to interpret your ideas, concerns, and wishes to your health care providers if you are too involved in labor to do so; will support you to the extent that he or she will not depend on you to determine what to do during difficult moments, but will be prepared enough to offer you help as needed, and will remain sensitive to your nonverbal as well as your verbal requests; is available to listen to you relive your birth experience afterward, whether it takes days, weeks, or months of actual sharing as you assimilate it into your life.

When I am asked what the most important factors were that enabled me to cope during my four labors, I always reply that it was a combination of the Lord's support and my husband's help. I can't imagine giving birth without the presence of either! Somehow my husband's masculinity gave me extra strength; he was a broad chest to lean on, strong arms to hold me, and large hands to rub my back. His protectiveness and gentleness conveyed the Lord's love to me in a very tangible way. Also, the bond between us grew with each baby that we birthed together as we shared the pain and joy of each delivery.

I also have had friends or family members present for extra help at each of my children's births. These were people with whom I could be myself and express my strongest emotions freely. That is not to say that they were there every minute—emphatically not! Instead, these were people who could be called on to relieve my husband, provide prayer support, or help in other ways when needed. This has always been a source of comfort to me, to know that I would never be left alone and that I was being prayed for by those who love me.

MAKING YOUR BIRTH EXPERIENCE ONE OF A KIND

There may be aspects of your baby's birth that are important for you to personalize. The birth attendant, place of birth, and labor companions you select will have an impact on how your labor goes. Beyond these, there are many ways to make each childbirth unique. The following are some ideas:

Music: Cassette tapes can be picked out ahead of time and played throughout labor. What music relaxes you? Some women even sing during labor!

Clothing: You need not wear a hospital gown that ties in the back, and is impossible for nursing discreetly. Simply bring a gown or two of your own to wear. Don't forget to take some socks or slippers.

Recording the birth: Photographs, tape recordings, home movies, and videotaping are all commonly used today by parents who wish to make a lasting record of their baby's birth. Check with the staff if you would like to gauge the light level ahead of time or if you need permission to use unusual types of cameras or equipment. Or, you might wish to make a journal or written account of the baby's birth.

Objects of visual interest: It helps to look at things other than a clock at the foot of your bed during labor. An extensive list of ideas can be found in chapter 9. Or you may discover that you prefer to keep your eyes closed.

Activity and labor position: Walking, bathing, showering, and rocking in a rocking chair may all be ways to help you feel more like yourself during labor, unless there is a specific reason for you to be in bed.

Prayer and Scripture: Use posters, cassette tapes, or handmade items to remind you of those prayers or Scriptures that are especially meaningful to you. Your labor companion may read aloud or hold the Bible for you to read to yourself. Constant prayer is very helpful in keeping your mind off any fear that you may feel. Or you may wish to choose a personalized "my" passage from Scripture to meditate on and use as your "word picture," such as "I love you, O Lord, my strength. The Lord is my rock, my fortress and my deliverer; my God is my rock, in whom I take refuge. He is my shield and the horn of my salvation, my stronghold" (Psalm 18:1, 2).

Drawing near to the Lord: The Bible is full of word pictures that describe the many attributes of God. You might find it helpful to picture the Lord as several of these "I ams" from the Bible, for example: "I am your shield, your very great reward" (Genesis 15:1); "I am God Almighty" (Genesis 17:1); "I am with you and will bless you" (Genesis 26:24), and many others. See Exodus 15:26; 16:12; 22:27; 31:13; Leviticus 11:45; Numbers 18:20; Song of Solomon 2:1; Isaiah 44:6; 45:22; 49:26; 51:12; Jeremiah 1:8; Matthew 11:29; 17:5; 28:20(KJV); Luke 22:27; John 6:48, 51; 8:12, 23; 10:11; 11:25; 14:6; 15:1; and Revelation 1:8, 18.

Remember, your birth experience will be greatly influenced by the what, who, and where of your choosing. Planning your baby's birth day, like planning your wedding, is a reflection of your personal needs, tastes, and preferences. Learn what is available in your community and make the decisions that will allow you to labor and give birth in an environment where you feel safe. No matter what you choose, the Lord will be right by your side as you look to him for protection, strength, and guidance.

Trust in the Lord and do good; dwell in the land and enjoy safe pasture. Delight yourself in the Lord and he will give you the desires of your heart (Psalm 37:3, 4).

CHAPTER EIGHT

Learning to Labor Together

"Two are better than one, because they have a good return for their work. . . . A cord of three strands is not quickly broken."
ECCLESIASTES 4:9, 12

When a woman labors to bring forth a child, she must travel a road that has been negotiated many times before by countless women through the ages. Yet, for each woman, the journey is different. Because of this, it is a journey that benefits from the companionship of a friend. When the going gets rough, the stronger can lift the other up. Also interwoven into this cord of friendship is a relationship with the Lord. He forms the third part of a friendship strand that is "not quickly broken."

A woman in labor is very sensitive to the presence of those who are around her. In fact, it's not at all uncommon for a woman to "fall in love" with her physician, or exaggerate the doctor's role in caring for her. A husband who works through labor with his wife helps to prevent this type of displaced affection as he asserts his role as a friend who "loves at all times."

Because some churches and fellowships discourage the presence of the husband during childbirth, it is important for you to prayerfully consider together what the Lord would have you do in this respect. Then you must act in accordance with what seems right for your individual situation.

Through this chapter, the primary labor companion is referred to as the husband because this has now become common practice. However, the activities and duties described here can be performed by whomever you choose to accompany you through labor.

There are three phases in your childbearing experience in which your labor companion should ideally be involved. These include prenatal preparation for labor, the birth itself, and the first six weeks after the baby's birth. (This last stage, called the postpartum phase, is discussed in chapters 9 and 15.)

PRENATAL PREPARATION

Since you will function as a team during childbirth, you must prepare for the experience together. As you read the rest of this chapter, remember that these prenatal preparations will help strengthen both of you, and ready you for a very special, unique time. (Chapter 9 covers what to do during labor and the birth.)

TALKING TO EXPERIENCED PARENTS
It is important for you to develop a relationship with a couple with whom you feel comfortable, who care for their child or children in a way that you would like to raise your child. This person-to-person contact is invaluable, even if it is fairly short-term due to changes or moves in your lives.

This sharing relationship enables the more experienced couple to teach by example, and to include the couple expecting a baby in many family activities. Having close friends to learn from is a true blessing.

PRAYING TOGETHER
Surprisingly enough, many Christian couples do not pray together regularly other than at mealtimes. The Lord promised that "where two or three come together in my name, there I am with them" (Matthew 18:20). I can remember when the impact of this promise hit home with my husband and myself, and we realized how Christ strengthened our marital bond when we prayed together.

We all have a lot to pray for. With each new child born into a family there comes additional responsibilities and relationships. There are nu-merous concerns and needs to be brought before the Lord. Scriptures such as 1 Thessalonians 5:17, James 5:16, Colossians 4:2, Romans 12:12, and Ephesians 6:18 show very clearly that, as Christians, we are called to pray continually.

Season all your preparations for your new baby with prayer. Share your concerns with the Lord together, and your union in him will reap the harvest of the prayers you sow.

SEEKING SPIRITUAL GUIDANCE
There may be times during your pregnancy when you find it is beyond your ability to cope with a certain situation. Within the body of Christ you may find those who can offer you the help you need. If you experience marital conflict (not uncommon during pregnancy), financial crisis, poor health, or any other difficulty that seems too much to handle, consider sharing your concerns with your pastor or another qualified person in your church.

Those in leadership roles in the church desire to serve others. By their example, our faith is increased. This is a wonderful benefit of fellowship with the body of Christ, and is the means through which we may experience God's love for us and serve one another in practical ways.

In Paul's first letter to the church in Corinth, he wrote: "If one part suffers, every part suffers with it; if one part is honored, every part rejoices

BENEFITS OF HUSBANDS AS LABOR COMPANIONS

When a husband is willing to support his wife through pregnancy and childbirth, a number of benefits result:
- The husband's compassion for and understanding of his wife's nature deepen.
- The bond that was shared through the act of love which created their child will widen to include the husband's participation in the birth as well.
- His sense of attachment to his wife and baby will become more real to him as he participates in his baby's life from the very first breath.
- His involvement in caring for his wife during childbirth will reinforce their sense of "oneness" and belonging to each other.

with it. Now you are the body of Christ, and each one of you is a part of it" (1 Corinthians 12:26, 27).

READING BOOKS

The past decade has been termed the most explosive in the earth's history for the written word. Thousands of books and publications in every area, including that of maternal and child health, are printed around the world each day. Today's selection of books on pregnancy, childbirth, breast-feeding, and parenting is overwhelming. These books, as well as numerous magazines and journals, are written from a variety of perspectives, some based on worldly philosophies or Eastern mysticism in one or several of its westernized forms. We need to follow 1 John 4:1-6, which cautions us to carefully consider the spirit behind what we are reading, hearing, seeing, or otherwise experiencing.

Christians should not condemn authors who hold a different view, but we should realize that some books are more educational than others, and do not include a strong feminist or mystical viewpoint. Sadly, there are very few books that promote the value of human life and the wisdom of the Lord's creation while at the same time offering an accurate account of childbearing or parenting. (A recommended reading list of helpful and informative materials is included in the back of this book. Also, most libraries now carry an excellent selection of books on these subjects.)

By reading books, you help supplement your experience with accurate information that helps you plan the birth, prepare your body for labor, learn about breast-feeding, and consider ways to parent your child. Books can be an invaluable resource, since practices pertaining to childbirth and parenting are now seldom passed from one generation to another.

TAKING CLASSES

Taking the following types of classes can provide you with reinforcement, camaraderie, demonstrations, motivation, a variety of views, and, most importantly, practice. As long as you remember to pick and choose from the information presented, taking any class that fits your needs will help you become better prepared for birth and beyond.

Be sure to inquire about prices, location, philosophy, the training of instructors, and the involvement of participants before enrolling. If a registered nurse is teaching, ask what additional training she has had to enable her to become an adult educator.

The availability of different types of childbirth classes varies widely among communities. The following types of programs may be offered where you live:

Early Pregnancy—Emphasis is placed on the prevention of birth defects and complication of pregnancy and childbirth. Discussions include nutrition, exercise, and the avoidance of substances harmful to the developing baby. Common complaints of the first six months are reviewed, and relief measures are offered. The emotional changes often related to the first months of pregnancy may also be presented.

Prenatal Fitness—Focuses on maintaining overall fitness, promoting relaxation habits, and strengthening the areas of the body most affected by pregnancy.

Infant Care Classes—Basic techniques of infant care are demonstrated and discussed, including bathing, diapering, comforting, feeding methods, and caring for a baby that is ill.

Preparation for Parenting—These programs may include the infant care skills listed above, as well as infant development and the financial, emotional, and practical aspects of early parenting.

Lamaze Classes—These are taught differently wherever they are offered, but basically they are taught from a viewpoint that emphasizes the active participation of both parents throughout the childbearing cycle. Most classes include use of visual aids (such as charts and movies), information on obstetrical procedures, and demonstrations of many types of relief measures. Self-help techniques are central to all Lamaze instruction.

Bradley Classes—This method emphasizes the participation of the father during childbirth and stresses muscular relaxation. The dangers of obstetric drugs and interventions also are discussed. The Bradley method is an extension of the Dick-Read method, both of which hold the philosophy of "natural childbirth" as their central theme.

Dick-Read or Natural Childbirth Classes—Advocates of this method focus on the importance of relaxation and prenatal exercise in preparation for birth. The process of childbirth is explained to alleviate fear and dispel any misconceptions a couple may have about birth.

Prenatal Yoga Classes—Yoga is not just a form of physical exercise, but it is intimately connected to the philosophy of Hinduism. There are other ways to relax that will not introduce the influence of Hinduism into the lives of Christians.

Birthing Center and Home Birth Classes—If you are planning an out-of-hospital birth in a freestanding birthing center, or in your home, it is wise to take the classes offered by the center or your midwife. These will help prepare you for the experience you have chosen, and inform you as to what to expect should any complications arise.

Breast-feeding Classes—In our culture, breast-feeding is an art that is not usually passed from mother to daughter. Understanding myths concerning breast-feeding and gaining accurate information are keys to successful lactation. Prenatal nipple preparation is demonstrated and visual aids such as slides and movies may be used.

Cesarean Birth Classes—With father participation in cesarean birth, a need has risen to prepare couples for going through such a birth together. Visual aids of the procedures involved are utilized, and pain relief measures, types of anesthesia, and emotional responses to having a baby by cesarean are discussed.

Vaginal Birth After Cesarean (V.B.A.C.)—The most recent type of birth preparation class is the V.B.A.C. series, which teaches women who have had a cesarean how to cope with labor and prepare for a vaginal birth.

Other types of classes are available; those included here are represented on a nationwide basis. Classes may be available through a C.E.A. (Childbirth Education Association run by a board of parents and professionals), your health care providers, hospitals and clinics, birth centers, community colleges, the Red Cross, a YMCA or YWCA, independent childbirth educators, and many other organizations.

For additional classes, consult the Yellow Pages in your phone book under "Childbirth education" or "Parents."

Classes specifically designed for Christian parents are becoming more widely available. *Genesia Childbirth Educators,* based in California, offers Lamaze classes from a Christian perspective. *Apple Tree Ministries* (A.T.M.), also based in California, offers a comprehensive program based on the Dick-Read method and includes information on sexuality, natural family planning, breast-feeding, and the Christian family.

GOING TO OFFICE VISITS

Office visits during pregnancy increase in frequency during the last trimester. There are many times when you would rather not wait alone, so why not go together? It is wonderful to hear the baby's heartbeat, and to discuss your birth plans with your health care provider as a couple. This way you both will have a clear understanding of what to expect during labor. Most health care providers welcome the father's presence at prenatal visits and are happy to discuss concerns with you both.

TOURING THE BABY'S BIRTHPLACE

It is beneficial to tour the setting where you plan to have your baby. This can be arranged through childbirth classes or directly through the hospital or center. During the tour, take notes and try to get a clear picture of what takes place where and what policies govern the maternity care offered.

STUDYING SCRIPTURE

Explore the Word for encouraging verses you can use during pregnancy and labor. There are many for you to discover!

Use what the Lord has so generously given to us for edification, strengthening, and instruction in his Scriptures. As Paul wrote in 2 Timothy 3:16, 17: "All Scripture is God-breathed and is useful for teaching, rebuking, correcting and training in righteousness, so that the man of God may be thoroughly equipped for every good work."

LEARNING AND PRACTICING PAIN RELIEF MEASURES

Noninvasive pain relief measures—measures you can use without physically invading or penetrating the body—are methods you can use yourself, or that your labor companion can do for you during labor to enhance your comfort. Needless suffering is pointless when there are safe ways to eliminate some pain during labor.

However, the use of drugs for pain relief is not a situation in which you either use drugs or you don't. There are advantages and disadvantages to any type of pain relief. Inadequate forms of pain relief could result in the mother feeling angry at her baby, or the Lord, for the pain. This also could lead to feelings of bitterness and possibly the desire to not have any more children.

You should discuss with your health care provider the types of medications generally used during labor, and learn the benefits and risks of those drugs.

Some specific times when anesthesia should be used include cesarean birth, a difficult forceps delivery, or when an episiotomy is necessary. These procedures represent additional trauma to the mother's body.

Know that you are free to choose what is best for you, and that you don't have to prove how tough or courageous you are to others or to the Lord. If you decide to use only noninvasive forms of pain relief, do so because that is what makes the most sense and seems the safest for you.

WHY USE NONINVASIVE PAIN RELIEF?

Here are some of the reasons noninvasive pain relief measures are emphasized in this book:

There is no existing drug that is without risk to, or completely safe for, the mother and child.

The use of anesthesia changes birth from a normal to a pathological state, and increases the likelihood of other types of obstetrical procedures being needed (e.g., forceps, hormonal stimulation of labor, or cesarean birth).

Analgesics and anesthetics tend to increase maternal dependence on the medical staff, and remove the mother from a central awareness of what is taking place, which may lower her inhibitions and undermine her self-esteem.

We must not fall into the harmful belief that there is a drug to deal with every discomfort; no drug completely takes away the work of labor. However, obstetrical pain relief methods should be used when medically necessary, or when a woman cannot tolerate the amount of pain she is experiencing in spite of using noninvasive pain relief measures.

ADVANTAGES OF
NONINVASIVE PAIN RELIEF
MEASURES

- Both parents are conscious and able to share in their baby's birth together, which enhances their partnership.
- Effective pain relief measures that are self-applied, or applied by a labor companion, affirm a woman's sense of dignity.
- Such techniques may reduce or eliminate the need for medication.
- The baby normally is not adversely affected by the use of noninvasive methods.
- A nonmedicated mother can consciously respond to the efforts of those caring for her during labor, and often is more alert and less fatigued following the birth.
- A satisfying birth experience enhances the mother's feelings of attachment to her baby.
- Greater participation in the birth process encourages personal and spiritual growth. Many drugs "numb" a person's sensitivity to the Lord, detracting from the mother's ability to pray and reach out to God for help during labor.
- Cooperating with the process of birth may avoid prolonging the labor.

CHAPTER NINE
Coping with Pain in Labor

"As the mountains surround Jerusalem, so the Lord surrounds his people both now and forevermore." PSALM 125:2

*I*t is very important to understand the causes of labor pain. Next to the fear of death, the fear of pain is the greatest fear that exists. People do not enjoy hurting, and will do whatever they can to avoid painful situations.

Pain usually is a protective mechanism that guards the body from sustained injury. If your finger touches a pan just after it leaves a hot oven, your automatic response will cause you to withdraw your hand from the source of pain. An injured muscle will go into a spasm to prevent further harm to the area, making a person move differently until the muscle heals.

Pain also can be purely psychological in origin, such as when a person experiences "phantom limb pain" in an arm or leg years after it has been amputated. There are many different types of pain, all of which can be complex and sometimes difficult to understand.

The function of pain during childbirth has been a challenging issue for many researchers. Birth is the one normal physiological event in the body that usually is accompanied by various degrees of discomfort, yet no injury typically takes place. A woman cannot withdraw the parts of her body from the pain's source, and no drug exists that is completely safe and can solve this problem.

Is this pain a result of Eve's transgression? Are women meant to suffer? As discussed in chapter 1, I believe the Lord wants us to look to him as we give birth. The painful toil of childbirth can result in our looking to him for strength and comfort.

Not only this, but it also helps us better appreciate the fruits of our labor. When a baby is born, his life can have an even greater significance because of the effort required for the birth. A woman who plays an active role in the birth of her baby, who sees her baby come into the world, often finds that her ability to protect and nurture her baby goes far beyond mere social expectations. The painful toil of childbirth ties her to her baby in a special, inimitable manner.

This is not unlike saving one's money for years to buy something valuable. The object holds greater meaning and will receive better care because it was costly. Our relationship with the Lord is similar to this as well. If following him costs us all we have (Matthew 19:16-22), then he truly is the "pearl of great price" (Matthew 13:44-46).

We need to remember how well the Lord knows us, how he loves and leads us. When we acknowledge the reality of Scripture and learn about childbirth, we can go through this special experience with dignity and without an attitude of suffering. We also become able to utilize the tools that modern medicine brings to the experience of childbirth to prevent loss of life and pain beyond that which women can bear.

THREE PHASES OF PAIN EXPERIENCE

There are three phases of pain experience: The anticipation of pain, its presence, and its aftermath. (See figure 1.) Remember that the Lord is with you and will help sustain you through each of these phases. In addition, review the "self-statements" in the chart on page 94, adapting them to your specific needs and situation. The things you think about during the three pain phases will influence your ability to cooperate with your body.

When we look at Mary's response to the angel's news that she would bear the Son of God (Luke 1:38), we realize that her attitude of submission is contrary to the spirit of the world. The biblical pattern expressed throughout the New Testament is radically different from the patterns of today.

The forcefulness of the gospel comes through its gentleness; its power through powerlessness; its victory through submission. As we learn this and work it into our hearts, we will avoid the world's temptations to "do it yourself," and rely on God's strength and help.

STRESS MANAGEMENT IN LABOR

For believers and nonbelievers alike in today's world, stress has become a major health problem. The challenge of coping with our concerns is great, and thousands of people are relying on transcendental meditation, hot tubs, drugs, and alcohol to get them through. Yet, a June 1983 cover story in *Time* magazine reported that an auto worker who had been laid off from three successive jobs was found by a researcher to be tremendously well-adjusted. Why? The man remarked that it was because his wife loved him and he attended church every Sunday!

What exactly *is* stress, and how can it affect childbearing? While there is no set definition, we do know that there are several different types of stress. *Thermal stress* is stress due to high or low temperatures; *physical stress* is due to vigorous bodily activity; *emotional stress* is due to personal situations and family life events; *mental stress* is due to the demand for a high level of mental performance; and *psychological stress* is due to a combination of factors associated with emotional and mental stress.

In childbearing, a combination of both the physical and psychological types of stress is experienced. Labor is physically, emotionally, mentally, and spiritually demanding. Yet it does not have to be stressful in a harmful way.

The Lord has built into our nervous system the capacity to go into action in a life-threatening or dangerous situation. This natural ability is called the "fight-or-flight" response. When we

THE THREE PHASES OF PAIN EXPERIENCE

FIGURE I

Anticipation	Presence	Aftermath
Looking ahead toward the experience	Actual experience	Looking back on the experience

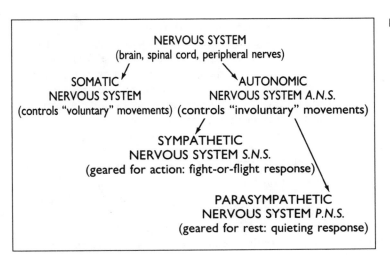

FIGURE 2

NERVOUS SYSTEM
(brain, spinal cord, peripheral nerves)

SOMATIC
NERVOUS SYSTEM
(controls "voluntary" movements)

AUTONOMIC
NERVOUS SYSTEM *A.N.S.*
(controls "involuntary" movements)

SYMPATHETIC
NERVOUS SYSTEM *S.N.S.*
(geared for action: fight-or-flight response)

PARASYMPATHETIC
NERVOUS SYSTEM *P.N.S.*
(geared for rest: quieting response)

become fearful, our body secretes chemical substances, which "turn on" this response. (See the chart on page 96 for the effects of adrenaline on the sympathetic nervous system.)

The *autonomic* (or "automatic") *nervous system* controls the large muscles in the fundus of the uterus during labor. The cervix, on the other hand, is influenced by the *sympathetic nervous system*. When fear stimulates the secretion of stress-related substances, the cervix may either stay closed or open very rapidly. This is a protective mechanism which allows the mother to flee to a place of safety, or quickly deliver her baby and then get away.

When no real danger exists, this can become a problem because labor may continue without progress or become so forceful that the baby is born too fast, not allowing the cervix and birth canal to stretch gradually. This is self-defeating, to say the least.

But be encouraged! The Lord also has built into our bodies a way to undo the effects of stress through the *parasympathetic nervous system*. When the P.N.S. is stimulated, we relax. Bodily processes slow down; energy is conserved. In labor, activation of the P.N.S. allows the body to function more normally, and with greater efficiency. (See figure 2.)

For this reason, it is important to learn how to turn on this nullifier of the fight-or-flight syndrome, called the "quieting response." This response counteracts the effects of stress on the body, allowing uterine contractions to open the cervix more gradually.

THE QUIETING RESPONSE

Read through the Twenty-third Psalm. What a beautiful word picture David has painted for us! Shepherd . . . not lacking anything . . . lying down in green pastures . . . quiet waters . . . restoration . . . paths of righteousness . . . God's presence, protection, guidance, and comfort. This is as solid a guarantee as we could want that God will, indeed, help us through all we experience.

Since stress management can take many forms, Christians should avoid any type of stress reduction exercise that places them into a suggestive state in a non-Christian context (hypnosis, guided trances, etc.). In my classes I am acutely aware of the power of suggestion as couples become physically and psychologically relaxed. For this reason, I use tapes recorded by Christian musicians and read psalms to remind participants of the Lord's presence. The quieting response is a God-given psychological phenomenon, and it's important to learn how to use it both properly and wisely.

THE "NATURAL" RESPONSE TO LABOR

Most people react to any type of abdominal pain by hunching forward, clutching their stomachs, and intermittently holding their breath. This is fairly automatic; it is a protective gesture made in response to intestinal upset.

Laboring women have a tendency to do the same kind of thing when uterine contractions become strong during childbirth. It is quite difficult to voluntarily relax the muscles one has control over while the uterus contracts involuntarily with great force. Learning in advance what to expect and practicing relaxation regularly will help prepare you to cooperate with your body when labor actually begins.

WHY RELAXING HELPS

A muscle requires energy in the form of oxygen and a basic sugar called glucose in order to work properly. This energy is provided through the blood, which circulates through the cells that make up all muscle tissue within the human body.

If oxygen intake, blood circulation, or energy absorption is impaired, a muscle cannot function effectively. Waste products build up in the muscle, causing discomfort; lack of oxygen results in cramping; overall fatigue sets in. This is the body's way of warning a person to slow down, or completely stop the action that is causing overexertion.

During labor contractions, it is important to conserve energy in parts of the body not directly involved in the birth process. This way, the uterus won't have to compete for oxygen and glucose being used by other tense muscles, or suffer from a lack of oxygen due to holding your breath.

This can be accomplished by voluntarily relaxing those muscles you can control and by breathing slowly during labor. All methods of childbirth are based on this physiological principle: "Contraction begins—I relax, I breathe."

As a Christian, you have an extra plus in that you are supported by God's strength and help. It is Jesus who will accompany and comfort you. Rather than becoming fearful and panicky from the uncontrollable pressure of labor, you can cooperate with the birth process by leaning on the Lord. This may take every ounce of determination you can muster at times, but it will be the most rewarding, and challenging, work you will ever do

These, then, are the purposes of relaxing and breathing calmly in response to labor:

- to provide adequate energy to the working muscles of the uterus
- to conserve energy by voluntarily relaxing all other muscles under your control
- to avoid resisting the pressure of the uterus as it moves the baby through your body and out into the world
- to avoid the stimulation of the fight-or-flight response and the secretion of adrenaline.

PREPARING TO RELAX DURING LABOR

All muscular activity taking place within the human body is mediated through the nervous system. Muscles cannot function independently under normal conditions. They can be moved only in response to signals sent to and from the brain along cablelike communication channels called nerves. When nervous impulses are blocked due to nerve damage or anesthesia, loss of sensation and decreased muscle activity result. (See appendix C for common drugs used for pain intervention during labor, and their effects.)

In preparing your body to adapt to the process of childbirth, you are training your will to respond constructively. Remember, the brain coordinates the behavior of the body; the will influences the brain. It is through the will that we direct our mind to inform parts of the body to relax.

Behavioral psychologists do not believe in the concept of the "will." Instead, they theorize that all behavior is the result of conditioning; human behavior is the result of genetic and environmental influences.

While this theory may contain elements of truth, as Christians we know that people are more than just organisms that adapt to a "path of least resistance." We know we have choices.

The Christian view asserts that all people are made up of body, mind, and spirit. As we present ourselves to the Lord and seek to live in accordance with his will, we discover the truth of Romans 12:1, 2. If we are merely the product of heredity and environment, how could we heed Christ's call to no longer "conform to the pattern of this world"? The Bible, in speaking of what we cannot know and do not see, refutes many of today's theories.

Therefore, the first step in preparing yourself to relax during labor is to strengthen your will. This will enable you to choose what is beneficial for your body during labor.

STRENGTHENING YOUR WILL

In the passage from Romans 12, what does the Lord say we are to do with our bodies and with our minds? As you prepare for labor, remember this passage. Acknowledge that it is the Lord who created you and the baby within you. Use your will to say, "I trust you, Lord. I belong to you; you are my God." Presenting yourself to the Lord in this way is your "spiritual worship."

Don't think about anything but concentrating on the Lord as you relax. Find scriptural passages that give you confidence, and think about them. Give thanks and praise the Lord for the many things he has done in your life.

It may help to picture yourself in one of these ways as you relax:

- leaning on the everlasting arms
- lying down in green pastures
- walking beside the still waters
- resting under the shadow of his wings.

There are many other word pictures for you to choose from.

As you rest, comfort yourself by thinking of the Lord being with you. In class, I read most of Psalm 139 as couples relax on floor mats or in chairs, using dim lights and soft praise songs playing in the background. Reading this psalm is so reassuring! What can possibly compare with the knowledge that the Lord is with you always?

RELAXING YOUR BODY

In labor, you won't be able to control the muscles of the uterus which must forcibly contract to press your baby down against the cervix to open it, then through the soft, stretchy tissue of your vagina. Cervical dilation takes place during the first stage of labor. Your greatest challenge will be to allow your body to complete this task by itself. You must cooperate constructively by keeping as calm as possible, breathing evenly, and staying in an upright position or walking to help gravity bring your baby down into your pelvis.

In preparing for this event it is helpful to relax once or twice daily in the following ways:

1. Choose a quiet environment. You may wish to dim the lights and play soothing music. Turn off the TV and unplug the phone to be free of interruptions.

2. Find a comfortable position. Upright positions are the best, such as sitting "Indian-style," semireclining with back support and pillows under your knees; straddling a chair with a pillow over its back and leaning into the back of the chair; or rocking in a rocking chair with your feet on a footstool.

3. Put aside your worries. This is the time to relax both your mind and body. You might try to spend an equivalent amount of time each day not worrying about anything.

4. Think about the Lord. Use whatever Bible verses, prayers, or poetry you wish. Spend these moments with God in appreciation for who he is and what he has done for you. This is not a time for intercessory prayer or petitioning. It is a time just to relax in God's presence and glorify him by being still before him.

5. Breathe slowly and evenly. As you relax, your breathing rate will slow to about half its normal rate. Check this, if you wish, by counting the number of breaths you breathe for twenty seconds, then multiplying that number by three. It is best to check your rate at the beginning of practice and toward the end, before you stretch and get up.

6. Relax your body. This can be done simply by "going limp," if relaxing comes naturally to you. Or you can use the method shown on page 83.

EVALUATING YOUR PROGRESS

If you are able to relax your body by stimulating its parasympathetic nervous system's quieting reflex, you will find that, as you become more skilled, several changes will take place. Your heart rate should drop to eighty or below (sixty-five or below if you're not pregnant). This can be checked by placing your index and middle fingers against the bone on the wrist, or pressing them lightly against the artery at the side of your neck.

As you relax, your breathing will become slower and deeper, reducing the rate to around half. Don't forget to check this rate both before you begin and after you have relaxed for about ten minutes, comparing the two figures.

Another noticeable change will be in your skin temperature, which lowers in response to stress and rises when you are relaxed. Check the temperature of your fingertips both before and after relaxing.

WORKING TOGETHER

A labor companion must watch for expressions of discomfort from the woman when she is in labor, determining what might be helpful and providing support in the use of pain relief measures.

You can effectively evaluate how a laboring woman is feeling by what she is saying, how she responds to her surroundings, how she moves her body, what sounds she makes, what her face does, how close she lets others get to her, how she shows her feelings, and how she relates to others. Consider these questions: Does her back look tense? Is her breathing raspy? Is she grimacing or irritable?

Husbands usually are very responsive to any expression of pain from their wives. The better you know one another, the easier it becomes to read nonverbal signals. This is another reason why husbands can be ideal labor companions: the intimacy of a marital relationship fosters a private language and a unique way of communicating feelings.

On the negative side, some husbands end up feeling helpless or directly responsible for causing the pain their wives are feeling during labor. It is important to keep in mind that you are not alone. The Lord is there to help both of you. Also, your health care team is able to provide additional support whenever it's needed.

Being a labor companion, laboring together, means that you can "lift her up" because your body isn't laboring in the same way. But it also means that you should empathize with her, and share in her feelings. After having our fourth child, I remember looking at my husband and thinking, *He looks as tired as I do!* Dave *was* tired. He labored with me, and we were very close throughout that birth. My love for him grew even greater because I was so thankful to have him caring for me during such a vulnerable time in my life. The presence of one's husband can be both reassuring and strengthening.

Easing Tension through Touching. An effective way to stimulate the parasympathetic nervous system (P.N.S.) is by stroking the skin

LEARNING TO RELAX YOUR BODY

STEP 1.

Do each exercise slowly, with an awareness of varying sensations as you tense the muscle area then relax it. After you have gone through the list a few times, go through it again releasing each muscle group without using tension as a comparison. Practicing this will enable you to fully relax all muscle groups consciously. Once you are confident in your ability to consciously relax these areas, proceed to Step 2.

AREA TO BE TENSED	HOW TO TENSE
Toes	Curl toes
Feet	Stretch toes
Ankles and calves	Pull toes and feet toward leg
Knees	Pull back on knee caps
Thighs	Press thighs together or onto floor
Buttocks	Press together
Pelvic floor	Pull up, front to back
Lower abdomen	Pull muscles in
Lower back	Tilt pelvis back, erase curve
Abdomen	Bulge out
Chest	Take deep breath, using chest muscles
Upper back	Press shoulder blades back
Shoulders	Pull shoulder blades toward ears
Fingers	Spread fingers apart
Entire arm	Tighten all arm, hand, and finger muscles (To release, start with fingers, then wrist, lower arm, elbow, upper arm, and shoulder.)
Neck	Pull tight
Jaw	Drop jaw and stretch
Tongue	Press against roof of mouth
Lips	Press together
Cheeks	Smile
Eyes	Shut eyes tight
Forehead	Raise eyebrows

(Remember, the tension is to show you a contrast, helping you learn how to relax these muscle groups naturally. As you tense each area, release it slowly and deliberately.)

STEP 2.

Large Muscle Groups. In this exercise, replace tensing with relaxing, thinking toward large muscle groups. Release further by exhaling, until you can feel that you are fully released.

The following large muscle groups are to be relaxed:

1. Right leg	4. Lower body	7. Both arms
2. Left leg	5. Right arm	8. Upper body
3. Both legs	6. Left arm	9. Entire body

(cont.)

STEP 3.

Relaxing with Distraction (Flexibility Games).

A. Tense one part of the body while relaxing tension in the rest of the body. For example: Tense your entire left leg. Have your labor companion check your arms and right leg to see if they are relaxed. Repeat this with your right leg and each arm. For a greater test, try tensing diagonally while relaxing opposite limbs (right leg, left arm).

B. Release with motion by tapping your finger or rotating your feet as you relax the rest of the body. Have your labor companion assess the level of muscular relaxation.

C. Relax in a public place, such as a shopping mall. Sit on a bench with your labor companion and have him discreetly check to see how relaxed you are.

D. Relax in tense situations, such as during prenatal exams or while driving.

THE LABOR COMPANION'S ROLE IN CONSCIOUS RELEASE EXERCISES

The labor companion monitors relaxation within two contexts: practice and labor. Practice creates a foundation of cooperation, making teamwork easier during labor. Make practice a special time when you convey your concern and support for each other.

Labor companions should realize that their touch speaks clearly to the laboring woman. Gentle support of each limb as relaxation is checked is important, as is the assurance that you, as a labor companion, enjoy helping and being with the woman in labor.

It's also important to develop a way to communicate your assessment of a situation. A spoken command, a distinct touch or glance can be ways of showing your thoughts.

Be certain to check thoroughly for relaxation. A fully relaxed leg feels heavy and moves freely as you guide it. You can encourage further relaxation through massage or by saying, "Let your leg fall into my hands."

Make it a point to suggest practicing every day, conveying your interest and enthusiasm to your partner. This is especially important during the final weeks of pregnancy, when your partner may be feeling as though labor will never happen!

The more you practice, the more confident you and your partner will grow. Be sure to ask questions during class if you don't understand key points. When labor finally does begin, try to stay calm and begin encouraging your partner to relax from the very beginning. Remember to use prayer, Scripture, and music to promote total relaxation.

PRACTICE RECORD

It's always a good idea to keep a record of your practice times. Also, you can use this record to jot down any questions you may have. Some headings you could use might include date, time, location, the exercise practiced, and questions.

in a light, soothing manner. (See figure 3.)

In our culture, we often are inhibited about touching others. We tend to think of touch as something sexual or erotic. Yet, if you consider the times when someone truly comforted you, it is likely that they expressed their concern and love in such practical ways as holding your hand, putting an arm around your shoulders, or embracing you.

On a recent visit to Mexico, I was pleasantly surprised by the warmth of the people there. Sisters walked arm in arm, and boys freely put their arms around the shoulders of their friends. Mexican family members seemed very close, and expressed their affection in physical ways. To my North American eyes, this looked pleasant but foreign. Yet, when I returned home, I really missed seeing people openly care for one another as I had seen them do in Mexico.

If you are married, nonsexual touching can be a positive way to support a partner through a time of stress. At the end of a long day, a back rub can revive one's sense of joy in living. In labor, massage may be confined to areas of the back, lower abdomen, and thighs. Determine what is the most soothing for you, and don't give up using this after the baby arrives—you'll need it to relax then, too!

Easing Pain through Attention Diversion. Since our minds can only interpret a limited amount of incoming information, looking at and listening to things that will hold your attention during labor can raise your pain threshold and help you feel less discomfort. The following are things you could have in your room to help in this way. Some may seem extravagant or unusual, but if you select things that are meaningful to you, they won't seem so once you're in labor.

These are not tools to be used as a way of inducing hypnosis, or a "mystical state." Instead, they are simply to be used as a way to distract your attention from the pain stimuli.

Two-dimensional items: Posters, photographs, art prints, drawings, paintings, slides projected on the wall. (Select for appealing colors, diversity, and meaningful content.)

Textiles: Weavings, tapestries, needlepoint, embroidery, fabrics, quilts. (Select large, bright, attention-getting items. Handmade items are especially unique.)

Religious objects: Statues, symbols, art, hand-lettered verses, hymns, songs, prayers. (Find things to remind you of your personal beliefs and to give you a greater perspective beyond the physical experience of labor.)

Baby items: Stuffed animals, toys, garments. (Bring things that will help reinforce attachment to your coming child.)

Living things: Plants, flowers, small aquarium, small pet, terrarium. (Pick those that have a pleasant odor and convey a sense of vitality.)

Light: Slides, diffused light, candles, kerosene lamp. (Be careful of eye strain—find sources of light that are attention-holding, fascinating.)

Small objects: Silk flowers, statues, art objects, motion figures, Magic Sand, pine bough or holiday ornaments. (Be creative in finding a few fun and interesting things.)

Surrounding environment: Tiles, wallpaper, clock, draperies, window/view, hardware, architectural features, facial features or hands of people around you, garments or jewelry they are wearing. (Look at parts of room or people that are nonthreatening and reassuring.)

Thermal Stimulation. Many women have been helped by applying heat or cold to areas that become cramped or tense during labor. Any of the following relief measures can be used, but avoid extremes in temperature. Always be careful not to burn or damage the skin.

Ideas for warm thermal stimulation include baths or showers, compresses (a slow cooker is ideal for keeping them warm), a hot water bottle, heating pads, warmed blankets, Mentholatum, and eucalyptus oil.

Cold thermal stimulation ideas include ice packs (commercial or self-sealing plastic bags), a hot water bottle filled with ice water (can also

USING STROKING DURING PREGNANCY AND CHILDBIRTH
FIGURE 3

BENEFITS:
- Stroking provides a focal point toward which the mother can concentrate her relaxation.
- Stroking promotes the circulation of blood through the body, enabling toxic wastes produced through the muscular activity of the uterus to be removed more quickly.
- Massage stimulates the parasympathetic nervous system (P.N.S.), provoking the quieting reflex.
- Being touched by a loved one helps the mother feel cared for, and provides a way for the labor companion to express affection and concern.
- The stimulation of the skin can raise a woman's tolerance to pain by sending impulses to the brain which interfere with other messages coming in regarding painful sensations.

TIPS FOR EFFECTIVE STROKING:
Stroking should be mild and light since the mother's circulating blood volume is much higher than normal. In addition, any massage should be patterned, repetitive, rhythmical, done with corn oil or cornstarch to minimize friction against the skin, performed skin-to-skin when possible to promote relaxation, and done when the mother is in a comfortable position.

*A SIMPLE TECHNIQUE FOR GIVING
A GOOD BACK RUB:*
This back rub technique is guaranteed to promote harmony in your home! It is especially nice when done at the end of a long day after showering or bathing.
- Circle sweeps: Lie on your side in a comfortable position. Have your labor partner place his/her hands at the base of your waist, and begin stroking with small, upward, sweeping circles that meet on either side of the spine and become larger in diameter to cover the shoulders. Upon reaching the shoulders, the movements should resume again from the base of the spine. This stroking should be rhythmical and always in an upward and outward direction.
- See-saw: Now have your labor partner place his/her hands next to one another, over the tops of your buttocks, with the thumb of the upper hand touching the small finger of the lower hand. Following the

contour of your body, your partner should firmly draw the hands outward, then inward, moving gradually up the back. Once the neck is reached, the stroking begins again at the *bottom* of the spine.
- Walking: Beginning at the base of the spine, your labor partner places his/her fingers on either side of the spine facing upward and slightly toward the spine. Alternating from left to right, your partner presses firmly and massages in a circular motion. This is continued in a "walking" motion up the back and begins again at the base of the back once the neck is reached.
- The harp: As a completion to these three types of stroking, have your labor partner begin at the neck, with fingertips at the right side of the spine, and draw his/her fingers quickly and lightly down the spine. As soon as the right hand begins, the left hand is placed at the left side of the neck, stroking downward in the same fashion as soon as the right hand completes its stroke. This should be a quick, rhythmical, alternating stroke.

TECHNIQUES FOR THE LOWER BACK:

Figure eight: With you in a comfortable side-lying position, have your labor partner use the flat of one hand to broadly stroke across the back of the pelvis. This may be done vertically or horizontally across the lower back. Your labor partner should use his/her free hand to hold your hipbone, stabilizing the pelvis.

Self-applied stroking: While lying on your side, you may stroke your own lower back by drawing the back of your hand firmly over that region. Firmer pressure may be applied if the thumb is hooked on the front of the hip, with the fingers reaching back in a broad circular motion over the lower back.

OTHER AREAS OF FOCUS:
The abdomen: Either you or your labor companion can do a light, rhythmical stroking with the fingertips on your bare abdomen over the area where a contraction is felt.

(cont.)

Low massage for cramping: Position fingertips on either side of the center of your pubic bone. Slowly draw fingers up and over the groin to the hip bones (iliac). Return hands to the original position, repeating rhythmically for the duration of the contraction. When in a sitting position, use both hands; when in a side-lying position, use one hand.

Light massage (effleurage): Position fingertips on either side of the navel. Draw fingers up, outward, then downward. Draw large circles, always returning through the center point of the abdomen. Be sure to keep touch light.

The thighs: Lie in a semi-lying position, with your legs relaxed on pillows or the bed raised under the knees. While facing you, your labor companion can stroke the muscles of the inner thigh beginning with hands placed over the inside of the calf. Hands should be drawn firmly up over the inner thigh and toward the groin, if comfortable. Every third or fourth stroke is swept up over the top of the thigh and completed by a firm movement down the outside of the leg, to the feet, and over the toes. Concentrate on relaxing into the stroke of your support person, and keeping the perineum relaxed.

use a hollow rolling pin or empty detergent bottle), cold compresses soaked in ice water, a spray mist of cool water, or pads soaked in witch hazel.

EASING FIRST STAGE OF LABOR THROUGH BREATHING TECHNIQUES

Patterned breathing is useful during the process of birth for several reasons. It can bring a greater measure of control to our reactions to challenging situations. Rhythmical breathing is distracting and places our focus on a positive body response to stress rather than on the stress itself. Also, adequate breathing insures adequate oxygenation, enabling the uterus to perform its work more effectively and efficiently.

Patterned breathing changes your usual response to large muscle contractions. Rather than tensing and holding your breath during a cramp, the breathing conditions you to think, "Contraction begins—I relax, I breathe."

Finally, breathing techniques keep a laboring woman's focus on coping with stress or pain. The attention is centered above the level of pelvic congestion and discomfort. Instead of passively observing what is happening, a woman interprets what is taking place within her body, and actively participates with its demand for oxygen.

PRACTICING BREATHING PATTERNS

The role of a labor companion begins during practice. As a labor companion you should learn and understand the patterns and techniques that will be useful during labor. During practice, work to develop ways of supporting your partner's breathing through verbal encouragement, eye contact, tapping, counting, or breathing in unison. Practice your signals so that you will not feel awkward using them during labor.

It is a good idea, while practicing, to periodically change roles, giving each partner a chance to be the "coach." Whoever is acting as the coach should call out the beginning, peak, and the end of each contraction to reinforce the use of breathing patterns. Be sure you both understand fully how each breathing pattern is done.

Another way to make these patterns a more natural response is to use them casually, at times other than practice. Do the patterns several times per day, especially during tense or uncomfortable moments for maximum benefit. (The slow breathing pattern is particularly soothing when you feel irritable, frustrated, or stressed.)

As you consider the different patterns, be flexible in choosing which pattern to use at any certain point in labor. They are interchangeable and need not be done in the order they are presented.

Remember the following key points:

1. Keep your breathing as relaxed and slow as possible for as long as possible. This saves energy. Always begin and end a contraction with "cleansing breaths," using first a "greeting breath" and then signaling the end of a contraction with a "completion breath."

2. When you make your breathing faster, don't breathe as deeply as when it was slow. Remember: As the rate goes up, the depth goes down. Quicker breathing means shallower breathing.

3. Be confident in your ability to "listen to what your body is saying," and change your breathing accordingly. Use only the patterns and rates that make you feel more comfortable.

4. Try to breathe in and out in equal amounts.

5. Try different patterns and variations until you discover what helps you relax the best.

Avoiding Hyperventilation. Hyperventilation occurs when an excess of oxygen builds up in the bloodstream. It can happen to a woman in labor when:

. . . she has not practiced her breathing techniques sufficiently before entering labor. When unsure of a breathing pattern, a woman in labor can easily breathe with too much force or too unevenly. Practice often, and be sure your instructor checks your progress.

. . . she increases her breathing rate without decreasing the depth of breathing during a contraction. The deeper and faster the breathing, the greater the oxygen consumption will be. Remember, as the rate goes up, the depth goes down.

. . . she gasps in air during a contraction due to anxiety, fatigue, or discomfort. Gasping results in a disruption of the oxygen balance in the bloodstream. Active labor support through your labor companion tapping, counting, or singing out a rhythm to regulate breathing can help you achieve a more even exchange of air.

The symptoms of hyperventilation are a tingling in the fingertips, lips, cheeks, and/or around the mouth; dizziness; numbness; and light-headedness. If you feel any of these symptoms during labor you will need active labor support that will provide you with a restoration of carbon dioxide in your bloodstream. One way to achieve this is by breathing into a paper bag or cupped hands for one or more contractions, or between contractions.

One thing you need to realize is that during labor your uterus will consume much more oxygen than it will during practice. Therefore, it is not uncommon for light-headedness to occur during practice of breathing patterns. If this does happen, simply take a break, then resume practice with mock contractions of no more than thirty seconds each. Be sure to rest between each "contraction" and avoid breathing too rapidly or deeply.

BREATHING PATTERNS
SLOW BREATHING

Function: To slow the rate and increase the depth of breathing to produce relaxation and calmness. This helps combat nausea, anxiety, and fatigue.

Pattern: Breathe in through the mouth or nose slowly and exhale the air through the mouth in a controlled, slow breath, similar to a deep sigh. The breathing is continuous, beginning the next breath without any pause. Experiment with letting the air expand your chest (chest breathing) and then your abdomen (abdominal breathing). Decide which way brings you the most comfort and relaxation.

Rate: The rate should be about half your normal breathing rate.

LIGHT BREATHING

Function: By keeping the breath lighter, pressure

on the uterus from the expansion of the abdominal wall is avoided.

Pattern: Basically a modified slow breathing pattern. Bring air in through nose, or mouth and nose, and exhale through the mouth. There may be a slight sound as the air is exhaled. This pattern, because it is more shallow, involves more of the upper chest which can expand out to the sides, if desired.

Rate: Should not exceed thirty breaths per minute.

COUNTED BREATHING

Function: To raise pain tolerance through an increased rate and decreased depth of breathing while encouraging concentration on a specific count. "Blow breaths" provide a break from the lighter pants.

Pattern: Breathe slowly in and out through the mouth, or in through the nose and out through the mouth. Shift rate and depth as you respond to the pressure of contractions.

Rate: Keep the rate as slow as possible, preferably less than thirty breaths per minute.

BLOW-BLOW

Function: To help relieve the urge to push if the mother is told that she cannot do so. It must be remembered that the urge to push is practically irresistible, and that the breathing does not *eliminate* the desire—it helps you to cope with it.

Pattern: When the urge to push is felt, whether merely a catching of the breath or a full-fledged desire to bear down, puff out air sharply and quickly. An extended blow can turn into a push, so make the puffs steady and fast.

SUMMARY

We have considered many ideas that you may use in coping with labor pain during the birth of your baby. Consider these as suggestions to be used as you see fit. It is important to try out a variety to discover which work best for you. Then, when labor begins, you can use those that make you feel better.

As you prepare together for this exciting event, you can fill it with pleasant words and a joyful anticipation. Remember these wise words from Proverbs 16:24: "Pleasant words are a honeycomb, sweet to the soul and healing to the bones." Make this a time that you both will look back on with fondness.

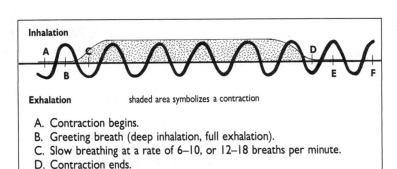

A. Contraction begins.
B. Greeting breath (deep inhalation, full exhalation).
C. Slow breathing at a rate of 6–10, or 12–18 breaths per minute.
D. Contraction ends.
E. Completion breath (deep inhalation, full exhalation) and thanksgiving that this contraction is gone forever!
F. Resume normal breathing rate.

SLOW BREATHING

LIGHT BREATHING

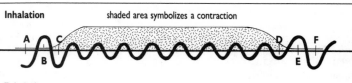

A. Contraction begins.
B. Greeting breath.
C. Light breathing at rate of 18–24 or 26–30 breaths per minute.
D. Contraction ends.
E. Completion breath and thanksgiving.
F. Resume normal rate.

45-second contraction: breathing rate and depth maintained throughout.
60-second contraction: breathing up at peak, down at depth.

COUNTED BREATHING 3:1

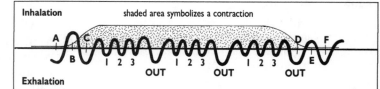

A. Contraction begins.
B. Greeting breath.
C. Count breathing with 3 lighter, more shallow breaths followed by 1 deeper, slower breath. Try for about 24–30 breaths per minute.
D. Contraction ends.
E. Completion breath and thanksgiving.
F. Resume normal breathing.

60-second contraction: 3 to 1 breathing maintained throughout.

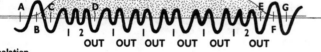

Inhalation

shaded area symbolizes a contraction

A C
B
1 2 3 4 1 2 3 4 1 2 3 4
OUT OUT OUT
D F
E

Exhalation

COUNTED BREATHING 4:1

A. Contraction begins.
B. Greeting breath.
C. Counted breathing with 4 lighter breaths followed by 1 deeper, slower breath (about 32–36 breaths per minute).
D. Contraction ends.
E. Completion breath and thanksgiving.
F. Resume normal breathing rate.

90-second contraction: 4 to 1, except at peak; 2 to 1 during peak.

Inhalation

shaded area symbolizes a contraction

A C D
B
1 2 1 1 1 1 1 2
OUT OUT OUT OUT OUT OUT
E G
F

Exhalation

COUNTED BREATHING 2:1, 1:1 FOR PEAK

A. Contraction begins.
B. Greeting breath.
C. Counted breathing at a rate of 2 shallow to 1 deeper breath.
D. Counted breathing at a rate of 1 shallow to 1 deep breath—no faster than 40 breaths per minute.
E. Contraction ends.
F. Completion breath and thanksgiving.
G. Resume normal breathing rate.

90-second contraction: 2 to 1 except at peak; 1 to 1 during peak.

I. BLOW-BLOW BREATHING WITH URGE TO PUSH AT PEAK

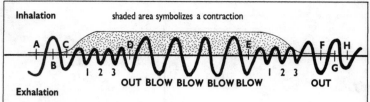

A. Contraction begins.
B. Greeting breath.
C. 3 to 1 counted breathing until urge to push develops.
D. Begin puffing air out after each inhalation.
E. Resume 3 to 1 counted breathing when urge to push subsides.
F. Contraction ends.
G. Completion breath and thanksgiving.
H. Resume normal breathing rate.

II. BLOW-BLOW WITH URGE TO PUSH DURING ENTIRE CONTRACTION

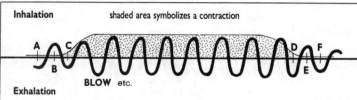

A. Contraction begins.
B. Greeting breath.
C. Begin blowing out continuously throughout contraction with light puff after adequate inhalations.
D. Contraction ends.
E. Completion breath with thanksgiving.
F. Resume normal breathing rate.

RELATIONSHIPS BETWEEN LABOR EVENTS AND PAIN

STAGE	EVENTS	POSSIBLE AFFECTED AREAS
1 Opening of the cervix	Effacement and dilation of cervix Uterine contractions Movement of baby deeper into pelvis	Pubic to umbilical region Upper thighs Lower back Hip joints
2 Movement of baby through birth canal	Uterine contractions Stretching of vagina, pelvic floor, and perineum Passage of baby through pelvis	Abdomen (especially with urge to push) Hip joints Lower back, tailbone Perineum, pelvic floor, vagina, and rectum
3 Expulsion of placenta	Passage of placenta through cervix and vagina Uterine contractions Repair of lacerations or incision in pelvic floor and perineum (episiotomy)	Pubic to umbilical region Lower back Upper thighs Perineum, vagina, pelvic floor, and rectum
4 Two-hour recovery period following childbirth	Uterine contractions Beginning of involution of the uterus Fundal massage Aggravated hemorrhoids Beginning of healing process (of episiotomy)	Pubic to umbilical region Lower back Rectum Perineum, pelvic floor, vagina
5 Six weeks following childbirth	Uterine contractions (for first few days) Healing of perineum Breast engorgement with onset of lactation (48 hours, then diminishes) Adjustment of nipples to nursing	Pubic to umbilical region Lower back Perineum, vagina, pelvic floor Rectum Entire chest wall Nipples

SELF-STATEMENTS DURING LABOR

During the three phases of pain experience (anticipation, presence, and aftermath), you must remember that the Lord is always with you. The following phrases contain suggestions that can help alleviate anxiety, fear, and worry. Review them, adapting them for your own use and keeping in mind that the things you think about during these three phases of pain will influence your ability to cooperate with your body.

STATEMENTS TO AVOID	STATEMENTS TO USE
ANTICIPATION PHASE	
Preparing for labor:	
This is going to be impossible.	O Lord, what must I do?
There is no way I can cope with labor.	I can cope with my labor with your help, Father. I can pray about this.
I'll just ignore this whole thing and deal with it when the time comes.	I will think and pray about what I have to do.
I'll probably panic when labor starts.	When I feel labor begin, the Lord will help me know what to do.
I feel better when I worry.	I won't worry; worrying is worthless.
This whole thing depresses me. Why does it have to be this way?	I can deal with the pain; the relief measures I've learned will help and the Lord will sustain me.
Nothing is going to help.	I have lots of ideas and strategies to call upon.
The Lord can't love me if this is what labor is. Pain means I lack faith.	I believe in God's love for me no matter how difficult things get.
I don't know how to relax. I've always been a tense person.	I'll take a few deep breaths now to relax, and remember Psalm 23.
The Bible can't help me.	Scriptural passages are my best defense.
PRESENCE PHASE	
Confronting and handling labor pain:	
I hate this.	I can meet this challenge with God's help.
God can't be with me and allow me to feel this way.	God is with me; he is my strength and hope.
I've never been able to handle pain. This is awful.	I have dealt with pain before; I can deal with it now.
I can't deal with this.	I'll take just one contraction at a time; God's grace is sufficient for me.

STATEMENTS TO AVOID	STATEMENTS TO USE
I can't get my mind off how I feel.	I'm not going to think about the pain; I'll look to the Lord and use my relief measures.
These contractions are terrible.	The tension in my uterus can be my ally, my cue to cope.
I can't get rid of this anxiety.	Anxiety is normal, but I can cast it on God.
No one will believe this—they'll think I'm exaggerating.	I don't need to prove myself to anyone, or try to pretend my pain isn't real. The Lord knows how I feel.
I can't do anything but hold my breath and curl up into a ball.	I'll just lean on God and use my breathing patterns.
Something's wrong—I *know* it.	I won't assume the worst, or jump to conclusions. God is in control.
This is a total waste.	There is something in this to feel good about; my child is coming into the world.
I don't care about doing anything right now. Leave me alone.	This feeling reminds me to use my relief measures and fix my eyes on Jesus.
I'm angry and I don't care.	Getting angry won't help this baby get born.
I'm really a failure.	Doubting myself is unnecessary; I know I can do this with God's help.

Coping with sensations/feelings at critical moments:

I can't do this. I've got to get rid of this pain.	I can't eliminate this pain completely; I *can* deal with it with God's help.
Maybe if I complain, everyone will feel sorry for me and that will make me feel better.	Complaining won't help; I will look to the God of my salvation instead.
This is completely out of control.	I can switch to a new relief measure at any point; it's my choice, something I can control.
There's nothing I can do to help.	What are the things I need to do?
The Lord has forgotten me.	Help me, Lord.
It helps to show my true feelings.	Feeling upset won't help; I know the Lord is with me.
If the pain gets worse, I'll ask them to knock me out. I can't stand it.	When the pain becomes intense, I will focus on Christ and on what I need to do.

STATEMENTS TO AVOID	STATEMENTS TO USE
AFTERMATH PHASE	
Self-defeating statements:	**Self-rewarding statements:**
I'm ashamed of myself.	Praise God, *that* contraction is gone forever!
	With God's help, I got through without getting upset.
Nothing works.	Alleluia! It worked!
I can't do anything right.	I knew I could do it through Christ who strengthens me.
I feel horrible.	That was hard, but I'm doing fine. Thanks, God.
I can't handle this.	I managed that pretty well, with God's help.
No one's going to know how badly I blew it.	I can't wait to tell everyone how the Lord helped me!
The Lord can't love me if he deserted me like this.	That was one of the hardest things I've ever had to deal with, but the Lord was with me all the way.

ADRENALINE:
ITS EFFECTS
AND HOW TO
COUNTER THEM

BODY FUNCTION	FIGHT-OR-FLIGHT EFFECTS	QUIETING RESPONSE EFFECTS
Heart rate	Faster	Slower
Breathing rate	Increased	Decreased
Blood pressure	Elevated	Lowered
Sweat production	Increased	Decreased
Metabolic processes	Speeded up	Slowed down
Circulation in large muscles	Greatly increased	Remains steady
S.N.S. activity	Increased	Decreased
P.N.S. activity	Decreased	Increased
ADDITIONAL FACTORS IN LABOR		
Uterine contractions	May stop or become stronger	Occur more rhythmically with gradual increase in strength
Cervical dilation	Cervix may resist opening or may open very quickly	Cervix opens with less resistance, in a more gradual process

PHYSICAL CAUSES OF PAIN IN CHILDBIRTH

- "Referred" pain: messages sent from the pelvic area to other places in the body
- Fast or prolonged labor
- Uterine function
- Pressure on pelvic floor
- Stretching of cervix
- Poor physical condition
- Pelvis size
- Mother's position
- Baby's position in uterus
- Physical disease or disability
- Pull on supporting ligaments
- Cramping and waste buildup in muscles
- Procedures done to mother

SOME FACTORS THAT INFLUENCE PAIN EXPERIENCE

- Your body's response and the cause of pain
- The meaning you give to pain
- The reaction of others
- What you've learned about this type of pain
- Your earlier experiences with pain
- Your age and personality
- The situation in which you experience pain
- The coping methods you choose
- Your ethnic and social background
- The accuracy of your expectations

CHAPTER TEN

Once Labor Begins: What to Expect and Do

"The eternal God is your refuge and underneath are the everlasting arms." DEUTERONOMY 33:27

When labor begins, you will experience new physical sensations and emotions. The details of labor are presented in this chapter, along with possible variations and descriptions of the roles played by your labor companion and health care provider. Consider this section of the book your practical labor guide. (You may even find it helpful to refer to these pages during labor, so don't forget to pack it in your things where it can be located conveniently!)

FIRST STAGE: EARLY, ACTIVE, AND TRANSITION PHASES

EARLY PHASE:
THE MOTHER'S EXPERIENCE

During the early phase of the first stage of labor the mother's experiences may include:

- periodic menstruallike cramps and backache that increase in strength, duration, and frequency over a relatively short time or over a number of days.
- the breaking of the bag of waters. (Check the color and odor and call health care provider.)
- a blood-tinged mucus discharge as the cervix thins out. (This may take place in advance of labor or as labor progresses.)
- stomach-flu-type symptoms of intestinal upset and diarrhea.
- anxiety about whether or not labor is beginning.

Use the following chart to help you determine whether or not you are in true labor, then seek your health care provider's opinion to confirm your suspicion.

To time your contractions, begin timing at the beginning of the contraction noting both when the contraction ends and the interval of rest until the next contraction begins. Combine the length of one contraction and one rest period to determine how far apart the contractions are. In other words, contractions are timed from the beginning of one to the beginning of the next. (See figure 1.)

While in this early stage, you may find it easier to sleep if you're given a back rub. (Don't worry

TRUE LABOR
CHART I

"TRUE" LABOR	"FALSE" LABOR
CONTRACTIONS	
● Get closer together ● Become more intense ● Last longer ● Feel crampy in front, or achy in back	● Average interval between contractions does not shorten ● Intensity and length stay the same
DISCHARGE	
● Thick, mucus discharge from cervix. May be clear, though usually blood-tinged	● None or clear, but not copious
CHANGES IN CERVIX	
● Effacement and dilation ● Process of birth resulting in baby's arrival	● Little or no effacement or dilation ● Symptoms stop; baby's arrival does not result

TIMING A CONTRACTION
FIGURE I

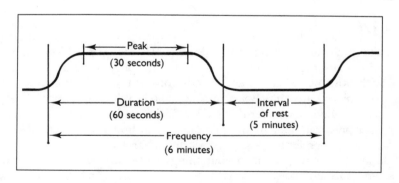

about sleeping too long; once you are in active labor, the contractions will definitely wake you up!) Also, a warm bath (if membranes are intact) or shower may help you relax. Eat and drink things that are easily digested, and that will give you energy. Walking sometimes is beneficial, since the increased pressure on the cervix from gravity has a tendency to stimulate labor.

With all the new sensations and feelings, you may be surprised by how labor feels and what happens. Try to accept it gracefully, and give thanks!

EARLY PHASE: THE HUSBAND'S/ LABOR COMPANION'S ROLE
As the labor companion, you can help establish the right perspective, regardless of circumstances. When the early phase begins, stay calm and help your wife to get comfortable. Remind her that it often takes 40 to 50 percent of the length of labor to reach three centimeters dilation.

Provide your wife with loving reassurance. Time the contractions, and call her health care provider if she asks you to. Also, notify any prayer partners or relatives and make arrangements for any other children you may have.

If you're leaving home for the birth, this would be the time to pack the suitcase and put it, and your pillows, in the car. Above all, be sure to tell your wife you love her, comforting her with your voice, touch, and presence.

Together, you can recall God's promises, praising him for your wife and baby. Rejoice together in the way God has designed the process of labor. Pray for his help and protection, giving thanks even though you may be tired, confused, or excited.

Meditate on the Lord as your Shepherd, and read Scriptures or play music to remind you of his living presence. Cast your anxiety on him, believing that he will deliver you, and will not allow you to undergo more than you can handle (1 Corinthians 10:13). Ask the Lord to assist each of you, giving you strength and guiding your health care providers.

EARLY PHASE: THE HEALTH CARE PROVIDER'S ROLE

Your health care provider should be available as needed, provide assistance in determining the appropriate time for transfer to the place of birth, evaluate the progress of labor, and recommend what the mother can do to be more comfortable and promote the health of herself and the baby.

EARLY PHASE: RELIEF MEASURES

- Proper spiritual perspective (See husband's role.)
- Eat and drink easily digested food and beverages
- Back rubs
- Shower; bath
- Thermal stimulation
- Walking; upright position
- Peaceful environment; dimmed lighting for resting
- Music
- Patience, forbearance; emotional support and

encouragement
- Acceptance of how labor feels
- Surrender of your labor to God, remembering everything is in his hands

ACTIVE PHASE: THE MOTHER'S EXPERIENCE

Normally, your cervix will have completed effacement (thinning out), and dilated from four to six centimeters. Your digestive processes slow down or stop, and you may be nauseated, burp frequently, or vomit. Your contractions become longer, often reaching peak strength and staying at peak longer, and the intervals between grow shorter (forty-five- to sixty-second contractions occurring every two to five minutes is normal).

You may want to be left alone and may feel like complaining. Be thankful instead! You will have to concentrate on pain relief measures, and may change to a lighter, faster breathing pattern. You should remember to urinate every thirty to forty-five minutes.

You probably will go to your chosen place of birth at this time, and you may be given a synthetic hormone, Pitocin, to make the contractions stronger. Also, your membranes may be artificially ruptured to stimulate labor.

You'll find it more difficult to get comfortable, and it may become more uncomfortable to walk. (But remember, walking between contractions may stimulate the progress of labor.) You may talk less, and need active labor support.

ACTIVE PHASE: THE HUSBAND'S/ LABOR COMPANION'S ROLE

At this point, your wife may require your undivided attention. Encourage her to relax, especially between contractions. Support her through praise, encouragement, and firm direction.

Your wife may feel a need for privacy to work through this stage on her own; if so, respect that need. If she wants you there, have a comfortable chair near the bed so you can sit when possible, and consider starting relief measures such as back massages, offering ice chips, etc. Remind her to keep her breathing at the slowest rate possible (to save strength) and rhythmical (to prevent hyperventilation).

Keep her informed of her progress. Remember to ask for help from staff when it's needed, and keep the room as quiet as possible, minimizing distractions. Also, you may wish to ask a nurse or friend to step in for you if you need to take a break.

ACTIVE PHASE: THE HEALTH CARE PROVIDER'S ROLE

The nurse or nurse-midwife will check fetal heart tones (baby's pulse); monitor the mother's blood pressure; perform vaginal checks to assess cervical effacement, dilation, and the descent of baby (station); help the mother and father relax; feel the fundus of the uterus through the abdominal wall (palpation of the fundus) to gauge the relative strength of contractions; recommend possible relief measures; keep the physician informed of the mother's progress, if applicable; inform parents of baby's condition and progress of labor; and make a record of the events taking place.

The physician or nurse-midwife will evaluate the mother's condition and recommend and perform treatments as needed.

ACTIVE PHASE: RELIEF MEASURES

- Prayer, music, Scripture
- Ice chips, cool washcloth
- Positive self-statements; emotional support and encouragement
- Upright body position for gravity
- Frequent urination (every thirty to forty-five minutes)
- Massage of back, leg, pubic area, thighs, and/or abdomen; counterpressure
- Change of position
- Extra pillows, blankets
- Quiet, soft music

- Thermal stimulation
  Use of focal point; auditory and visual distraction
- Clean bed linens and underpad; clean, dry socks
- Lollipop, Chapstick
- Fresh gown
- Quieting response; breathing techniques
- Analgesia (usually a low dosage of Demerol with Phenergan or Vistaril) or anesthesia (possibly a paracervical or epidural block)

THE TRANSITION PHASE

Transition is the term used to describe the third phase of the first stage of labor. This phase occurs between seven and ten centimeters dilation, and involves the final stretching of the cervix over the baby's head (or presenting part).

"Transition" means to progress from one state to another. So, in this phase, you move from the first to the second stage of labor. Remember the example of pulling a tight turtleneck sweater over your head? At first your head enters the sweater easily, but as it nears the tight outlet, you must pull with greater force.

During transition, the uterus contracts for longer periods at shorter intervals to accomplish the final stretching. The contractions may be as long as 90 to 120 seconds with as little as 20 to 30 seconds between. You may well feel as though one contraction leads into another. Transition is completed when the cervix has stretched enough to allow the baby's head to pass through. The cervix width usually is about ten centimeters at this point.

For most women, transition lasts for twenty to thirty contractions with their first baby, and ten to twenty contractions for successive births. It is an especially difficult phase of labor because of the longer contractions and shorter rest periods, and because the mother often is tired from the first two phases. Also, several other symptoms occur because of the tremendous physical effort needed in this stage. (*See chart 2.*)

CHART 2   COMMON TRANSITION PHASE SYMPTOMS

SYMPTOM	RELIEF MEASURES (for labor partners to perform)
● Mood change (caused by fatigue, demands of accelerated pace of labor, little rest).	Remember the Lord's presence; play tapes of Christian recording artists; give encouragement and reassurance; get help when needed; give a sense of goal; stay calm; be aggressive in offering help; read psalms aloud.
● Withdrawal, resistance to helpers (caused by pain and lack of control).	Respect the effort involved in labor; stay positive; express acceptance of her feelings; don't leave, just be more quiet; continue in prayer, for wife and baby, out loud.
● Trembling, shaking (caused by exertion of uterus, alteration of metabolism).	Gentle, firm, rhythmical massage; warm blanket; encouragement and reminders that this soon will subside.
● Backache (caused by pressure of baby moving through pelvis, uterine activity, and position of mother).	Warm or cool compresses; counterpressure to affected area; firm massage; appropriate position; reminder that the baby is approaching the birth canal.
● Hot flashes (caused by increased activity of uterus and altered metabolism).	Remove clothing; close drapes and pull window blinds shut; place cool washcloths over body; lower room temperature if possible.
● Cold extremities, chills (caused by decreased circulation to hands and feet due to uterine demand for increased blood circulation).	Clean, warm socks; warm blanket fluffed over feet; raise room temperature if possible.
● Dry mouth (caused by medication and/or breathing techniques).	Ice chips; sucker; cool washcloth; Chapstick; slower breathing, especially between contractions.
● "I want to give up" attitude (caused by stresses, pain, and shorter rest periods in labor).	Pain relief techniques; praise and prayer; active support; perspective—"not much longer"; reassurance and encouragement; analgesia in small doses.
● Hyperventilation (caused by overbreathing or erratic patterned breathing).	Establish even rhythm to breathing by breathing with her; slow down breathing; have the mother breathe into a paper bag to restore her CO_2 level.
● "Urge to push" reflex (caused by descent of baby into pelvis).	Light breathing with quick puffs to release abdominals; ask physician to check dilation; have mother change to active pushing when given the OK.

(cont.)

SYMPTOM	RELIEF MEASURES (for labor partners to perform)
● Rectal pressure—similar to the urge to have a bowel movement (caused by baby's head compressing rectum while passing through pelvis).	Remind her that it's the baby, not a bowel movement; suggest that she fully release pelvic floor as pressure is felt; encourage by stating that the baby is getting closer.
● Pressure below pubic bone (caused by passage of baby under pubic bone).	Massage over pubic bone area; warm or cool compresses; change of position; reassurance.
● Cervical pain (caused by pressure of baby's head against cervix during last phase of stretching).	Conscious release of muscle tension; faster, lighter breathing at peak of contractions; encouragement; possible administering of anesthesia to cervix (paracervical block).

NOTE: While each of these symptoms is common, no one woman will experience them all!

COPING WITH BACK PAIN DURING LABOR

Most women have at least some degree of backache some time during labor. This pain may be temporary, or it may persist throughout labor. Often called "back labor," this back pain is caused by at least one of the following:

- The baby's head is large for your pelvis and exerts a great deal of pressure against the pelvis as it passes through.
- The back of the baby's head is toward your back and is pressing against the back of the pelvis. This is a "posterior presentation."
- Your position is causing gravity to pull the baby's head down against your back.
- The baby's head is at an awkward angle as it comes through the pelvis.
- The wide ligaments anchoring the uterus to the lower back are stretched as the uterus contracts.

One way to help relieve back labor is through the mother's position. A side-lying position, in which the mother lies on either side, propped with pillows, helps keep the weight of the baby off the back and makes the mother's back available for massage.

Standing, Indian-style sitting, and sitting upright have several advantages. An upright posi-

tion in labor allows gravity to bring the baby's head closer to the cervix and can encourage dilation. The baby's head is pulled into the pelvis rather than onto the back, and the mother can lean forward to receive back massage. Also, the bed can be raised to a ninety-degree angle for extra support.

In an all-fours position, the baby's weight is taken off the mother's back entirely. However, this position may be difficult to sustain with intense contractions.

Massage also is good relief from back pain during labor. A firm, low back massage, done with steady, rhythmical, repetitive movements can be done with contractions and/or during the intervals between contractions. Be sure to use oil, lotion, or cornstarch to reduce friction and ensure the smoothness of the massage.

If the baby's head is pressed against the mother's pelvis during contractions, it may help to provide counterpressure by pressing inward against the pelvis at the place where the baby is pressing outward. Do this with the hand, forearm, a clean paint roller, or the foot (when you're too exhausted to use your hand or arm!). A constant pressure exerted during contractions will help greatly.

Some women find that passive pelvic rock,

rocking the pelvis between and/or during contractions while it is supported by a labor partner, provides relief. This technique mainly promotes relaxation of muscles connected to the pelvis. With the mother on her right side, the labor partner should grasp the mother's hip bone with his left hand and place the right hand over the back of the pelvis, fingers pointing downward as they touch the tip of the spine. As the mother gently rocks her pelvis, the labor partner presses downward when the pelvis tilts forward and relaxes his hand as the pelvis returns to its normal position.

Something the labor partner should keep in mind is that he must try to stay calm if he wishes to be of help to his wife during times of back pain. Backache in labor hurts a great deal, and it can be difficult to keep cool when supporting a woman who is hurting. Your presence, words of encouragement, and willingness to participate will be helpful even if she doesn't seem to notice your concern. Above all, remind her often of the final goal of labor, and keep her informed of her progress.

Medication for Back Pain. Many women find that back pain in labor is quite difficult to manage with just noninvasive pain relief measures. In deciding whether or not you would benefit from pain relief medication during this time, keep the following in mind:

- Drugs given for pain relief during the first stage of labor usually are not anesthetics. That means they don't take away the pain. Rather, they act on the brain and encourage a feeling of apathy and nonconcern. The pain may stay intense, but you care less about it.
- Analgesics can be counterproductive to women who want to stay alert during labor. The tendency to doze off between contractions may make it difficult to use pain relief measures for the entire duration of a contraction.
- Analgesia may enable a very anxious or tense mother to relax, which can encourage labor to

progress. Aggressive emotional support, however, often can have the same effect.

SECOND STAGE: GIVING BIRTH THROUGH ACTIVE PARTICIPATION

THE MOTHER'S EXPERIENCE

In the second stage of labor, your cervix will have completed dilation, and your uterus will contract forcibly at the top (fundus) to press your child through the birth canal. The contractions will have changed in strength, length, and interval time.

Your efforts now change from release to expulsion, and from light breathing to concentrated pushing. Your position should allow as much comfort as possible while enabling you to work with gravity. You may feel a great urge to bear down with contractions. If so, listen to your body; it will help you know what kind of effort to make. If you don't feel like pushing, you may need more active labor support for direction.

As the baby moves down the birth canal, you may feel tremendous pressure on the pelvic floor. As the baby's head distends the pelvic floor, you may feel pressure on the rectum and a stinging sensation around the vaginal outlet. You will need to push into the sensation you feel, even if it is painful. In fact, you probably will feel that you've never worked as hard in your life before!

THE HUSBAND'S/ LABOR COMPANION'S ROLE

Help the mother into an effective, comfortable position. Direct her actively in her breathing efforts through praise, encouragement, and reassurance. Watch for the baby, and inform the mother of anything you see happening.

Place your hand on her lower abdomen, just below her navel, telling her to "bulge out" this area into your hand as she presses down with her upper abdominal muscles. Support her physically during her pushing efforts. Remind her to release into the pressure, and ease any fears she might have of tearing or having a bowel movement.

You especially need to encourage her to relax between contractions, and follow her doctor's recommendations. Wiping her brow with a cool washcloth can help. Minimize distractions, keeping the room as dim and quiet as possible.

THE HEALTH CARE PROVIDER'S ROLE

The nurse or nurse-midwife will continue the actions described for the active phase of labor, as well as check for progress of the baby as descent through the pelvis takes place. Then the physician or nurse-midwife will assist the mother during the baby's birth by supporting the perineum, making an incision as needed to prevent damage to this area. He or she will also be available to perform emergency treatment if it is needed.

SECOND STAGE POSITIONS

The mother's positions in the second stage of labor should be as follows:

Semi-sitting: back of bed up, legs relaxed (open with supports), pelvis tilted forward, back of pelvis flat on bed.

Side-lying: lie on side, curled forward with labor partner holding legs up. (This position is best if your baby is posterior.)

Kneeling: keep bed upright and legs wide apart, resting against the bed between contractions. Hold self up by placing arms on knees during contractions.

Squatting: support position with legs wide apart and bed upright.

Standing: lean buttocks against edge of bed or table with physical assistance; used until baby "crowns."

SECOND STAGE EFFORTS

Remember the angle of the baby's descent; push down . . . up . . . out. Also, actively release the pelvic floor upon feeling pressure, pushing into the sensation.

Relax the lower abdominal muscles, bulging the lower abdomen out. Contract upper abdominal muscles, using them as levers on top of the uterus.

Keep your eyes open, watching for the baby. And stop pushing upon feeling a burning sensation at the vaginal opening or upon doctor's orders.

BREATHING

Use the following breathing techniques, testing to see which is most effective for you:

- *Pushing with breath held briefly at bottom of throat*—As the contraction begins, take a deep greeting breath. Take a medium breath for the second breath; hold it at the back of the throat and keep breath blocked for three to five seconds. Be sure to contract upper abdominal muscles to maximize your effort, keeping them taut between breaths.

- *Pushing with forced expiration*—As contraction begins, take a deep greeting breath. Follow with a breath in that isn't as deep, blocking it at the back of the throat to fix abdominal muscles taut. Force air through taut lips as you bring upper abdominal muscles in and down against the top of your uterus. Keep muscles taut between breaths. End with one or more full breaths. Relax your muscles between contractions, breathing slowly and deeply.

- *Light breathing for final expulsion*—When the baby's head reaches the perineum, it is imperative that you push only when someone tells you to. Rather than breathing to enhance the work of the uterus, you must breathe to detract from the uterine effort. Just follow your greeting breaths with light breathing or puffs of air (blow-blow breathing, see page 89). This allows your baby to be born less forcefully and helps you to prevent injury to your perineal area.

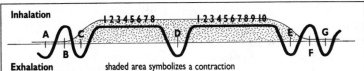

BLOCKED BREATHING FOR PUSHING

shaded area symbolizes a contraction

A. Contraction begins.
B. Greeting breath.
C. Inhale medium-sized breath, blocked at base of throat by using the "glottis" muscle. Hold breath for no longer than 8–10 seconds while using abdominal muscles to push.
D. After 3–5 seconds, exhale breath quickly, inhale and block next breath for 3–5 seconds. The mother does not release her abdominal muscles during this exchange of air, but continues to push throughout the contraction.
E. Contraction ends.
F. Completion breath and thanksgiving.
G. Resume normal breathing rate.

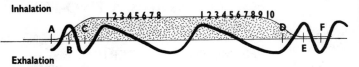

FORCED EXPIRATION FOR PUSHING

A. Contraction begins.
B. Greeting breath.
C. Quickly inhale medium-sized breath, then slowly but forcibly exhale for 8–10 seconds. The breath should be somewhat blocked at the back of the throat, but the glottis muscle is partially open to allow air to slowly pass out of the lungs. Be prepared . . . this gets noisy, but birthing noises are a sure sign of progress during birth!
D. Contraction.
E. Completion breath and thanksgiving.
F. Resume normal breathing rate.

THIRD STAGE: THE BIRTH OF THE PLACENTA

THE MOTHER'S EXPERIENCE

During the third stage of labor, you will feel cramplike contractions of the uterus as it works to shed the placenta. Expect a certain amount of blood loss (approximately eight ounces total) as the placenta detaches and the uterus grows smaller in size.

Normally within five to fifteen minutes after the birth, you will feel the placenta slide into your vagina, and will push it out with your health care provider's help. Occasionally chills and involuntary shaking due to hormonal and physiological changes will occur at this time.

If conditions permit, you can hold and nurse your baby immediately after giving birth. Don't be surprised if you feel relieved, exhilarated, and exhausted all at once.

You may receive an injection of the synthetic form of the hormone oxytocin, called Pitocin, through your IV or in your upper arm. Oxytocin causes contractions of the uterus and diminishes the flow of blood from the placental site. This hormone also is produced when the baby nurses at the breast.

Your baby will be checked and given an Apgar score based on his color, reflexes, breathing, heart rate, and muscle tone. This score is determined at one, five, and ten minutes of age. The five categories can receive zero to two points each, with ten being a perfect score. Initial scores of seven or above are considered normal. A score of six or below indicates that your baby requires medical assistance.

THE HUSBAND'S/
LABOR COMPANION'S ROLE

Now is your time to participate in the first moments of the baby's life outside the womb through touch, picture taking, celebrating, and praising the mother for her effort on her baby's behalf. Help the mother hold her baby as soon as possible, and enjoy this time together.

When the mother is experiencing the expulsion of the placenta, help her maintain her breathing rhythms.

THE HEALTH CARE
PROVIDER'S ROLE

The nurse will administer Pitocin upon request of the nurse-midwife or physician during this stage of labor. She also will assist with the delivery of the placenta if necessary, give the baby Apgar scores and otherwise evaluate the baby's adjustment to extra-uterine life, encourage the mother to relax and bond with her child, and provide warm blankets as needed.

The physician or midwife will assist the mother in delivery of the placenta, monitor blood loss and the state of the uterus following the birth, and provide medical assistance to the baby if necessary.

RELIEF MEASURES

- Maintain as upright a position as possible
- Relax your pelvic floor to facilitate the birth of placenta
- Use light or counted breathing if cramps are felt
- Focus your attention on the baby
- Use warm blankets
- Cooperate with your physician or nurse-midwife's efforts to assist you with the placenta
- Use prayer, praise, and Scripture to thank God for his help
- Nurse your baby, if possible, to encourage your uterus to contract as well as for you to marvel at your newborn child

FOURTH STAGE: A TWO-HOUR TRANSITION PERIOD

THE MOTHER'S EXPERIENCE

During this two-hour stage, you will continue to feel cramps or "afterpains" while the uterus contracts. Your blood pressure and pulse will be checked frequently to determine how your body is adjusting after your baby's birth.

Your episiotomy, or any tears, will be repaired with sutures, and you probably will be given a local anesthetic (if it wasn't administered during late second stage). You will be moved—or you may walk—to a labor or recovery room (if you had your baby in a delivery room), and you may find you are quite hungry and thirsty.

The fundus of your uterus will be checked and massaged if necessary. Also, your blood flow will be monitored.

Your emotions will be varied, and you may or may not feel like making phone calls or receiving visitors. Interact with your baby and nurse as you desire (if your baby is doing well).

THE HUSBAND'S/
LABOR COMPANION'S ROLE

During the fundal massage, remind the mother

to use light or counted breathing. Be sensitive to her reactions to the birth and to her continued need for companionship and support. Encourage her to interact with the baby.

THE HEALTH CARE PROVIDER'S ROLE

The nurses will assist the physician or nurse-midwife with the repair of the episiotomy, provide appropriate care for the baby, evaluate the mother's and baby's progress, monitor the physical status of the mother, perform fundal massage, adjust medications as needed, bring the mother food and beverages as desired, and inform the physician or nurse-midwife as to the mother's progress.

The nurse-midwife or physician will examine the cervix, vagina, and perineum and make repairs as needed. He or she also will monitor the mother's condition (usually based on the nurse's reports), and perform procedures or prescribe medications as needed.

RELIEF MEASURES

- Rest and relax
- Use patterned breathing for cramps and fundal massage
- Get a clean gown and socks
- Shower
- Consume food and beverages as desired
- Have uninterrupted closeness with the baby, if possible
- Use an ice bag for swollen perineum

SELF-CHECK QUIZ FOR LABOR

Take this quiz after you have read chapters 7 through 10, and have practiced the techniques you have learned. For the greatest benefit, use it as a "rehearsal" for labor during late pregnancy.

PRELABOR AND EARLY LABOR

- What signs are associated with prelabor?
- How are Braxton-Hicks (prelabor) contractions different from labor contractions?
- How will you know labor is beginning?
- You awaken at 4 A.M. and use the toilet. On the tissue you notice a slightly bloody vaginal discharge. How might you respond?
- How do you think you'll feel when your labor begins?
- You begin having menstruallike contractions in the late afternoon. What will you do?
- What types of foods and beverages might be ideal (easily digestible) for prelabor and very early labor? What activities safely stimulate labor? (See chapter 11.)
- As labor begins, what will you expect your labor partner's role to be? What kinds of com-

fort measures might be useful?
- At what point will you begin breathing patterns? Which type will you use?

Things to Do:
- Practice breathing patterns for early labor.
- Rehearse early labor contractions with relaxation, breathing, and attention-focusing.
- Review hospital admission procedures from your tour.

ACTIVE LABOR

- How may the quality of your labor change between four and six centimeters cervical dilation?
- What feelings and reactions are typical for this phase of labor?
- How will you know when to change breathing patterns and which ones to use?
- What procedures may be done at this time? According to your health care provider, what medications may be offered?
- What can you do for dry lips and mouth? Cold feet? Backache?

- How can your labor companion help you to relax, especially between contractions?
- You have been in labor for twelve hours and are three centimeters dilated. Your doctor decides to stimulate your labor. What might he do?
- Your membranes rupture spontaneously. What can you expect to happen and how might you respond?
- Your back has hurt since the beginning of labor and you feel the contractions mostly in the lower back area. What can be done?
- Your fingers and lips feel tingly. What's happening and what can be done?
- Your labor is moving very rapidly and the contractions are very intense. How can you cope, and what can your labor companion do to help?

Things to Do:
- Practice breathing patterns for active labor.
- Review positions and pain relief measures for basic labor.
- Practice contractions in which you become tense and breathe erratically. Have your labor companion coach you in alleviating tension and anxiety.

TRANSITION
- You are irritable, tired, and your legs are shaky. What's happening? How might you cope? What other symptoms are common in this period of labor and what comfort measures might be used?
- What can your labor companion say and do to help you during transition?
- You have one urge to push but are not fully dilated. What can you do to alleviate this?
Things to Do:
- Practice breathing patterns and relief measures for transition.

PUSHING AND BIRTH
- How might your mood change during pushing? What will happen to the quality of your contractions?
- What physical sensations are associated with the second stage of labor?
- You will be asked not to push or give a series of small pushes. Why?
Things to Do:
- Practice pushing.
- Practice breathing for crowning and birth.
- Try several positions and breathing techniques.

AN OVERVIEW OF PHYSICAL ADJUSTMENTS OCCURRING AFTER BIRTH (POSTPARTUM)

- *Uterus*—During pregnancy, the amount of muscle fibers and blood carried in the uterus increases as it expands. After the placenta separates from the lining of the uterus (during the third stage of labor), contraction of the muscle fibers must take place to close off the open blood vessels where the placenta was attached. This causes the uterus to drastically reduce in size and to sink into the pelvic cavity.

These contractions or "afterpains," which continue as the uterus breaks down and reabsorbs unneeded muscle cells, are most intense while breast-feeding or if Pitocin is given. They occur with greater intensity after each successive child. Conscious release and breathing techniques may help to decrease your discomfort. Pain medication, such as Tylenol 3 or Darvon, may be taken if cramping is severe.

Just prior to your baby's birth, your uterus weighs about two pounds, and is under your ribs. After the placenta is expulsed, your uterus is below the navel and about the size of a large grapefruit. It stays this size for about forty-eight hours. By the third day, your uterus begins to decrease in size and weight until it reaches its normal size, about six weeks after the birth.

● *Lochia*—A bloody discharge, this begins to flow after the third stage. It is made up of blood and debris (such as shed muscle cells) from the uterus. Most of this discharge comes from the place where the placenta was attached. This site usually takes between six and seven weeks to heal completely. The discharge color changes from bright red during the first few days to a reddish-brown, then turns yellow-white around the eighth or tenth day, becoming watery before ceasing. Sanitary napkins are preferable to vaginal tampons since they allow the discharge to flow more freely and pose less risk of infection.

The amount, rate, and duration of the flow of lochia varies between women and between subsequent pregnancies. At first, because of the accumulation of lochia while lying flat, the flow may become heavier as you stand after resting. The red lochia may persist for longer than a week, or may occur only off and on. If the flow lasts more than twenty-one days or becomes

REVIEW OF NORMAL PROBLEMS AND HELPS

Problem	Help
Fatigue	Good food, rest—especially when baby rests
Chills after birth	Warm blanket
Backache	Slow breathing, pelvic rock, massage, heat
Body aches	Warm shower, heating pad
Mood swings	Talk about how you feel and accept your feelings
Afterpains	Relief techniques, pain medication
Change in color of lochia back to red	Take it easy
Sore perineum, itching	Ointment, sitz baths, pain medication, gauze pads soaked in witch hazel
Numbness or bruises in area where IV was placed	Warm, wet compresses
Abdominal wall flabbiness	Curl-ups, tightening, pelvic rock, leg sliding
Engorgement, leaking breasts, sore nipples	Prop towel or cotton pad under breasts, air dry, change position often (see page 59)

SYMPTOMS FOR WHICH YOU SHOULD NOTIFY YOUR DOCTOR

● Temperature over 101° F
● Chills
● Bad-smelling vaginal discharge
● Severe headache
● Faintness, dizziness
● Vaginal bleeding soaking more than one pad per hour over a couple hours
● Heavy gush of red blood from vagina after flow has tapered off or changed color
● Passage of several clots accompanied by heavy bleeding
● Severe back, abdominal, chest, or leg pain
● Burning with and increased frequency of urination
● Reddened area in breast that feels sore and hot (especially when accompanied by fever, and flu-ish feeling)
● Any other symptom your doctor tells you to report

heavy enough to soak a sanitary napkin in an hour, call your physician.

If the flow tapers off, then gets heavier, you may be doing too much too soon. Try resting more and taking it easy with activities such as housecleaning and lifting. Another way to deal with a bout of heavier bleeding is, if breast-feeding, to put the baby to the breast—if he will cooperate.

If you pass blood clots, it needn't be cause for alarm. As long as a clot is not followed by persistent, bright red bleeding, and if you don't pass clots for a period longer than six hours, it usually is just blood that has coagulated. However, if either of the two conditions mentioned occur, call your physician.

If the lochia develops a foul odor, and is accompanied by vaginal itching (not associated with the healing of the episiotomy), and/or has a green or frothy appearance, get in touch with your doctor. These may be indications of an infection, which needs treatment.

Finally, do not douche without your doctor's consent. External cleansing of the perineal area normally is sufficient.

• *Breasts and Nipples*—Your breasts undergo several changes during pregnancy in anticipation of lactation. There is an increase in blood and lymph fluid to that area and the amount of glandular tissue increases. Small bumps develop in the areola (pigmented area around the nipples), which secrete a fatty substance that helps moisturize and protect nipples from infection.

After your baby is born, the breasts stay the same size for the first few days. The process of lactation, however, is triggered at the time the placenta separates from the uterine lining. During this period, before milk is produced, your baby receives a concentrated liquid called colostrum. This is made in the breasts during the latter part of pregnancy. It is high in antibodies, a laxative, and helps to break up mucus in the baby's digestive tract. There is no substitute on the market for this remarkable substance.

The breasts usually undergo engorgement, or marked swelling, as the milk "comes in" on the second to fourth day. For women who choose to bottle-feed, engorgement may be a problem even though a lactation suppressant probably will be administered. If this happens, most likely it will last twenty-four to forty-eight hours.

Usually the milk supply will diminish in the absence of suckling. Liquid intake may be reduced to aid in this process, although it's important to drink some fluids throughout the day. Ice packs may be put on the breasts for ten to fifteen minutes every few hours and the breasts may be bound firmly with a towel.

Nipple care is covered in chapter 6, and should be followed if you wish to help your nipples adapt to nursing. Cleansing of the nipples with warm water can be done, and is especially helpful during the first few days as secretions of colostrum dry and collect on the nipple.

• *Abdominal Wall*—Similar to a corset, the abdominal wall, if stretched for a prolonged period of time, tends to lose its resiliency. After your baby's birth, your abdominal muscles will feel quite loose and will not complete the process of returning to their normal state for about six weeks.

If it has lost its tone, the abdominal wall may remain less firm than you might want even after that time. The section on basic pregnancy fitness exercises in chapter 6 gives several easy toning exercises for this area which can be started soon after giving birth. These exercises may be followed up by a more strenuous program with your doctor's consent after your six-week checkup.

When you go to the hospital, be sure to take a pair of loose-fitting (or maternity) slacks to wear when you go home. It may take you awhile to fit into your regular clothes, though this is not always the case. Try to remember that your body has several weeks (up to two months) of recuperating to do, and it's best not to expect too much too soon.

● *Vagina, Genitalia, and Related Structures*—The vagina is a muscle membrane which, due to hormones, softens during pregnancy in preparation for giving birth. It stretches considerably during a vaginal birth, and remains slack until it reduces in size during your recovery. Pelvic floor exercises hasten healing of this area and help you regain muscle tone after giving birth. See the section on the pelvic floor (chapter 6) for discussion of the significance of these exercises.

The lips around the vagina, the labia minora and labia majora, also stretch considerably during a vaginal birth. Occasionally they have surface lacerations due to the stretching, which may sting during urination. Try to lean on the toilet seat so that the flow of urine is directed away from the burning. The lips may stay somewhat flabby after the birth.

Other structures that undergo changes are the oviducts (fallopian tubes), ovaries, and the suspensory ligaments which support them. After being stretched during pregnancy, they will resume their normal position in the pelvic cavity in the weeks following the birth.

Likewise, the cervix is soft and flabby right after birth. By the end of the first week, its opening narrows and it firms up.

In general, by the sixth week after your baby is born, much healing has taken place and you've nearly completed the cycle of parturition, or giving birth to your child.

● *Weight Loss*—The average amount of weight lost after giving birth is twelve pounds, though this varies from woman to woman. The twelve pounds include a seven-pound baby, a one- to two-pound placenta, one to two pounds of amniotic fluid, and two pounds of body fluid and blood. Three or more pounds may be lost as the body rids itself of excess fluids, and a few more pounds may be lost by the end of six weeks when the uterus resumes its normal size.

The main variables seem to be the amount of fluid retained during pregnancy due to high sodium concentrations and the amount of fatty tissue stored by the body. If needed, talk with your doctor about a moderate weight reduction plan at your postpartum checkup.

● *Energy Level*—You may find that you become tired easily during the weeks that your body is returning to its pre-pregnant condition. Fluctuations in hormone levels, the stress of healing, and being up with the baby are a few of the factors leading to fatigue in new mothers.

During the first few weeks, it's important to try to sleep when the baby's sleeping, keeping in mind that your body is working at healing itself. If you cooperate with this process by getting good nourishment, plenty of liquids, and sufficient rest, then you probably will encounter fewer roadblocks on your way to recovery.

● *Other Things to Consider*

Hemorrhoids—Some women are affected by hemorrhoids, the enlarged blood vessels that may protrude as the anus distends during the pushing stage of labor. If you have them, you must avoid straining while having a bowel movement since that can aggravate the condition.

The pain and itching of hemorrhoids can be helped by soaking in a sitz bath; applying special ointment; pressing them back into the rectum with a clean, lubricated fingertip followed by up to ten minutes of contracting the anal sphincter; and/or applying an anesthetic cream or gauze pad (such as Tucks), which is premoistened with soothing liquid or witch hazel.

You probably will experience a decrease in this problem within two weeks following the birth. If not, make sure your physician examines you at your postnatal checkup.

Constipation—You may not have a bowel movement until the second or third day after giving birth. The intestines seem to be less effective in moving substances and you may have been thoroughly "cleaned out" by an enema prior to the birth.

Drink lots of liquids to make the first bowel movement easier. Raisins, prunes, bran, and other laxative foods can be eaten to enhance the process. If you're afraid of putting pressure on the healing perineum, wash your hands thoroughly and place a clean gauze pad on the perineum for support as you have your bowel movement. Stool softeners are readily available if all else fails.

Hair Loss—Due to hormone levels during pregnancy, many women gain extra body hair. This diminishes during the first few months after giving birth. Hair loss from the scalp is common, and usually takes place from four to six months after the birth and should not last more than two weeks.

GRAPHIC LABOR CHART

(This chart may be copied and used during your labor as a general guide. Feel free to adapt it to your own birthing pattern.)

STAGE	ONE		
PHASE	Early	Active	Transition
WORK DONE	Cervical effacement and dilation Baby moved deeper into pelvis		
CONTRACTIONS A) DURATION	15–30 seconds 5+ seconds	30–60 seconds 20+ seconds	60–120 seconds 40+ seconds
Intensity and Peak			
B) LENGTH APART	20+ minutes to 5 minutes	5 minutes to 2 minutes	2 minutes to 30 seconds
DILATION (cm)	1 2 3 4	5 6 7	8 9 10
APPROXIMATE DURATION	40-50% (4–8+ hours)	30% (2–6+ hours)	10% (30 minutes–1½ hours)
POSSIBLE BREATHING PATTERNS			
Description of Pattern	Slow Light	3:1 2:1	1:1 Blow-blow
RELIEF MEASURES **(REMEMBER: Position is important!)**	Release, relax, and rest Back massage for relaxation Nourishing liquids Use most comfortable position Begin deep breathing if anxious or tense Get professional help if needed Warm shower Cuddle with labor partner	Urinate often Ice chips, lollipop Counterpressure, passive pelvic rock, and low back rubs (active and transition phases) Dim lights Change breathing as contractions intensify Warm compresses Praise and encouragement Medication if desired	Perspective: Last part is hardest but shortest Adapt breathing to contractions Eliminate fear; accept what is happening Get professional help whenever it's needed Remember: Your baby is almost here! Socks for cold feet Blow out to relieve urge to push

Graphic Labor Chart (cont.)

STAGE	ONE		
PHASE	Early	Active	Transition
WHAT'S HAPPENING (You may experience a variety, but not all of these symptoms.)	Loss of mucus plug likely Soft b.m.'s Low backache Crampy feeling in lower abdomen Effacement of cervix Membranes may break	Baby moving deeper into pelvis Contractions progressively longer Digestion slows down Nausea, vomiting Backache	Leg shaking Irritability; mood change Decreased desire to talk Nausea, digestive disturbance Hot or cold flashes Rectal and back pressure Early urge to push
EMOTIONAL RESPONSE	Excited Anxious Unsure it's the "real thing" until examination	Greater concentration on use of comfort measures Concern, determination Increased dependence on labor partner and health care providers	Introspective, withdrawn May feel discouraged, panicky, fed-up Stress reaction: anger, crying, etc.
SPIRITUAL RESPONSE	Praise Thanksgiving Perspective Prayer and Scripture throughout entire labor	Control of thought patterns Avoid fear and anxiety by setting your mind on "things above" Contemplate word pictures from Scripture	Total dependence on the Lord's strength Call upon the name of Jesus Ask for the Lord's help

STAGE	TWO	THREE	FOUR
WORK DONE	Birth	Expulsion of placenta and membranes	Involution of uterus begins
CONTRACTIONS	45–90 seconds	45–90 seconds	30 + seconds
A) DURATION	30 + seconds		
Intensity and Peak			
B) LENGTH APART	1–2 minutes		sporadic
DILATION (cm)	Complete	Cervix closes after birth as uterus contracts	
APPROXIMATE DURATION	10–20% (10 min. to 2 + hours)	5–20 minutes	45–60 minutes

Graphic Labor Chart (cont.)

STAGE	TWO		THREE	FOUR
BREATHING PATTERN				
Description of Pattern	Forced expiration	Breath block	Crowning—Blow out or slow pant	After birth—Slow
COMFORT MEASURES	Remember C-curve as you push down, up, and out Eyes open. Look for baby! Release perineum and lower abdominals Utilize upper abdominals Rock pelvis back to lift baby forward Release and pant for crowning Local anesthetic for episiotomy		Hold your baby and enjoy the fruit of your labor Give slow push for placenta Focus attention on baby for repair of episiotomy and use slow or pant-blow breathing, if needed Nurse baby if he/she wants to suck	Warm blankets Juice, food—birthday cake! Hold and nurse baby Slow breathing for massage and contractions Urinate Ice bag for episiotomy may help Pads for lochia (vaginal discharge after birth)
WHAT'S HAPPENING (You may experience a variety, but not all of these symptoms.)	Pressure in vagina and on perineum Back pressure Rectal pressure Strength of urge to push varies Baby moves onto soft tissue and is born! Deep guttural sounds result from pushing		Expulsion of placenta and membranes Repair of episiotomy Baby given Apgar scores; initial exam May hold baby for first time Separation of placenta signals onset of lactation	Recovery room Vital signs checked Uterus checked and massaged if necessary Blood flow is checked Breast-feeding is beneficial to both mother and baby at this time
EMOTIONAL RESPONSE	Complete involvement with work being done Rest periods; withdrawn, sleepy, attempting to conserve energy Disbelief that cause of pressure is baby's head		Awe, exhilaration, relief, gratitude Concern for baby's well-being Irritable about repair of episiotomy, post-birth	Many different feelings arise; both parents are emotionally sensitive Accept the way you feel, even if it isn't all positive
SPIRITUAL RESPONSE	Draw on the Lord's strength Be thankful for the new life about to be born		Praise Thanksgiving Give the glory to God	Pray for your new baby Rest in the Lord

FIRST AND SECOND STAGE ACTIVITIES: YOUR RECORD

Use this form to take notes in class or to keep notes from this book.

1. EARLY PHASE (1–3 cm)
   Quality of contractions

   Physical manifestations

   Comfort measures and stimulation of labor

   Companion's role

   Signs indicating medical attention is needed

2. ACTIVE PHASE (4–6 cm)
   Quality of contractions

   Physical manifestations

   Routine procedures/possible alternatives

   Sources of discomfort/comfort measures

   Companion's role

   Nurse's or midwife's role

Your Record (cont.)

3. TRANSITION PHASE (7–10 cm)
Quality of contractions

Physical manifestations

Sources of discomfort/comfort measures

Companion's role

Nurse's or midwife's role

4. SECOND STAGE (pushing)
Quality of contractions

Physical manifestations

Sources of discomfort/comfort measures

Options for birth

Companion's role

Nurse's role

4. Doctor's or midwife's role

Positions attempted during practice

1.

2.

3.

How they felt

Breathing: Which feels best? Are you confident in your body's ability to signal you as to what to do?

Other considerations
   Pushing is good for your baby if this stage isn't overly long. The contractions that occur while your baby passes through the birth canal squeeze fluid and mucus from your baby's breathing passages and stimulate the surface of your baby's skin.

CHAPTER ELEVEN

God Works for Good in All Things

"So do not fear, for I am with you; do not be dismayed, for I am your God. I will strengthen you and help you; I will uphold you with my hand." ISAIAH 41:10

With the many factors interacting to make each labor and birth unique, it's impossible to predict what will take place in any given situation. There are many variations on a basic theme in birth, and many "what-ifs" that create uncertainty during the months of waiting. No one can assure you that all will be normal, and that your baby will be just what you hope he or she will be . . . but the Lord can and does assure you that, ultimately, all will be as it should be (Romans 8:28).

The Lord's love to his children is unconditional, immeasurable, and sovereign. Serving Jesus means obeying and loving him, surrendering all that you are and have to him. Consider the words of the old hymn, "I Surrender All":

All to Jesus I surrender,
All to him I freely give;
I will ever love and trust him,
In his presence daily live.

All to Jesus I surrender,
Humbly at his feet I bow,

Worldly pleasures all forsaken,
Take me Jesus, take me now.

All to Jesus I surrender,
Make me, Savior, wholly thine;
Let me feel the Holy Spirit,
Truly know that Thou art mine.

All to Jesus I surrender,
Lord, I give myself to Thee.
Fill me with Thy love and power,
Let Thy blessing fall on me.

I surrender all, I surrender all,
All to Thee my blessed Savior,
I surrender all.

As you consider the upcoming labor and unborn child, can you say from the depths of your heart, "I surrender all"? Let any fear you may have be dispelled by reading God's words in Matthew 11:29, 30: "Take my yoke upon you and learn from me, for I am gentle and humble in heart, and you will find rest for your souls. For my yoke is easy and my burden is light."

It's natural to make our surrender to God a conditional one. But as we grow in him, we learn more of his nature and begin to lay more and more at his feet. We can trust that God will not disappoint us. He knows our needs even before we bring them to him, and he *will* respond (Matthew 7:7-11).

MEETING THE CHALLENGE OF UNEXPECTED EVENTS

Unexpected things have a way of happening to all of us. During childbearing many things can come up, from having a girl (when you really wanted a boy), to going three weeks past your due date (when the doctor said you'd be three weeks early), to more serious complications involving the baby or you.

If something unexpected happens during your childbirth, whether with you or with your baby, don't be afraid. Call on your heavenly Father for help. Place yourself and your baby before God, remembering his love for you both.

Almost every labor has its panicky moments. Here are some ideas for coping if something unexpected happens to you:

WHILE IT IS HAPPENING—

- Stay calm. The Lord is with you and he will strengthen you so you can cope with feelings of disappointment, anger, or loss. He truly is the "God of all comfort" (2 Corinthians 1:3). Present your requests to God, petitioning him in prayer (Philippians 4:6).
- Accept your feelings. Don't be ashamed of the way you feel; the Lord understands and he is patient. David honestly expressed many of his feelings, and so did Abraham . . . yet look how much the Lord loved them. Their faith in God drew them to him for answers to their questions.
- Get accurate information. Don't be afraid to

ask questions! Be involved in what's going on so that you can better understand how you can help, what can be done, and what the true outlook is.

- Pray for those caring for you. Pray that the Lord will guide the hands and thoughts of your health care providers. Ask him to help them make the right decisions and use the best treatments for your situation.
- Picture Jesus as being "in the same boat" with you. Remember the story of Jesus calming the storm when in the boat with his disciples? Call on his name and trust him to answer you with his calming presence.

AFTERWARD—

- Remember: Others have experienced similar situations, so you are not alone. Other parents have lived through what you are experiencing, many of whom are willing to offer support and information. Don't isolate yourself, denying the benefits of allowing others to reach out to you. Ask for a referral from your health care provider or your church.
- Keep your options open. Don't make irreversible decisions. The more critical the situation, the greater the psychological stress . . . so try to get all the facts before making any ethically complex decisions (e.g., termination of life support systems). Ask your pastor to pray with you if you feel overwhelmed by the circumstances.
- Allow time to heal your hurt. Whenever loss is experienced, whether loss of hopes or loss of a life, emotional hurt is produced. Such wounds cannot be healed by doctors. Only God, through time and the help of capable people, can heal in this area.
- Don't compare. Your birth or baby may not fit your picture of what is "ideal." It is natural to compare, but keep in mind that each situation is unique. Try not to compare your experience to what you may consider the "norm." Instead, be attentive to what the Lord

would have you learn from your situation.

- Realize that any loss brings grief. Grieving is a process marked by a variety of emotions including disbelief, denial, sorrow, loneliness, anger, depression, physical manifestations of stress, irritability, frustration, upset in interpersonal communication, restlessness, fantasy, disorganization, and a desire to talk about what is causing the grief.

Normal grief is a process, which runs its course and eventually leads to restoration of well-being. Complicated grief that becomes prolonged, intensified, or delayed can prevent a person from dealing with life productively. Because of this, the person suffering such a grief may benefit from professional counseling or pastoral care. Read Psalm 77:1-15 and 86:1-7 to discover a picture of the reality of grief and the determination to rely on the Lord.

- Seek pastoral or professional support as needed. Never hesitate to ask for help. There are times when even the strongest among us needs ministering. If your relationship with the Lord or with those around you has been disrupted, don't let things become even more complicated by refusing to accept professional help. Seek help compatible with your beliefs, and make a sincere effort to follow recommendations you are given.

- Try to get adequate rest and avoid substances that aggravate stress. It's impossible to feel clearheaded if the need for sleep and balanced meals is neglected. Avoid excessive caffeine intake, nicotine, and sugary foods, which promote nervousness. Instead, drink herbal teas with honey and lemon, or Postum. Buy nutritious, easy-to-fix foods such as those listed in the snack menus in the Family Nutrition Guide (appendix A).

- Realize that placing blame won't help or change the situation. Blaming began in the garden when Adam tried to say, "It was Eve's fault." The chances are good that everyone involved in your situation did their best, and no one is at fault. Don't waste your precious energy and thoughts on blame . . . or guilt.

- Make peace with the Lord. You may never know why things happened as they did. Accept that God heard your prayers, knew your desires and expectations, and answered them in this way for reasons that only he can understand. Be honest with your feelings, presenting them to him and allowing him to help you work through them. Let him be your help and support, as he has promised (Psalm 46).

SPECIFIC SITUATIONS

The following situations, though far from common, can occur during birth. It is hoped that you will find the suggestions here helpful and informative, and that you will use them as a part of your preparation. This way, should you find yourself experiencing any of these situations, you will be able to understand and cope with them.

Many of these conditions are reasons for having a baby by cesarean, and all warrant medical or professional care. For a more thorough discussion of these conditions, talk with your health care provider.

PREMATURE LABOR

Recent studies indicate that between 7 and 8 percent of babies born in the U.S. today are "premature" or "low birth weight" babies. The premature infant is one who is born before the thirty-eighth week of pregnancy. A low birth weight infant is one who may be any gestational age, but weighs less than five and a half pounds at birth. Babies in these two categories may have similar problems in adjusting to life outside the womb.

Babies born before "term" (thirty-nine to forty-two weeks) generally have greater difficulty handling the stress of labor; an immaturity of the digestive tract; poor self-regulation of body temperature; and poor absorption of oxygen due to a less developed respiratory tract. Fortunately, there are many neonatal intensive care units (N.I.C.U.s) in regional centers throughout the country. These units are equipped to provide an environment for pre-term infants who need oxygen, temperature-controlled surroundings, and special feedings to survive. Also, there have been medical technological advances in recent years that have increased pre-term infants' chances of survival.

There are numerous factors that can cause prematurity and low birth weight including:

- malnutrition
- heavy cigarette smoking
- alcohol and drug abuse
- high blood pressure in the mother (maternal hypertension)
- diabetes
- multiple gestation (more than one baby in the womb)
- teenage pregnancy
- placental insufficiency
- poverty.

If labor began prematurely, your health care provider would likely admit you to the hospital, and prescribe bed rest and medication for you that hopefully would quiet your uterus. If the contractions stopped, you would be sent home. Should the membranes rupture spontaneously, the possibility of infection would necessitate hospital admission and close medical supervision. Your physician would have to weigh permitting labor to take place or performing a cesarean to avoid infection against the risks of prematurity.

In premature labor, electronic fetal monitoring permits a continuous readout of the baby's heart rate. When labor seems to adversely affect the baby's well-being, a cesarean birth would be advisable. Analgesics or anesthetics during labor or a cesarean birth would need to be selected in light of the baby's needs.

When there are multiple concerns involved in childbearing, the situation is considered "high risk." Such pregnancies require special medical attention and the services of a skilled obstetrician—a specialist trained in the management of such situations. Two of the newest branches of medicine, neonatology and perinatology, have developed to promote the survival of high risk babies.

When a baby has to stay in the N.I.C.U., parents are encouraged to spend time with the infant. They can provide the necessary factor of tender love and care in the midst of a stressful, sterile environment of IVs, blipping monitors, and concerned medical teams. Also, the mother's breast milk often can be used to feed her infant, rendering benefits unattainable from any other source.

Recently I asked the head nurse of the N.I.C.U. at the hospital where I work what I could share in this book with expectant parents who might be faced with having a baby early. Mary, a Christian, responded, "Tell them to put their trust in the Lord. That's the single most important piece of advice I can offer." I couldn't agree with her more!

POST-TERM LABOR

When a baby is overdue (born more than two weeks past his due date), he may be "postmature." Between 6 and 12 percent of babies carried longer than forty-two weeks are served by an "aging" placenta, one that is beginning to shut down. When placental function is impaired, the danger to the baby is increased.

A postmature infant may be larger, making vaginal birth more difficult. To facilitate the birth, labor may be induced artificially through intravenous administration of Pitocin. Should labor be too stressful for the mother or the baby, a cesarean birth would be performed. Your health care provider often will use a fetal monitor at this point to observe the infant's response to motion and/or simulated labor to help determine which procedure would be best.

DIFFICULTIES WITH THE PLACENTA

Since the placenta develops from the initial cluster of cells that join together at the time of fertilization, it is a "temporary" gland. It secretes the hormones that maintain the pregnancy after the early weeks of gestation. Firmly attached to the lining of the uterus (until the third stage of labor), your baby's nutritional and excretory needs are met through a complete exchange of substances that takes place through the placenta.

Usually, the placenta is attached to the upper portion of the uterus, on the front or back uterine wall. Sometimes, however, it adheres to the lower part of the uterus, covering the cervix. When it is attached between the baby and the cervix, it is called a *placenta previa*. This condition is suspected if an expectant mother experiences vaginal bleeding during pregnancy. It can be confirmed by using ultrasound to make a diagnosis. Placenta previa is a serious condition that may necessitate bed rest during pregnancy, the avoidance of sexual intercourse, or even hospitalization.

The safest route of delivery for the baby when the placenta is covering much of the cervix is a cesarean. This is because the baby's source of oxygen would be interfered with if the placenta began to detach prior to the baby's birth as the cervix dilated during labor. This condition occurs in about 1 out of 300 pregnancies.

Another placental condition, where the placenta begins to loosen its grip on the uterus before the baby is born and breathing on his own, is referred to as an "abruption of the placenta," or *abruptio placentae*. Symptoms of this condition tion include vaginal bleeding and sharp abdominal pains. Immediate delivery by cesarean normally is advisable. This condition can be caused by malnutrition, shortness of the umbilical cord, elevated blood pressure, overly long (tetanic) labor contractions, or grand multiparity (a woman having more than five babies). It occurs in about one percent of all labors, with varying degrees of severity in the abruption.

MULTIPLE PREGNANCY

The incidence of twins being born among whites in the U.S. is about once in every ninety-three births; among non-whites it's one in seventy-eight. Having a multiple pregnancy requires a greater focus on providing yourself with adequate nutrients, appropriate exercise, and plenty of rest. Multiple births are more likely to be accomplished via the cesarean route, unless the size and position of twins allows for their safe passage. Triplets and quadruplets often are born prematurely and invariably are delivered by cesarean.

Sharing the uterus means sharing oxygen, nutrients, and space. As a result, babies born together may be of lower birth weight and have a greater tendency to be born pre-term. Positioning can be awkward, making passage through the pelvis trickier. Cord problems are not uncommon, and the mother may be more likely to experience high blood pressure and swelling. The risks to both the mother and baby may be reduced substantially through proper prenatal care.

LARGE BABY, SMALL PELVIS

When a discrepancy exists between the size of your baby's head and the size of your pelvic passageway, it is termed a cephalopelvic disproportion, or C.P.D. This may be diagnosed through the use of ultrasound or by doing an X-ray pelvimetry, where the distance between the bones in your pelvis is determined through measurement on X-ray films. This diagnosis occasionally is made prior to the onset of labor, but more commonly it's done after some labor has taken place without the baby sufficiently moving down into the pelvis.

Upright positioning and walking during labor will encourage the descent of the head when there is adequate space and should be used to promote the progress of labor. These techniques also can help borderline, but not absolute, disproportion.

DIFFICULT POSITION

When a baby presents his buttocks, feet, shoulders, face, brow, or chin toward his mother's cervix, it means that his birth through the vagina will be difficult, if not impossible. The health care provider should check for the baby's position during prenatal visits, suggesting exercises to encourage the baby's head to descend into the pelvis. Some midwives and physicians will attempt to manually "turn" the baby to a head-first position. If the baby does not change position, a cesarean may be required.

RUPTURED MEMBRANES

Most health care providers recommend that mothers be checked or enter the hospital after the bag of waters breaks. If you're unsure whether the baby is well engaged in the pelvis when this happens, you should lie on your side as much as possible until the baby's position is checked. This is because the cord may descend ahead of the baby, when some of the fluid escapes, and interfere with the baby's oxygen supply. Called "cord prolapse," this would require an immediate cesarean.

When the amniotic sac breaks, it feels almost like an internal balloon popping. There is a release of fluid from the vagina and some relief of pressure. It's important to check the color and odor of the fluid, making certain it is clear and fairly odorless.

Occasionally, the baby will have had a bowel movement in reaction to stress and the fluid will have flecks of stool in it, or be a dark greenish color. This condition, called "meconium staining," occurs in about 11 percent of all births. Meconium staining requires that the baby's breathing passages be thoroughly cleaned after birth, usually through a catheter, to prevent him from inhaling any of the irritating fluid into the lungs. Many physicians also recommend that the baby's heart rate be monitored continuously during labor if meconium is present in the amniotic fluid.

SLOWLY PROGRESSING LABOR

Many labors get off to a slow start, and many women experience intermittent menstrual- or flu-like abdominal cramping off and on for twenty-four hours or longer without having labor "kick into gear." Other women check into the hospital to discover they are dilated to two or three centimeters, then labor for eight hours or more without any change in the cervix.

If you feel your labor needs to begin or be stimulated, you might try the following:

- Relax your body; don't resist labor. Let your uterus do its work and avoid tensing in response.
- Create a quiet environment with guaranteed total privacy for at least thirty minutes.
- Take a warm bath or shower to encourage relaxation if your membranes or bag of waters hasn't broken yet.
- Identify and overcome any fears or inhibitions you have about giving birth.
- Walk or sit upright, if you're not confined to bed. Walking is a fabulous way to stimulate labor. It gets the baby down against the cervix, exerting greater pressure on it to open up. Sitting upright on your bed or in a chair will help, too.
- Breathe slowly and deeply, as if you were sleeping. Slowing down and deepening your breathing will get extra oxygen to your baby and working muscles.
- Massage your nipples by pulling them out rhythmically and intermittently (one minute on, one minute off) to mimic a baby's sucking, or use an electric breast pump. Recent studies in Israel have demonstrated that nipple stimulation is effective in starting or augmenting labor because the hormone oxytocin is secreted when the nerve endings in the nipples are stimulated. Oxytocin works on two main areas: uterine muscle fibers, and cells in the breast that contract to eject milk from the glandular cells where it is stored. The Lord made our

bodies so that when a baby nurses in the days after birth, the uterus will contract to close up the wound left by the placenta and thereby reduce bleeding. Nipple stimulation prior to the baby's birth also contracts the uterus and can enhance or induce labor.

Your health care provider also can do several things to induce labor, such as:

- Administer an enema to promote contractions and the evacuation of the lower intestines. (This may be self-applied at home, but check with your health care provider first.)
- Artificially rupture the membranes. This commonly used procedure, called "amniotomy," makes contractions stronger and may make labor more productive.
- Intravenously administer Pitocin. When medically required, and if the above measures are ineffective, uterine contractions may be induced using Pitocin, the synthetic form of oxytocin. If this, too, proves unsuccessful, the baby will be delivered by cesarean. Inductions should be performed only in a hospital setting under obstetrical supervision.

Most health care providers want the baby, if it is full term, to be born within twenty-four hours after the membranes have ruptured. This is due to an increased incidence of infection (sepsis) for the mother and baby after this period of time.

MATERNAL COMPLICATIONS

Several health concerns can become aggravated during pregnancy. A mother's body must adapt in many ways during gestation, and these changes can aggravate health concerns that existed before the pregnancy, or even initiate new conditions related to the pregnancy itself. Following are some conditions that may require special care throughout pregnancy and which often

make a cesarean birth necessary for the safety of both mother and baby:

- diabetes
- anemia
- vaginal bleeding during pregnancy
- lung, kidney, or heart disease
- genital herpes infection
- narrow pelvis, or pelvic infection
- high blood pressure
- incompetent cervix
- previous cesarean birth (vertical incision)
- mother's age being under eighteen or over thirty-five
- malnutrition
- Rh blood incompatibility between maternal and fetal blood
- preeclampsia, eclampsia, and toxemia

Should any of these conditions exist, it is even more important to eat balanced meals and follow the Daily Food Plan in appendix A. Also, use a physician who can closely monitor your pregnancy. Your life-style will be more affected, of course, if your pregnancy is high risk. Adequate rest and relaxation is essential to help your baby grow.

Medical complications of any kind during pregnancy or childbirth can be both physically and emotionally trying. It's natural to worry and think the worst. Be willing to discuss your thoughts with your husband, or with your pastor. Reread the parts in chapters 4 and 5 that present ways to strengthen your heart, mind, and family relationships by drawing closer to the Lord.

Avoid comparing yourself to women you know who have had "easy" pregnancies and births. This usually leads to self-pity and depression. Remember, Jesus is with you every step of the way, and he will give you everything you need to meet the particular challenges you face.

CHAPTER TWELVE
Preparing for a Cesarean Birth

*A*lthough few women would choose to have their baby by cesarean, it is important to keep in mind that it is a possibility for any woman giving birth today. In fact, though the rate varies with location, about 10 to 25 percent of births are by cesarean. Because of this, it is wise to learn what takes place during cesarean birth and during the recovery, so that if this should be necessary for you, your level of participation in the birth of your child is enhanced.

"Cesarean section" is the term applied to an operation in which the baby is born through incisions made in the abdominal wall and uterus. It is a necessary method of delivery when vaginal birth would endanger the health of the mother and/or the baby. Also, when the baby's size and/or position make passage through the pelvis abnormally difficult or impossible, a cesarean is performed.

Occasionally your physician will determine that you will need a cesarean birth prior to the onset of labor, though he may have you go into labor on a trial basis before choosing this route.

Special diagnostic procedures may be used to support this decision. If you know ahead of time that you will have a cesarean, you may want to talk with others who have had the same experience. Generally, the decision for first-time cesarean births (primary cesareans) is made during labor, if the need arises.

Once the choice of performing a cesarean is made, the following procedures will take place before the surgery:

- *Admission and surgery consent forms are signed.*
- *Blood and urine samples are taken, and weight and vital signs are taken and recorded.*
- *Fetal heart tones are monitored.*
- *Your medical history is taken, and a physical may be done.*
- *You and your anesthesiologist will discuss the type of medication you will have and its effects. If you have a preference, discuss this to determine whether or not it would be suitable for your situation. Now is the time to bring up*

any questions. Carefully consider the pros and cons of the anesthesia available to you.

FATHER-ATTENDED CESAREAN BIRTH

The news that a cesarean needs to be performed does not necessarily mean that your planning and anticipation of being involved in the baby's birth has been in vain. Many hospitals will allow a father to attend his child's arrival by cesarean under certain conditions. (Understandably, in an emergency situation, many hospitals prefer to have the father wait outside the operating room.)

This decision rests primarily with the anesthesiologist, because the surgery requires regional or general anesthesia, which is administered and monitored by a specialist. The attending obstetrician will perform the surgery; the anesthesiologist will safeguard the response of the mother to the anesthetic and the surgery. The anesthesiologist "rules the roost," so to speak, and must feel comfortable in order to perform his or her job.

The following conditions normally are used as criteria for permitting a father's presence during surgery:

1. The father should be prepared for what to expect through prenatal classes, a film or videotape, or by talking directly to the labor nurse, obstetrician, or anesthesiologist.

2. He should assess his ability to be involved in a medical situation.

3. The mother often is required to be awake during the birth if the father is to be present.

4. The father should be of good health and free of infectious disease.

If you are allowed to stay during the birth, you will be at the head of the table to talk to and touch your wife. At this point, your role is to assure your wife, encouraging her to think of the end result and reminding her to relax by using the level of breathing appropriate to her tension level. Your emotions probably will fluctuate between apprehension and anticipation, so remember the Lord is with you both. Recall the Scriptures you used to prepare for the birth, and pray frequently.

It is becoming standard practice to have a father hold his baby as soon after it is born as possible. The father, mother, and their new child often are able to spend ten to twenty minutes together if all is going well. After this, the father might accompany the baby to the nursery and be included in the baby's care. Once the mother's surgery is over, the family may get back together in the recovery room as conditions permit.

If you can't be present for the birth, you will be shown where to wait for about thirty to ninety minutes. Occasionally fathers are allowed to be in the hall outside the operating room and can hold the baby almost immediately after birth. Otherwise, you will be notified when you can see the baby in the nursery. If possible, you will be reunited with your wife in the recovery room. If you and your wife haven't been with the baby yet, you might ask if the three of you could be together.

PREPARING FOR SURGERY: THE FATHER

There are many things you as a father can do in preparation for being present during the cesarean birth. Be sure to eat a light, nongreasy meal an hour or two before the surgery. This will help you be less queasy. Remember to focus on your wife and the Lord during the entire procedure, not on the other people in the room. It's easy to become fascinated, or nervous, because of all the activity. You aren't there to pretend you're a physician, but to give spiritual and emotional support to your wife and to say hello to your newly born child.

Help your wife relax by praying with her and reminding her that the Lord is near. Maintain body contact with her throughout the time you are there—hold her hand, stroke her cheek, give her a few kisses, place your hand on her head.

These things will convey your concern and affection to her, and will help alleviate her anxiety. Also, share your excitement about the baby's birth with her. She will benefit from knowing how proud you are of her, and how you feel about the baby.

Pay attention to any requests the hospital staff may make. Take slow, deep breaths if you begin to feel light-headed or nauseated. Don't watch procedures that make you feel faint, and remember to relax! Ask any questions tactfully if you don't understand what's happening, or are uncertain where you should be. Be assured, the staff wouldn't let you be there if they didn't want you a part of what's going on.

PREPARING FOR SURGERY: THE MOTHER

As you go through this experience, remember to relax, concentrating on the Lord and all you have learned in preparation for your child's birth. If you feel afraid or anxious, share your feelings with Jesus, laying your burdens at his feet. Try to pray, continually thanking and praising God for watching over you, letting you know you are not alone!

If your husband is present, listen to what he is saying. Respond to his voice, touch, and his love for you. Touch your baby as soon after birth as is possible, sharing that love and joy with this new child you have labored together to bring into the world.

Just after the baby's birth you may feel nauseated or uncomfortable. You also may not feel like interacting much until after the anesthetic wears off and you are on a more mild form of pain medication. Don't worry about this. Your first responsibility is to help your body cope with the surgery. Don't try to live up to an imagined ideal of the perfect birth and bonding experience. Just be yourself, and follow the Lord's lead.

WHAT TO EXPECT

BEFORE THE BIRTH

Just before the surgery, a small, narrow tube or catheter is placed through the urethra to the bladder so that urine may be continuously drained, keeping the bladder out of the way of the surgery. If the catheter is inserted prior to the administration of the anesthetic, it may be somewhat uncomfortable. Use a focal point, conscious release, and slow breathing. Push out as you feel the tube being inserted.

You may or may not be given preoperative medication to help you relax. If an IV hasn't been started, it will be begun with a solution of sterile water, salt, and basic sugar. It also is used to

GENERAL ANESTHESIA: LOSS OF CONSCIOUSNESS

Pros	Cons
1. The mother is asleep and unaware of the surgery.	1. The mother is asleep and unaware of the birth.
2. Total pain relief.	2. The husband is not allowed to be present.
3. Little risk of fetal depression resulting from the anesthetic, if given properly.	3. Drug depression of baby is more common with general anesthesia than regional anesthesia.
4. The obstetrician may find the operating room condition more suitable.	4. Changes in mother's heart performance occur related to intubation.
5. General anesthesia is preferable in certain situations such as in an emergency when the mother's blood pressure is low.	5. May be difficult with intubation of mother.

administer other medications, fluids, and blood when necessary. Armboards will be attached to the operating table on which to rest your arms. (Sometimes one arm is fastened securely onto the table. If this is done, you may want to request it be released so you can touch your baby following birth.)

Your blood pressure will be monitored during surgery, so the cuff will be put on your arm. There also will be two discs attached to your chest to record your heartbeat. Your abdomen will be draped with sterile sheets and a screen will be placed at your shoulders, above your breasts, to keep you from contaminating the sterile field (this also blocks your view of the operation). A loose-fitting cap will be placed on your head to cover your hair.

You will be given an anesthetic either to numb your body from just above the top of your uterus down or to put you to sleep. You may be given extra oxygen during surgery through a mask placed over your nose and mouth.

THE BIRTH ITSELF

A cesarean takes forty-five minutes to over an hour to perform. Incisions are made in the skin, abdominal muscles, lining of the pelvic cavity, and the uterus. The incision on the uterus will be about six inches long and will be vertical (classical) or horizontal (pfannenstiel). The membranes are ruptured and the amniotic fluid is suctioned out. Then the baby is lifted from the abdominal cavity, and the umbilical cord is quickly clamped. It is approximately ten minutes from the beginning of the surgery to this point.

The repair of the uterus and the abdominal walls, which takes the most time, is begun by removing the placenta and administering an oxytocic drug to stimulate uterine contractions. (Vaginal discharge and afterbirth contractions are the same as after vaginal birth, so be certain to read the section describing these occurrences on pages 111-114.)

Flexible rooming-in (which may require a private room) will allow you to choose your rest times and the extent of contact with your new baby. Your husband can visit at any time, and can help you with the baby and in moving around.

Breast-feeding your baby may require pillow support over the abdomen, or that you lie on your side to feel relaxed and comfortable. If your

REGIONAL ANESTHESIA: LOSS OF SENSATION FROM THE TORSO TO THE FEET
(Mother Remains Conscious)

Pros	Cons
1. Mother is awake and experiences the birth.	1. Mother is awake and aware of the surgery.
2. Little risk of drug depression for baby.	2. Anesthetic sometimes does not take effect as it should, resulting in inadequate block of sensation. More anesthetic may be required.
3. Risks related to intubation are avoided.	3. Mother's blood pressure may be lowered.
4. Less chance of aspiration.	4. Chance of postspinal or epidural headache.
5. Partner may be present under certain circumstances.	5. May be situations when regular anesthesia can't be used (emergencies, low blood pressure, etc.).
	6. Regional anesthetic may affect the mother's breathing.

baby seems to be sleeping because of the medication you received, gently stimulate his or her back and soles of the feet while making certain he or she isn't so bundled up that it's producing extra drowsiness.

Realize that mood swings in the first few days are common, especially if you are disappointed about not giving birth vaginally, or if your husband was not able to be present. Share your feelings with your husband and the Lord, living through and resolving them.

RECOVERY

The IV is kept going after the surgery, and probably will be left in for twenty-four to forty-eight hours to fight infection and provide fluids and energy. The catheter will be removed after about twenty-four hours, too. If you find it difficult to urinate, drink plenty of fluids once you are able and use your pelvic floor release exercise.

Discomfort in the shoulders may be due to the accumulation of blood and air under your diaphragm, irritating the nerves going to your shoulders. Pain medication can be adjusted to your needs, but be sure you are informed as to what you are being given and why. If you are breast-feeding, there are safe drugs to use. While drugs may help reduce pain, some may make it hard for you to feel like being with your baby.

Get up and walk as soon as possible. This will stimulate your processes of digestion and elimination. Support your incision with both hands at first, taking short steps. Try to stand tall, even though you'll feel like swaying and shuffling. You may feel pain and pulling at the incision; extra support will help and each time it gets easier. Discomfort from the incision will be noticeably less each day and will have decreased significantly by the seventh or tenth day. Any involuntary movements of your abdominal muscles may hurt. If you anticipate a cough, sneeze, or laugh, support the incision with your hand.

Gas pains signal the return of digestive function and until then you won't be allowed to eat solid foods. You will be on a liquid diet until gas is passed. Try lying on your side with the underside leg bent and the leg on top straight or in the Sims'-lateral position to get rid of gas. Movement also helps. Avoid carbonated beverages and apple juice.

MAKING RECOVERY EASIER AFTER A CESAREAN BIRTH

IN THE HOSPITAL

As soon as your flow is less heavy, use beltless sanitary pads. Sanitary belts can rub on the incision and be a source of discomfort. Tampons may be used with your doctor's OK.

Get up and walk as soon as they will allow. You will find it gets easier each time and you'll feel better with the improved circulation. A small wedge heel on your slippers will help you to stand and walk more comfortably the first few days.

"Crawl" into your bed on all fours to avoid using your abdominal muscles. Use slow breathing to help calm yourself, relieve tension, and deal with discomfort. You may find sleeping on your stomach to be more comfortable during this time.

Select nutritious meals, and eat as soon as you are allowed. This gives you more energy and helps you regain your strength. A reducing diet can be started by avoiding "empty calorie" foods that are high in calories but low in nutrients. After six weeks, you may lower your calorie intake to help shed unwanted pounds, as long as you have your doctor's approval.

Before leaving the hospital, make sure your doctor discusses your limitations and postbirth care. If your husband can be present, it will help him plan how to help you at home. Ask questions freely, so that small concerns don't grow. Have things explained to your satisfaction. Also, acknowledge and accept your feelings. Don't allow others to dismiss your joy, anger, pain, or insights. You feel as you do for a reason.

Keep your visitors during the first few days to a minimum. Each day will bring renewed strength, more energy, and a brighter outlook. Visitors are entertaining, but they also can be exhausting.

Because the human body heals faster after childbirth than at any other time, recovery following a cesarean birth is amazingly fast if there are no complications. Postsurgical pain has a reason: If you keep your hurting abdominal muscles inactive, you help them to heal. The discomfort will seem greatest as you doze off and wake up, but take heart! This will subside soon. Talk things over with your husband, but realize that he can't meet all your emotional and physical needs. He's tired and adjusting, too. Learn to rely on close friends, a relative, or your pastor as well as your husband.

TIPS FOR DAD
WHILE AT THE HOSPITAL

You can help your wife after a cesarean birth by keeping her lips moist with ice chips, a cool cloth, and fluids when they are allowed. Help her to sip (but don't use a straw). Other small but important ways to help would be freshening her pillow by turning it over, brushing her hair, giving her a gentle back rub, and adjusting her bed position (sometimes raising her knees helps to relax the pelvic region).

Realize that your wife will be tired at first. Encourage her to rest. If you help her change positions, be careful not to pull on her IV or catheter tubing. Help her use slow breathing by placing your hands on either side of her chest along the ribs and having her breathe expansively into your hands several times. Rotate her feet at the ankles to improve circulation. You might also consider spending the night if your wife is in a private room and your presence seems helpful.

WHEN YOU GET HOME

When you finally get back home, forget about the housework! Rest, with your feet up, as much as possible for at least two weeks. Fatigue is your No. 1 enemy; be ruthless about getting rest.

Prepare simple meals before you go into labor and freeze them. There are many put-it-in-all-at-once meals that taste great and involve little time or expertise. Stock up on canned goods and juices. Buy lots of paper plates and cups. Crockpots are a real blessing! Keep taking your prenatal vitamins daily. Extra protein may be helpful as well.

Keep a small pillow in the car to place under the seat belt while your incision is still tender. At night, keep a nightlight on in your room. Bring your baby in with you and keep him or her in a bassinet or cradle nearby. Keep diapers next to your bed, and a pitcher of ice water and a glass at your bedside. Night care of your baby will be much easier if done this way. If this is disturbing for Dad, maybe he can sleep in another room for a short while.

Finally, remember to pamper yourself, making sure you have at least ten minutes completely to yourself every day! Don't feel guilty about this time; we all need time alone, especially when getting used to the new demands of parenthood.

BODY CONDITIONING EXERCISES AFTER CESAREAN BIRTH

(Be certain to talk to your nurse or physician before doing any of these exercises.)

Use these exercises for the first three to seven days:

A. Breathing to clear lungs of mucus—If a general anesthetic was used, your lungs may collect some mucus due to the slowing of your breathing rate. Expand your chest with two breaths as follows: Breathe in, "filling" your abdomen up with air, then breathe out, flattening the abdomen. Next, place your hands under your armpits and breathe in, expanding the chest wall sideways.

B. Foot movements—To increase circulation,

the following exercise should be done several times a day (discontinue if you are up and walking throughout the day): Hold legs out straight or bent at knees over a pillow. First, bend and stretch your feet at the ankles for sixty seconds, then rotate your ankles in circles for one additional minute.

C. Leg bracing—To increase circulation in your legs and prepare for walking, put your legs out straight with your ankles crossed. Tighten all the muscles in your legs, press your knees down, and squeeze your buttocks together. Hold for two to three seconds, then relax.

D. Bend and straighten knees—To prepare for walking, lie on your back with one leg bent at the knee, and the other leg straight. Slide the heel of your bent leg down the bed, then back to its starting position. Repeat with the other leg. This can be varied by bending and straightening your legs alternately, working them at the same time.

E. Abdominal tightening—Relieve discomfort of trapped air (gas pains) and stimulate sluggish intestinal activity by lying on your back or side with your knees bent. Flatten the lower back by contracting abdominal and buttock muscles. Contract the muscles on a breath out, then relax on a breath in.

After ten to fourteen days do this exercise:

Tailor sit—Relieve back strain by sitting with your legs bent, knees falling outward. Keep your back slightly rounded, allowing the muscles in your back to relax. (See chapter 6 for more exercises.)

It is my hope that the information in this chapter will help guide you through what can be a very difficult and trying situation. Use this material as a supplement to the medical and pastoral care you receive. And, in all situations, always remember the presence and protection of the Lord are with you; he is more than able to sustain you through tough times, as David so beautifully reminds us in Psalm 91:1-6 and 9-15(NASB):

He who dwells in the shelter of the Most High will abide in the shadow of the Almighty. I will say to the Lord, "My refuge and my fortress, my God, in whom I trust!" For it is He who delivers you from the snare of the trapper, and from the deadly pestilence. He will cover you with His pinions, and under His wings you may seek refuge; His faithfulness is a shield and bulwark.

You will not be afraid of the terror by night, or of the arrow that flies by day; of the pestilence that stalks in darkness, or of the destruction that lays waste at noon.

For you have made the Lord, my refuge, even the Most High, your dwelling place. No evil will befall you, nor will any plague come near your tent.

For He will give His angels charge concerning you, to guard you in all your ways. They will bear you up in their hands, lest you strike your foot against a stone. You will tread upon the lion and cobra, the young lion and the serpent you will trample down.

"Because he has loved Me, therefore I will deliver him; I will set him securely on high, because he has known My name. He will call upon Me, and I will answer him; I will be with him in trouble; I will rescue him, and honor him."

CHAPTER THIRTEEN
A Baby Learns about Love

"And he said: 'I tell you the truth, unless you change and become like little children, you will never enter the kingdom of heaven. And whoever welcomes a little child like this in my name welcomes me.'"
MATTHEW 18:3, 5

Where did you come from, baby dear?
  Out of the everywhere into here.
Where did you get your eyes so blue?
  Out of the sky as I came through.
What makes the light in them sparkle and spin?
  Some of the starry spikes left in.
Where did you get that little tear?
  I found it waiting when I got here.
What makes your forehead so smooth and high?
  A soft hand stroked it as I went by.
What makes your cheek like a warm white rose?
  I saw something better than anyone knows.
Whence that three-cornered smile of bliss?
  Three angels gave me at once a kiss.
Where did you get this pearly ear?
  God spoke, and it came out to hear.
Where did you get those arms and hands?
  Love made itself into hooks and bands.
Feet, whence did you come, you darling things?
  From the same box as the cherubs' wings.
How did they all just come to be you?
  God thought about me, and so I grew.
But how did you come to us, you dear?
  God thought about you, and so I am here.
  —*George MacDonald*

My initial glimpse of our first child stirred up many emotions in my heart. I was overcome with a sense of awe that two small cells became our baby. At the same time, I felt the incredible weight of responsibility for her new life falling right between my shoulders. I was amazed at how much a part of her I was while at the same moment realizing that she was a person I had never met before.

I marveled at the smoothness of her skin as I stroked her back, still covered with its protective creamy coating called vernix. I wanted to wrap her up and snuggle her close, knowing that the world she had just entered was full of danger and sin as well as life and joy. I shed tears of concern while grinning with happiness. Birth is a bittersweet moment, when heaven and earth collide in a profusion of possibilities, hopes, and expectations.

How could I teach Joanna about Jesus? Would she come to trust him as her own Lord and Savior someday? Would she question me as I had questioned my own mother? Who would she become? What did life have in store for her?

There is no way to answer most of these questions. Only time reveals what the patterns of life bring to each person. Jesus' mother, Mary, was probably aware of these same concerns as she held her infant and nurtured him during the early years of his life. In Luke we read that "Mary treasured up all these things and pondered them in her heart" (Luke 2:19). Mary had no way of knowing what lay ahead. She had to trust the Lord day by day, and we must do the same.

When your baby is born you will discover what it means to trust the Lord in a new way. Your love for your son or daughter will teach you to rely more heavily on the Lord. Opening your heart to completely love another person involves risk-taking, personal growth, and an abiding faith in the sovereignty of God the Father.

WELCOMING YOUR BABY

Your baby can learn about Jesus from the first moment of life. By loving and accepting your child, you will demonstrate in a real way what the Lord has done for you. You can affirm your baby right away through touch, warmth, words, eye contact, and milk. In saying, "I'm thankful you are here" and "I will take care of you," you tell yourself as well as your infant that you accept him and will meet his needs as well as you can. Your baby will be listening to the tone and timbre of your voice, and will recognize you immediately. After all, he has heard you for many months, since the sense of hearing normally develops prenatally!

The sooner you can touch and talk to your baby after birth, the better. The reason for this is that the Lord has designed healthy newborn babies to be quietly alert for two to three hours after birth. If a mother is not heavily medicated and the baby is doing well, these hours can provide a very special opportunity to get acquainted "face to face." Most women find that they experience a surge of energy after an uncomplicated

birth and are anxious to begin mothering their baby as soon as possible.

You may want to touch your baby as he emerges from your body, still warm and slippery with vernix and amniotic fluid. While this does not appeal to all women, some mothers are exhilarated by the first sight and touch, regardless of how moist the baby is! The routine initial care of the baby can be performed entirely "in arms" if you desire. This is becoming a common practice, but it is a good idea to discuss it with your physician in advance. You may request that the baby be wrapped loosely in a blanket for holding if you are uncertain about keeping a sure grip otherwise!

As you greet your baby for the first time, remember that your baby already knows your voice and can see the shape of your face; your baby's mouth is the most sensitive place on his body, and his sense of touch signals your presence; he sees you best from a distance of about twelve inches—the distance between holding him in your arms at chest height and your face; and you can "talk" to your baby with your eyes, your hands, and your milk as well as by your voice.

I am convinced that God made babies to be lovable! Although they can be exasperating at times, babies thrive on a mother's milk and the tender loving care that is expressed through cuddling, rocking, singing, bathing, stroking, and keeping the baby near. A baby's needs and wants seem to be inseparable until later in the first year of life. The Lord expects us to respond to our baby's needs for food, protection, warmth, and physical affection throughout every day and night. (Why else would he have designed them to eat every two to three hours?)

Babies who receive an inadequate amount of physical affection can become victims of a syndrome described as "failure to thrive." Earlier in this century, it was discovered that institutionalized infants could actually die of a disease called "marasmus," caused by not being held. The idea of keeping babies in cribs, infant seats, and playpens for hours on end so as not to "spoil" them is not based on a factual view of the needs of infants.

You need to find a balance between meeting the baby's needs while meeting your own needs and those of other family members. Finding this balance takes time. Still, it is possible to keep your baby close by, hold your baby often, and have everyone happier as a result. Why? Because satisfied babies cry less and their mothers find it easier to relax!

KEEPING YOUR BABY CLOSE

Unless there is a medical reason for your baby to be out of your sight, it really makes sense to keep your baby close by. This encourages the continuing development of the bond between the two of you that began while your baby was still inside your womb. The process of attachment, or bonding, is not as automatic as it might seem. If the baby is the "wrong" sex (not what you were hoping for), ill, fussy, overly active, or generally not what you expected, the bond can be strained. Togetherness fosters attachment and attachment fosters a parent's ability to take care of the baby. The father's presence is included here as well, even though breast-feeding is God's gift to the mother alone.

"Rooming in" is available at most hospitals for the purpose of encouraging families to be together during the first few days after birth. Some couples opt to go home after four to twenty-four hours because they feel they can relax, adjust, and recover better in familiar surroundings. The usual postpartum stay is two to three days for a vaginal birth and five to seven days for a cesarean birth. Private rooms provide the greatest degree of privacy and flexibility. If we continue the wedding analogy introduced in chapter 9, this time compares to the honeymoon period. Sheila Kitzinger, a well-known childcare author, refers to it as the "babymoon" instead![1]

Your baby will be weighed, measured, and thoroughly checked after birth. A prophylactic eye treatment against gonococcus is usually required (by state law) to be administered within two hours of the baby's birth. Silver nitrate was used for this purpose until recently. Now you can request that an antibiotic be used instead, since the application of silver nitrate irritates the mucous membrane of the eye, and may temporarily interfere with the baby's ability to interact with you visually.

All of these procedures may be done at your bedside or with you watching in the nursery, if you choose to arrange it. (To have the baby suddenly disappear to the nursery is not unlike having the groom vanish after the ceremony while the reception is taking place!)

The "babymoon" begins in earnest when the parents are alone with their baby for the first time, with no nurses, physicians, or grandparents present—just the family. There is a real need for privacy at this time and for a lack of interruptions. Post a "Do Not Disturb" sign on the door and turn the phone off! This is a time of discovery that shouldn't be interrupted, even by well-wishers and advisors.

Your baby probably will have a strong desire to suck and nurse during the first few hours, then will fall into a deep sleep. The alternating patterns of activity and sleep vary from baby to baby. It is wonderful to hold a sleeping baby against your chest. You will find that you can gaze for hours, but you will need sleep too. (Chapter 15 presents ways to obtain the nutrients and rest you will need during the fifth stage of labor.)

The idea that keeping the baby near "tires the mother out" is an odd notion. I have found that mothers and babies sleep better when they are in close proximity to one another. This is because they have been "as one" for nine months and being close is reassuring, comforting, and soothing. Remember how you first felt about your mate? While you were falling in love, your engrossment in his life was profound. The more you were together, the closer you felt.

Likewise, the babymoon is a time to devote to learning to love your baby. It is a time to embrace what it means to be a mother or a father, and learn the rhythm of your baby's personality and temperament. It's a time to take a break from everyday worries and duties. Your relationship as a parent to this child-person will be built on these early weeks together.

EASING THE TRANSITION FROM THE WOMB TO THE WORLD

While your baby was growing in your uterus, he never experienced hunger, cold temperatures, bright light, or loud noises. Intrauterine life provided the warmth of your inner body, the rhythmical movement of your digestion, breathing, circulation, and bodily activities such as walking. It provided the constant sounds of your heart beating, blood pumping, lungs breathing, and intestines rumbling; a mixture of nutrients transferred directly from your blood through the placenta and umbilical cord into the baby's circulatory system; diffused light through your abdominal wall; and muffled sounds from the world outside. In effect, you were mothering your baby perfectly without thinking about it much!

When your baby moves from life inside your womb to existence on the outside, you can ease this transition by thinking about how to continue meeting your baby's needs for warmth, movement, sound, nutrients, and visual stimulation. A bright nursery lit up by fluorescent lights twenty-four hours a day with babies lined up in isolettes must be a rather rude awakening for newborns. The Lord has equipped mothers to provide just what their babies need. All we mothers have to do is realize it!

When you cradle a baby in your arms, he still hears your heartbeat and your breathing; when you swaddle him in a blanket, you provide a feeling of security and warmth; when you nurse your baby on demand, you give him the perfect follow-up to nutrients he received inside your womb; and when you respond quickly to his cries for comfort, you teach him that you are dependable. Recent studies have demonstrated that babies who are provided with close physical contact learn to be independent earlier and that a baby can be soothed more effectively if responded to quickly.

Babies like to be held firmly, with a good grip placed on the thigh or buttocks. They prefer the peaceful sound of your heart to lots of "baby talk" while nursing. Babies are fussiest and experience colicky episodes at the end of a long day when Mom and Dad are tired and tense. Relax! Did you do much housework or errand-running or meeting-attending during your honeymoon? While in the hospital or at home during the early weeks, a comfortable rocking chair and clean bed should be the places you like the best!

PERSPECTIVE

Your baby will be growing away from you from the moment of birth. T. Berry Brazleton has said that "the goal of attachment is detachment." This means that the parent-child relationship begins with the dependence of a child and should aim toward moving the child away from the parents into a productive life of his own. Your baby needs you to be there responsively in order to learn a basic sense of trust.

This seems like a big task until we look at the larger picture. Each day will bring new capabilities to your infant, as well as new growth. It is a process that takes only a few years, and then you will have a child who is capable of doing a great deal all by himself. The early period of complete dependence will gradually dissolve into independence. Trust me—it happens!

The art of parenting requires sensitivity to the changing needs and perceptions of children. The way I express my love to my first daughter, who is now in junior high school, is substantially different from how I express it to my youngest son, a preschooler. The Apostle Paul describes this well as he compares spiritual maturity to human development: "I gave you milk, not solid food, for you were not yet ready for it" (1 Corinthians 3:2).

Your baby will need you to be available to meet his needs in a physical, tangible way. Later on, he will challenge you to be available in a much wider sense: intellectually, spiritually, and emotionally. Babyhood is a unique time during which Christ's love can be expressed in terms of comfort, warmth, milk, and protection.

CHAPTER FOURTEEN
Feeding Your Baby

"For you will nurse and be satisfied at her comforting breasts: you will drink deeply and delight in her overflowing abundance."
ISAIAH 66:11

"But we proved to be gentle among you, as a nursing mother tenderly cares for her own children." 1 THESSALONIANS 2:7, NASB

*T*he analogy of breast-feeding is used in the above verses to describe satisfaction and love— and rightly so! It is in the arms of his mother that a baby first receives warmth, food, and affection. As an infant's hunger vanishes and his need to suck is provided for, he learns what it means to "delight in her overflowing abundance." The Lord designed maternal breasts to supply just the right nutrients and soothing skin-to-skin contact for the youngest among us. Breast-feeding is a lovely expression of God's provision for nurturing new life.

You may choose to feed your baby at your breast or with formula in a bottle. Breast-feeding is no longer universal and does not need to be believed in with religious fervor. In fact, the decision you make regarding how you will feed your baby is completely up to you and your husband. Nursing a baby can be one of life's most interesting and gratifying experiences, but only if you are comfortable doing it. Carefully consider what each method is like and discuss your impressions with your husband. Whatever you

decide together about feeding your baby is fine. Your infant will be satisfied and comforted either way if you respond to his needs to be held, fed, and allowed to suck.

From the beginning of history until the middle years of this century human milk was almost exclusively used by mothers and wet nurses to feed infants. It is important to remember that the importance of hand washing as a means to prevent infection was not discovered until the 1840s and not used widely until twenty to forty years later. Modern technology did not make bottle-feeding possible until the 1920s. Commercially produced formulas, bottles, and sterilizers gained popularity over several decades so that bottle-feeding became the method chosen by most women during the fifties and sixties. Breast-feeding came to be viewed as an old-fashioned, unattractive, messy nuisance, while bottle-feeding was considered a modern wonder. Consequently, the majority of women who are currently of childbearing age were bottle-fed. Even if they were breast-fed, very few were nursed longer than two months.

The prevalence of bottle-feeding and early weaning has been noted throughout the world as an accompaniment to industrialization and is not unique to the United States. In less industrialized cultures, breast-feeding has remained essential to the health of children under the age of two years. This is because mothers who live in poorer countries do not have enough money to buy formula. Neither can they pay for the medical care that often becomes necessary when unsanitary water is used in formula preparation.

Breast milk provides both immunities and organisms that protect the gastrointestinal tract against infection. Bottle-feeding is only appropriate when proper hygiene is possible and when antibiotics are available. It is a "luxury" that only a small percentage of the world's population has been able to afford!

If bottle-feeding is truly the "modern" way to feed a baby and a symbol of status in many parts of the world, why are so many women choosing to return to the practice of breast-feeding? The primary reasons for this change seem to be: (1) numerous research studies performed during the past fifteen years emphasizing the physiological and psychological benefits of breast-feeding; (2) the promotion of breast-feeding by professional organizations such as the American Academy of Pediatrics, through mother-to-mother help made available through groups like La Leche League, and in childbirth preparation classes; (3) the "back to nature" trend which has reacted to the high costs of technology by stressing the value of healthier and simpler life-styles.

These and other factors have contributed to a widespread change in popular opinion and breast-feeding is once again the feeding method used by the majority of American mothers. Complications, however, are not uncommon. Many women discontinue breast-feeding within eight weeks after giving birth.

Why do so many decide to wean their babies from the breast so soon? Possibly it is because few women are prepared for what nursing a baby will be like when the time comes. Breast-feeding is viewed as the "natural" way to feed a baby. As a result, many people believe it will be an uncomplicated, easy-to-learn, instinctive process. Not so! Breast-feeding must be learned from other women who have breast-fed, and in our culture few of us were raised in households where long-term nursing was practiced.

Also, we live in a country where breasts are primarily thought of as sexual objects and erogenous zones rather than viewed simply as mammary glands. Living in a culture that views breast exposure as taboo makes it difficult to learn about breast-feeding from others. In addition to these cultural factors, many women have unrealistic expectations about what nursing a baby involves. They compare it to the experience of bottle-feeding: put the baby to the nipple, let the baby suck, and the feeding is over when the milk is gone.

Breast-feeding is an entirely different process than bottle-feeding, and requires the mother to respond in a flexible way to her baby's signals of hunger and satisfaction. If a mother lacks accurate information about breast-feeding, she will not understand how it differs from bottle-feeding and will become anxious about the frequency and duration of her baby's feedings. Bottles often become necessary as she limits nursing her baby to scheduled times. Her milk supply diminishes as the baby's times at the breast become too brief and too infrequent to stimulate an adequate production of milk. Such a woman receives little support from friends and relatives who question the frequency of feedings and offer to feed the baby to "let her get some rest," not knowing that she needs rest from housework, laundry, cooking, shopping, and outside employment instead!

According to Dana Raphael, director of the Human Lactation Center in Connecticut, the keys to successful breast-feeding are as follows:

1. Understanding the process
2. Discounting confusing folklore

3. Knowing the benefits
4. Mothering the mother

If you follow Dr. Raphael's recommendations, breast-feeding can be a satisfying experience for all involved. Before making your decision to breast- or bottle-feed your baby, it is helpful to compare the advantages and disadvantages of each.

MAKING THE DECISION TO BREAST- OR BOTTLE-FEED

Your prenatal preparation is but one of the factors that will influence your decision to breast- or bottle-feed your newborn. Your life-style, beliefs, plans for the future, upbringing, family, health care provider, and feelings about your body are all going to have an impact on the decision. Considering these things ahead of time may enable you to be more comfortable with your decision after the baby is born.

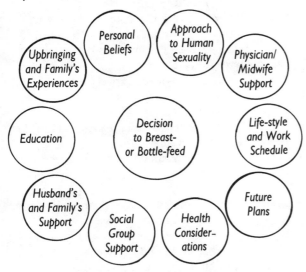

COMPARING THE PROS AND CONS

Although your background and personality play an important part in your decision, there are pros and cons to each method which may also be considered. Here is a list of some of the advantages and disadvantages of breast-feeding and bottle-feeding. Several others may come to mind as you reflect on your own personal experiences.

Breast-feeding

Advantages:

- A substance called colostrum is produced by the breasts from the sixth month of pregnancy to the onset of lactation (about two to four days after giving birth). It contains water, minerals, sugar, proteins, and a high number of antibodies. Even a few days of nursing provides your baby with this "transition diet."

- Breast milk requires no preparation, is readily available at just the right temperature, and is free of pathological organisms (germs).

- Breast milk is the Lord's intended diet for the human species; that is to say, it is "species specific" and suitable for all human infants. As long as the mother's diet is appropriate, it cannot be too thick, too rich, or allergy-provoking.

- Breast milk rarely causes digestive problems such as constipation or diarrhea. This is due to the organisms in the milk which keep the intestinal tract healthy.

- Outings are easy when Baby comes along. You can forget about any bottle preparation.

- In the immediate postpartum period, breast-feeding causes contractions of the uterus, which help to diminish bleeding and hasten the return of the uterus to its normal size. These contractions may be uncomfortable, however, and may interfere with a woman's desire to nurse.

- Baby's milk is "free," but it is a product of the food the mother eats. It is ecological; there is no waste. No costly energy is used to make, refrigerate, and heat the formula or to prepare the bottles.

Disadvantages:

- Leaving Baby home requires special planning and/or expression of milk for bottles in your absence.

- Night feedings disrupt sleep unless you learn to rest as your baby nurses or you sleep with your baby.
- The baby is physiologically tied to the mother in a breast-feeding relationship; fatigue, anxiety, stress, diet, and medication all can affect the milk supply in various ways.
- The baby is dependent on the mother for feedings. This is especially true during the first six weeks of life when frequent nursing is necessary for the establishment of lactation.
- Breast milk naturally varies in fat content and nutrients depending on the age of the child, the phase of the feeding, and the time of day.
- Breast exposure is necessary, but may be limited by using appropriate clothing and a shawl or blanket.
- Breast milk is not measured. Therefore, you do not see how much your baby is getting. Allowing the baby to suck on demand stimulates milk production so that the supply is determined by your baby's needs. Overfeeding is not as likely as it is with bottle-feeding.
- While the baby is totally breast-feeding the return of menses is often delayed, especially when all the baby's sucking needs are being met by the breast. The vaginal lining may be drier and more tender due to lower estrogen production.
- Breast-feeding requires physical intimacy between mother and child and is enhanced or interfered with according to the relationship the woman has with her body. Since the mother and her baby are intertwined psychologically as well as physiologically, a woman's uneasiness or satisfaction would be perceived by her offspring.
- The physical discomforts associated with the onset of breast-feeding may be difficult to get beyond. Although nipple soreness and swelling of the breasts rarely last more than one or two weeks, they can be a deterrent to an enjoyable feeding experience.
- To "make" breast milk, an extra 500 to 800 calories per day are needed. A nursing mother also needs a well-balanced diet and adequate liquids daily. It is often easier to lose weight by eliminating high calorie foods that are low in nutritive value (fats, sugar, starches).
- Leaking milk, plugged ducts, and/or breast infections (mastitis) can be a problem for some nursing mothers. These can be avoided or coped with if a woman is familiar with how to manage these common problems.

Bottle-feeding

Advantages:
- If you are more comfortable being out and leaving Baby home, little extra planning for bottle preparation is needed.
- Bottle-fed babies often sleep for longer periods at night sooner than breast-fed babies since formula takes longer to digest than breast milk.
- The baby is physically separated and is unaffected by the mother's physiology.
- The mother can give the baby to others to feed. This is an important advantage to mothers who are separated from their babies on a regular basis.
- Formula is the same concentration (unless prepared differently) throughout each feeding, each day, and for all ages.
- The baby may be fed anywhere without embarrassment or special clothing.
- Periods are usually resumed six to eight weeks postpartum and hormone levels return to their pre-pregnant state.
- Lack of nipple stimulation keeps contractions from occurring with much intensity.
- Bottle-feeding requires no exclusive intimacy between mother and child. However, a baby actively interacts with his or her caretakers during feedings and picks up on their feelings while eating.
- No special diet for the mother is required. Losing weight will require cutting back on daily caloric intake and increased exercise.

Disadvantages:

- There is no product that is equivalent to colostrum.
- Traveling with Baby requires that equipment and formula be taken along.
- The body's return to a pre-pregnant state is unaided.
- Formula must be heated while a hungry baby waits. Mother doesn't necessarily need to wake and feed Baby if someone else is available.
- Bottles must be stored safely and carefully prepared according to directions provided by the manufacturer. Some warming is usually necessary.
- Occasionally a trial period is required for babies who react to certain types of formula. This in turn results in the extra expense of physician's office calls and higher priced special formulas. During an allergic reaction, a baby may be more irritable as well.
- Most babies do well on formula, but a few have trouble digesting formula that is not diluted. Stools are much firmer, constipation is more common, and inflammation of the intestinal tract (gastroenteritis) is more frequently seen in bottle-fed babies.
- The amount of formula is determined by the person who prepares the bottles. Overfeeding is more frequently seen due to giving the baby larger amounts less often and also due to more

A SUMMARY OF BENEFITS AND PRODUCTION REQUIREMENTS

BREAST-FEEDING	BOTTLE-FEEDING
• Species-specific.	• Less frequent feedings.
• "Living" fluid with antibodies and organisms to promote health, possibly less illness.	• Anyone can give the baby a bottle.
• Allergy-free.	• Outings and separation from baby are easier to accommodate.
• Readily available, no preparation or storage.	• Baby is not physically tied to the mother. She can eat, drink, take medications without affecting the milk.
• Promotes physical closeness and skin-to-skin contact.	
• Better oro-facial development due to stronger sucking.	• No breast exposure; it is culturally acceptable in public.
• Periods often delayed six to twelve months.	• Return to normal hormonal levels is accomplished sooner.
• Exclusive bond between mother and baby.	• Night feedings often do not continue for as long a period.
• Physical recovery after birth promoted.	• The amount of formula taken by the baby can be seen.
• Considerably less expensive.	• Adequate formula production relies on:
• Adequate breast milk production relies on:	
• Fostering and understanding the let-down process and principle of supply and demand.	• Commercial availability.
	• Hygienic preparation.
	• Financial ability to buy equipment and formula.
• Discounting confusing folklore.	• Understanding the baby's nutritional requirements.
• Knowing the benefits.	
• Sufficient mother-baby contact.	

rapid intake. A baby must suck much more strenuously at the breast than at the bottle.

- The breasts may be tender and swell as the mother's body adjusts to not breast-feeding, although the breasts have usually returned to their usual state within one or two weeks.
- The baby's feeding is independent of the mother's eating habits. Formula must be purchased commercially. The purchase of equipment incurs a substantial initial investment.
- There is waste and energy consumption involved in bottle-feeding.

THE LET-DOWN REFLEX

When you nurse your baby, his sucking will stimulate sensitive nerve endings in your breast, which will send a specific signal to your brain's "regulatory center." When this area (the hypothalamus) receives the right information, it will cause your pituitary gland to secrete two hormones into your bloodstream: oxytocin and prolactin. The circulation of blood through your body occurs at a rapid rate and will quickly carry these substances to cells in your breast. Within thirty to ninety seconds, the secretion of oxytocin will normally be at a sufficient level to cause milk

to be ejected from the glandular cells in your breasts where the milk is produced. (See figure 1.) Thousands of tiny cells will then contract in unison in what is termed the "let-down reflex," compressing milk out of nearby secretory (gland) cells. The milk then will flow into vessels that will carry it to large collecting ducts and eventually to the milk sinuses.

If you can picture the trunk of a tree leading to smaller branches, which in turn split into thousands of twigs, then you have an idea of how this system in your breast will function. The trunk is like the sinus; the branches, the larger milk ducts; the twigs, the smaller ducts; and, if the analogy is taken even further, the clusters of leaves, the milk glands.

In order for oxytocin to be secreted efficiently, you will need to get plenty of rest and enjoy your baby. Tension, fear, pain, fatigue, and worry can interfere with the release of oxytocin into your bloodstream. (See figure 2.) This hormone will also cause your uterus to contract as it is resuming a smaller size after your baby's birth. The system through which a baby receives nourishment while promoting the mother's recovery was created by the Lord and is not merely a biological accident.

THE LET-DOWN REFLEX
FIGURE I

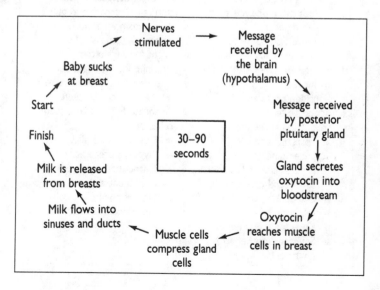

FIGURE 2   THE LET-DOWN REFLEX

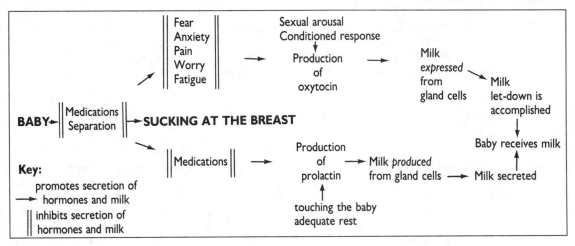

The hormone prolactin will cause the gland cells in your breast to actually manufacture the milk from nutrients in your bloodstream. It is a highly selective process and one that will occur without much effort on your part. The sucking of your baby is all you will need in order for prolactin to be released.

Avoid using any medication without your physician's advice, as there are a few drugs that can interfere with the secretion of these hormones. Figure 2 shows what factors can promote and inhibit the process of lactation.

THE PRINCIPLE OF SUPPLY AND DEMAND

The most common mistake made by nursing mothers is trying to schedule feedings by the clock. Your baby will accept your breast when you offer to nurse him if he wants to suck. Don't be afraid to do so since your milk supply will be abundant if your baby's demands are frequent.

A baby may nurse several times on each breast before he is satisfied. You must rely on him to be your guide! Otherwise, if you restrict the length of time according to your idea of how much nursing is "enough," you may interfere with your milk supply. Supplemental bottles, feeding schedules, and misinformation about the physiology of lactation are the greatest threats to successful breast-feeding.

On the other hand, if you grasp the beauty of the supply and demand system, you will discover that the Lord's wisdom is truly behind this process. On some days, your baby will nurse more, on others, less. Your supply will reflect your baby's varying requirements if you feel confident in freely responding to his needs. All this takes place without your giving it a second thought!

The general rule of thumb is to nurse ten minutes on the first side and as long as your baby seems to want to nurse on the other side. Most of the milk in your breast will be given to your baby in ten minutes. Since milk does not flow during the entire nursing, much of your baby's feeding is to satisfy his need to suck. Pacifiers and thumb-sucking are possible replacements that can be used if you find that unlimited nursing is not possible.

However, frequent breast-feeding has a nice advantage: the sucking of your baby will inhibit your ovulatory cycle and tends to delay the return of your menses. This is God's way of protecting your baby's nutrient source. (If you do become pregnant while nursing, your milk supply will likely diminish significantly.) In the majority of cases, a baby does not need any other food or liquid beside breast milk for about the first half year of life. After this time, his digestive system will become more mature and he will be able to chew and swallow foods other than your milk. Our Creator is truly magnificent!

GETTING STARTED

Your first consideration in beginning to breast-feed your baby should concern when and where your first nursing experience will take place. Ideally, if both of your conditions permit, the earliest time will benefit both of you.

While your comfort and choice at that time may be influenced by many things, it is important that you understand the benefit of breast-feeding immediately following your baby's birth, if the birth was uncomplicated. Here are several reasons why early and frequent feedings at the breast promote successful lactation:

1. The infant's sucking reflex is most intense during the first twenty to thirty minutes after birth. Delaying gratification of this reflex can make it more difficult for the baby to learn the sucking process later.
2. The baby begins to immediately receive the immunities that are in colostrum (and at peak levels during the first twenty-four hours following birth).
3. The baby's digestive processes will be stimulated by nursing; this has a laxative effect on the baby's bowels.
4. Later breast engorgement can be alleviated somewhat by the early and frequent removal of colostrum from the breast.
5. The baby's sucking stimulates contractions of the uterus, aids the expulsion of the placenta, and helps to control excessive blood loss, all of which benefit the mother after giving birth.

6. The process of milk production is accelerated and the milk appears sooner when the baby is encouraged to nurse upon delivery and frequently thereafter. This, in turn, diminishes the baby's total weight loss after birth.
7. Attachment or bonding is prompted at a time when both mother and baby are particularly sensitive and ready for this attachment to occur.

Nursing soon after delivery requires your statement of this preference to your health care provider. You can wait, see how things go, and decide when the time comes when you would prefer to begin. The expulsion of the placenta and the repair of the episiotomy may be distracting. However, many mothers have found that having their baby in their arms at this time is an ideal way to focus on something much more rewarding! If you wish to begin nursing soon after birth, one of your health care providers will check the baby for any conditions that would interfere with your baby's ability to breast-feed. After this brief check, your position must be such that nursing will be easy to accomplish.

Your decision on when to begin should be based on what is happening, how you feel, and how the baby is doing. Find out ahead of time whether your health care provider encourages or discourages breast-feeding immediately after birth. If he or she is against it, perhaps you could discuss this concern during a prenatal visit. The decision is yours, but it also may help to consider the viewpoint of your birth attendant and the situation you encounter upon giving birth.

THE FIRST FEEDING

When you are ready to begin:

1. Have your labor companion or a nurse help you get into a comfortable position. If you are trembling following the exertion of giving birth, ask for a warm blanket to help soothe you. If thirsty, request a glass of juice or water. A semi-sitting position is good, unless you have had a spinal anesthetic. If you have had a spinal and/or a cesarean birth, you may

begin nursing lying on your left side if you are right-handed (the right side if you're left-handed) with a few pillows behind your back to prop you up.

2. Check your nipple to be sure it is erect. Gently grasp your nipple and pull it slightly outward. This will make it easier for your baby to suck. Compress the areola (the circular area of darker skin surrounding the nipple) between your thumb and forefinger and grasp firmly. Make sure the nipple is shaped to fit comfortably into the baby's mouth.

3. Hold your baby securely in the crook of your arm. Turn your baby toward you so that you are "tummy to tummy," rather than holding him with his body facing up. If your baby tries to put his hand in his mouth before your nipple, wrap a blanket firmly around your baby in swaddling fashion with the arms tucked inside, or tuck his arm under your arm. With your free hand, grasp your breast, with your thumb on top and two fingers beneath, then brush the baby's cheek with your nipple. The baby will turn in the direction of this signal and open his mouth in what is known as the rooting reflex.

4. Firmly place your nipple and a portion of the areola in your baby's mouth while aiming toward his palate (roof of the mouth), behind the upper gums. Hold your nipple there until the baby grasps it. This may take several seconds or even minutes. Some babies do not decide to suck vigorously right away; they prefer to nuzzle, lick, and sniff the skin on your breast. This is all part of your baby's getting to know you. Try again a few minutes later.

5. Don't forget to include Dad! Make sure your husband gets the opportunity to hold and touch your new son or daughter.

A QUICK REFERENCE GUIDE FOR NURSING YOUR BABY

I. POSITION YOURSELF.

Using pillows as necessary, sit up in bed or in a rocking chair with your baby held comfortably by placing your knee, a pillow, or the arm of the chair under your elbow that's cradling the baby's head. Pillows are a nursing mother's friend; they help prevent back strain and promote relaxation.

2. POSITION YOUR BABY.

Whenever possible, undress your baby (leaving the diaper on, of course!) to promote skin contact and keep your baby alert. Cuddle your baby in your arms with his head in the crook of your arm, his bottom in your hand, and his back supported by your forearm. His head should be on an even plane with his body; it is neither bent forward nor arched backward. Also, his head is not turned to the side, but his whole body faces you, "tummy to tummy," with his head directly facing your breast.

3. MANUALLY EXPRESS A FEW DROPS OF COLOSTRUM

or milk to get started. This moistens the nipple and areola and makes the nipple less rigid so that your baby can grasp it more readily.

4. CUP YOUR BREAST WITH YOUR FREE HAND.

Support your breast by holding it with several fingers underneath and your thumb on top.

5. ENCOURAGE YOUR BABY TO OPEN HIS MOUTH WIDE.

Stroke his cheek nearest to your breast to stimulate the rooting reflex. As he turns to face your breast, he will open his mouth and hunt for the nipple. Tickle his lips with your milk-moistened nipple. When his mouth opens wider, press your shaped, supported nipple and areola in his mouth toward the area behind his upper gums. His tongue should lie underneath your nipple, with his lips relaxed but not quite visible. If you do not get enough of the areola into his mouth, the pressure will be directed onto the nipple and feel painful. When this happens, pull his lower jaw downward with your thumb placed on his chin. Break the suction and start again if he doesn't cooperate. Encouraging him to do it right from the start is vital. Many babies have no trouble sucking correctly; others need to be taught.

6. Allow your baby to suck as long as he seems interested. Break the suction by inserting the forefinger of your free hand into your baby's mouth. Then resume nursing on the opposite side if your baby wishes. Contrary to some opinion, nursing by demand does not increase nipple soreness. There is data to support unlimited nursing time if the mother and baby are willing. Limiting the time at the breast merely postpones the adaptation of the nipples to lactation. Make sure to follow the guidelines for nipple care in chapter 6. (Remember: When you encourage your baby to nurse on demand this will stimulate your milk supply, toughen the nipples, and cause the baby to suck less vigorously than when feedings are delayed or limited.)

WHY DO BABIES SUCK SO OFTEN?

The idea of a "schedule" for a breast-fed baby is a misconception; the only schedule your baby knows is determined by his individual needs. Keep in mind that the supply and demand principle is the foundation of successful breast-feeding and means that your baby's demand determines the amount of milk that you produce. Clockwatching interferes with the development of a mother's ability to respond to her baby's cues.

The majority of infants learn to nurse in a pattern which best suits their biological and emotional needs. Nursing on demand can be tiring for Mom and a threat to continued nursing if you try to fit your baby into an inflexible feeding pattern. Adapting your sleeping habits and activities to incorporate demand feeding is appropriate. In fact, it's just good common sense.

Understanding the biological design of demand feeding may help you to accept your baby's feeding patterns more easily. The following factors influence the frequency of nursing and your breast-feeding relationship:

1. Your baby sucks as long and as often as his nutritional needs require him to nurse.

   While some babies obtain 80 to 90 percent of the milk in the first five minutes of nursing, others are less efficient. Some women have a stronger let-down reflex compared to other women who have several let-downs during a feeding. Your baby's cues are the only "timer" to use.

   You may find that your baby prefers to switch sides. There is intelligence at work here: on the first breast, your baby might obtain thinner milk, called foremilk, for the first few minutes. Continued sucking stimulates the let-down reflex and brings a greater abundance of creamier milk. While your baby nurses on one side, the other side leaks foremilk. In switching to the other breast midway through the feeding, your baby receives the more satisfying hindmilk. Who says babies aren't very smart?

2. The fat content in your milk varies not only within the feeding itself, but with the time of day and throughout the months that you nurse your child.

   Babies often nurse more frequently at times of the day when the fat content is lowest since the fat makes them feel more satisfied. Late afternoon and early evening are the most frequently noticed times for this to occur.

3. Your baby will digest your milk much more quickly than he would formula since it is more easily assimilated by the digestive system.

   Since he will not feel full for as long a period, he will probably nurse more often than he would if he were bottle-fed.

4. You will have days when the baby will want to eat more frequently. At around six weeks and three months, for example, babies go through a growth spurt which increases the amount of milk they need in accordance with their growth pattern. A more detailed consideration of this can be found in the section

later in this chapter titled "Questions to Consider."

5. Many babies enjoy nonnutritive sucking which satisfies emotional rather than physical needs.

6. One- or two-minute feedings are not unusual. These satisfy your baby's thirst, rather than his hunger, by giving him the more watery, less-filling foremilk. Trust your baby to adjust the frequency and length of his feedings to obtain the more watery foremilk when he is thirsty, get more calories when he is growing, and seek the fattier hindmilk when he is hungry. Because it isn't possible for you to measure or interpret these differences, you will do best when you let your baby be the guide.

Remember that your breast milk differs in fat content and calories. It cannot be matched by any formula currently available. Comparing the feeding patterns of a breast-fed baby to a bottle-fed baby denies this fundamental fact and can be discouraging. Know that demand feeding and variable calories control obesity and encourage appetite control, thereby promoting a healthy approach to eating habits beyond infancy.

ADDITIONAL REASONS THE LORD DESIGNED BABIES TO NURSE FREQUENTLY

1. The fifth stage of labor lasts six weeks; this means that your body needs rest. If your baby is nursing eight to twelve times per day, it's unlikely that you'll be overdoing it. Nursing makes moms sit down and put their feet up!

2. You need to get to know your newborn. Extensive nursing allows mothers to spend time cuddling their babies and to learn all about this new little person. No matter how many children you have, you'll still need to get to know the unique character of each one. Time at the breast promotes becoming well acquainted with one another through touch, smell, eye contact, and speech.

3. Your baby needs you; a newborn baby is totally dependent on others for sustenance. Being together is insured by a frequent nursing pattern.

NURSING A SLEEPY BABY

Some babies fall asleep after sucking only a short time. This is discouraging and sometimes can be overcome by:

- Undressing your baby to increase skin-to-skin contact.
- Keeping your baby's attention by talking.
- Manually expressing milk just before nursing to soften your breasts, thus allowing your "little sleepy head" to get more of the areola into his mouth. Compression of the areola during nursing will enable him to get milk more easily from the ducts underlying this area.
- Tickle, tap, or nibble to awaken him as he starts to lose interest and doze off. It needn't be excessive or desperate; just have fun!
- Use the "bubble and switch" technique. Remove him from the breast if you've done all of the above. Sit him up, allowing the air bubble in his stomach to rise, and then burp him. Often, the jostling and thumping of bubbling will wake a baby up and you can resume nursing on the second breast. Repeat as necessary.
- Relax! Your baby eventually will outgrow this tendency. Small babies, jaundiced babies, and contented babies are more likely to be sleepers than fussy babies, babies who love to suck, and babies who are more alarmed by noises. Avoid being anxious and get some sleep yourself!

COPING WITH FUSSY PERIODS

Crying, regardless of popular opinion, is not a sign of health but is largely of reflex origin. It is not a voluntary expression in young infants. That is, your baby doesn't diabolically plot out how he can get you to pick him up because he is lonely. Neither does he think to himself, as far as anyone knows, "I'm hungry. Let's see now. I think I will cry to get my way."

Experts are beginning to question the concepts of "spoiling" and "normal fussiness." These concepts miss the point: Babies cry in response to pain, loneliness, and hunger. Some babies seem to be fussier by nature, possessing a temperament that makes them more reactive to their environment and their feelings. Fussy babies are more demanding and more difficult to parent than more placid babies.

Here are a few suggestions that may help you cope if you are the mother of a more expressive child:

- Realize it's not your fault. Babies seem to fuss because of their own orientation to life and not your mothering abilities.

- Adjust your expectations. Perhaps you've imagined a fantasy baby based on TV commercials, shows, magazines, stories, etc. Let's face it—no television show has ever shown what life with a new baby is really like! Experienced parents (of fussy babies) will help you to understand that your baby is more normal than you realize.

- Fussy babies often grow up to be above-average, intelligent, creative children. This calls for above-average, intelligent, creative parenting and acceptance of your baby's potential.

- Infants do not cry to annoy, consciously manipulate, or take advantage of their parents. They cry to express a need. Ignoring the cry equals ignoring the need. Not meeting these needs decreases your baby's ability to trust you and increases dependency (spoiling). Meeting the need promotes trust and independence.

- Responding to your baby's crying in the first weeks of life may make your baby less likely to cry uncontrollably later. According to research on personality and childhood behavior, the development of trust and a basic sense of security early in life seem to be an important factor in the development of your baby's personality.

- Arrange for frequent contact that is interrupted as little as possible from the moment of birth. Feeding on demand, skin-to-skin contact, and the cloth infant carriers promote maternal-infant bonding. Given this contact, fussiness is kept to a minimum.

- Use stress management and relaxation techniques when you're tense and tired.

- Figure out when your baby's fussiest period of the day is likely to be and plan for it. Use his happiest periods for play and learning activities. During his grouchiest times (often between 4:00 and 8:00 P.M.) promote peace and quiet with crockpot meals, decreased activity, less noise, and a backrub for Mom.

- Your fussy baby will likely make you and the entire family fussy. Marital tension rises! Talk together and spend moments loving rather than fussing once the baby stops being crabby! Don't forget to "pamper" yourself!

- Make sure there is no physical cause of the fussiness. A thorough examination by your baby's physician is important as a means of ruling out this factor. Colic is different than mere fussiness and needs to be dealt with more specifically. If your baby is given a clean bill of health, consider allergens in your milk, cigarette smoke, hair sprays, and the like as possible irritants. If there are not physical reasons (and there often aren't!) fussiness may be alleviated by:

    Praying for your baby out loud, using a soothing voice.

    Motion and physical contact.

    Baby massage.

    Bathing with a parent in the "big bath."

    Music, mechanical sounds (dryer, car, dishwasher, vacuum, etc.).

- Seek help from those who will listen, empathize, and offer you genuine help. Avoid people who will offer quick advice ("Let him cry!"). What you need is support, not advice.

You will benefit from hearing:

"It's okay to have these feelings."

"Your love is what he needs most."

"He's not taking advantage of you."

"It's normal to resent your baby sometimes; what really matters is that you love him far more than you resent him."

"Your baby is changing daily; you'll feel less tied down soon."

Take each day one at a time. Pray often. Remember, it's not your fault. And enjoy the cuddling, snuggling, and close times that far outweigh the intense periods of fussiness.

TIPS FOR TREATING A COLICKY BABY

- Feed and burp your baby in an upright position.
- Burp early and frequently.
- Feed your baby in a quiet, dimly lit room. Make sure that you relax, too!
- If using a bottle, enlarge the nipple hole. If breast-feeding and you have a strong letdown, allow the initial spray to drain onto a cloth diaper or towel.
- Keep your baby in an upright position with gentle motion for a half hour after nursing.
- Try a different position for burping. Carry your baby in the "football-hold" position holding him horizontally in front of you, with your hand supporting his abdomen, facing him away from you.
- Hold your baby in a relaxed and secure fashion. A baby carrier that can be worn in the front may be useful.
- Clear his nasal passages; mouth breathing may increase air swallowing.
- Avoid sudden noises that may startle him.
- Consider the possibility of allergies (substances in your diet passed into the milk that could be eliminated). Examples: iron supplements, dairy products, caffeine-containing beverages, citrus fruits and juices.

- Seek help from support groups, that is, other people who really are capable of empathizing, not criticizing or scrutinizing!
- Don't forget: colic usually disappears between three and six months. Pray that it will be over even sooner!

QUESTIONS TO CONSIDER

The following ideas are taken from a La Leche League reprint. If you think your milk production is low or inadequate, if you're not sure that your baby is getting enough milk, ask yourself these questions:

Have I used both breasts for at least ten minutes at each feeding?

The best pattern for ensuring an adequate supply is ten minutes on the first side, then as long as your baby wishes to nurse on the other side. Make sure to begin nursing on the side you left off on at the next feeding. Occasionally, babies get too much milk if you use both breasts. You will be able to recognize if this is happening because your baby will spit up large amounts of milk after nursing on both sides. This means you have an ample supply and perhaps should nurse your baby on one side for a longer period of time.

Am I nursing my baby for as long as he's interested and content to nurse?

If you forget about that clock and let your baby be your guide, you will be a happier nursing "couple" and make more milk as well.

Am I feeding him when he's hungry?

Often babies will nurse for only a short period of time and then must eat more frequently. Nurse according to your baby's cues. Also, remember that one feeding does not mean just the allotted time at each breast. A feeding is however long it takes your baby to finish eating and be satisfied.

Are there at least six soaking-wet diapers in a twenty-four hour period?

A baby who has at least this many wet diapers is receiving an adequate amount from the breast.

How much liquid am I drinking?

Most nursing moms desire two to four quarts of liquid per day, with a substantial portion of this being water. Any beverage that contains caffeine should be avoided, since caffeine enters the milk and will interfere with both you and your baby's ability to sleep. Never force fluids; drink to satisfy thirst. Just be sure to drink the necessary amount of two to four quarts.

Is my diet balanced and am I eating regularly?

The quality of your milk is partly a reflection of the quality of your diet. Six small meals per day are better and more satisfying than three large meals. Brewer's yeast reportedly causes the milk supply to be increased, but may make you and your baby "gassy."

Do I understand the principles of supply and demand and the let-down reflex?

The amount of milk you produce is directly related to the amount of milk that is removed from your breasts. The amount of milk your baby gets is related to your ability to relax and establish the let-down reflex. The production of milk requires your baby's suckling, the giving of milk, and your peace of mind. Any supplements, rigid schedules, or upsets will interfere with your body's ability to nurse your baby.

Am I worried about my milk supply?

Many women in our culture become concerned about their milk supply. They also tend to be much less aware of the things that contribute to successful breast-feeding than successful bottle-feeding! The two methods are very different in terms of how they work. Once you understand the principles of successful nursing—relax! Think positively about making milk and sharing yourself with your baby in this unique way. Avoid giving thought to the comments of friends or relatives who are unfamiliar with lactation. Just worrying too much can affect the release of oxytocin and the process of letting-down your milk.

Have I started solids too soon?

In most cases, babies are not going to physiologically need any solid food until about the middle of the first year of life (five to seven months). If you are following the ideas you've learned and are applying the principles to your experience, your milk will be the ideal food for your baby to receive in most situations. If you must begin solids earlier, be sure to nurse your baby before offering solids so that your milk supply is maintained.

Do I compare my baby with babies who are bottle-fed?

This can lead to apprehension and confusion! A baby who is breast-fed: (1) digests breast milk much more rapidly, (2) excretes it more easily, with less waste, (3) must work harder by sucking more vigorously to obtain milk, and (4) should be fed on demand since there is no way to determine how much your baby is getting. Sleeping and nursing patterns may reflect this, just as they do with babies who are not receiving breast milk.

At six weeks old is my baby going longer between feedings?

If so, this may reduce your milk supply. Although some longer spans of time between nursings newborns are fine, remember that frequent nursing stimulates your breasts to make more milk. Encourage your infant to nurse at least once every four hours, with possibly one longer stretch in a twenty-four-hour period (every five to six hours).

Is my baby acting hungry all the time and not satisfied with the usual number of feedings per day?

"Nursing binges" are common at times when your baby must stimulate a greater production of milk. During a growth spurt, particularly around six weeks and three months, your baby will nurse more frequently for twenty-four to forty-eight hours. This will be followed by a reduction in the frequency of nursing once your baby is satisfied that your milk supply has increased enough to meet his needs. Some other situations when "frequency days" may be expected: during an illness (yours or your baby's), following a hectic couple of days (when you may have nursed less often), while traveling (because your baby picks up your tension or your let-down reflex is not up to par), on weekends if you're working and separated during the week.

DISCOUNTING THE FOLKLORE

When you make the decision to breast-feed, you may find yourself becoming the target of all sorts of comments and advice. Many of the things you hear will be based on what was thought about breast-feeding many years ago. Discount any breast-feeding advice if it is based on belief rather than fact. Also discount it if it's an idea left over from "someone else's" unsuccessful attempts at nursing; received from any books published prior to 1976; or aimed at proving the person right or easing her concern for you, rather than at providing you with genuine support and accurate information.

The most helpful source of information, other than books, is another woman who enjoyed nursing her baby and who breast-fed for at least eight months. Your health care provider can also be an excellent source of information if he or she values breast-feeding as a special relationship that involves you and the baby, instead of simply a means to get nutrients into your child.

The following statements are commonly made by people who don't understand the process of breast-feeding. If you hear any of them—and believe me, you will—realize that you don't have to defend yourself or prove that what you're doing is correct. Misinformation about breast-feeding is the norm rather than the exception, and you can politely refuse to be affected by it!

- "Are you sure your milk is rich enough?" (See pages 145.)
- "He couldn't possibly be getting enough . . . you just nursed him twenty minutes ago." (See pages 152.)
- "You'll spoil him if you nurse him every time he acts hungry." (See pages 152, 154.)
- "You'll be lucky if you have enough milk; I didn't." (See pages 149.)
- "I'd be able to help you more if I could feed the baby for you." (See page 144.)

There are many reasons why people make comments like these to nursing mothers: disappointment at personal failure with breast-feeding, feelings of exclusion, a desire to have you mother your baby in the way that seems "right" to the person speaking, or concern for your baby's health. In Proverbs 15:1, we find that "a gentle answer turns away wrath." Through understanding why someone would feel led to make critical or hurtful remarks, you will find it easier to answer the advice you receive.

When you are faced with comments that reflect a lack of understanding about the process of breast-feeding, keep in mind Proverbs 15:23: "A man finds joy in giving an apt reply—and how good is a timely word!" You will find that an "apt reply" or a "timely word" will clear the air and prevent later misunderstandings. Try to be kind and gentle; demonstrate your commitment to your relationship with the Lord as well as your commitment to breast-feeding your baby.

EXPRESSION AND STORAGE OF BREAST MILK

While you are breast-feeding you may have times when you either need or want to be apart from your baby. Sometimes it is possible to time your separations so that you don't miss a feeding. This is ideal, because your breasts will not become uncomfortably full if you nurse your baby every two to three hours. Also, it is important to remember that regular, frequent nursing stimulates your milk supply and ensures that your baby is getting enough milk.

If you find it is necessary that the baby miss one or more feedings you can plan ahead and express breast milk to be used in your absence. The advantages of supplementing with breast milk rather than formula are he will have (1) fewer digestive upsets, (2) continued protection against infections, (3) no risk of an allergic reaction, and (4) breast milk is the best source of nourishment for your baby.

You may express your milk by hand or with a breast pump. The best time of day to obtain milk is when your milk supply is highest, usually in the morning. Don't be discouraged if you only get one ounce at first. It takes a while to become adept at expressing milk and for the let-down reflex to respond to the stimulus of manual expression.

To establish a let-down reflex (without which little milk is expressed) in response to expression, relax. Avoid expressing when you are under pressure to obtain milk. Plan in advance, practice in a calm setting (in the tub or while taking a shower), and realize that you won't get much at first. You are learning a new skill, just as you learned to breast-feed. At first, it can seem awkward, but before long it will seem perfectly natural.

The type of pump I recommend that is commercially available is made up of two plastic cylinders with a cup on one that fits against the end of your breast. These pumps are available at many drug and department stores in town. They can be purchased for fifteen to twenty-five dollars. If you are going to be returning to work and will be expressing milk several times a day, a pump would be a worthwhile investment and is more efficient than hand expression for many mothers. Follow the directions from the manufacturer and give yourself time to learn how to get the best results.

Hand expression involves no equipment and can work well once you learn the technique. Your hand is placed with your thumb above the nipple with several fingers beneath. Press your breast against your chest wall for greater pressure and then press inward with your fingers. This is done in a fairly quick movement and repeated rhythmically: press and squeeze, press and squeeze, etc. Sooner or later the milk sprays out of several openings in the nipple, slowly accumulating in a very clean bowl, cup, or plastic bottle. Rotate your hand so that you obtain milk from all the ducts underlying the areola. You will be able to tell if you are doing this correctly when you see milk spraying out of different openings when you change positions.

If you find it difficult, you can apply warm compresses and massage your breasts prior to expressing in the same way that you were shown for prenatal preparation. This will encourage the ducts to open and your milk to let-down.

You can express one breast or both breasts at a time, using one or two bags or jars. This is not appealing to some women and can only be done successfully if you're comfortable touching your breasts in this way.

Freeze the milk, even if you are able to obtain only one or two ounces. The next time you express, chill the milk thoroughly and add it to the frozen milk until you have four ounces. Freeze four-ounce quantities to avoid waste. Never thaw the milk at room temperature; only in the refrigerator or under slightly cool running water—and do not warm it beyond skin temperature (feels neither warm nor cool when dropped on your wrist). Once the milk is thawed it must be used within twenty-four hours. Once you've warmed it, any remaining milk must be discarded. Breast milk is full of living organisms that are beneficial to your baby, but keep in mind that these same organisms are an ideal culture for the wrong kind of bacteria.

Breast milk may be stored up to forty-eight hours in the refrigerator, two months in your freezer, or one year in a deep freeze. If you plan ahead and are careful about preparing and storing the bottles, breast milk supplements can be the ideal way for someone else to feed your baby while you are away.

BREAST-FEEDING AND WORKING

Only you and your husband can decide whether or not you should resume or begin working before your baby is weaned from the breast. Your decision to go to work or attend school doesn't have to mean that you must wean your baby. It will take special effort and planning on your part to make the necessary arrangements to continue breast-feeding, however.

Do the advantages of nursing outweigh the disadvantages? Let's consider some positive aspects of nursing and working:

a. Breast-feeding offers an exclusive bond between you and your child.

b. There are many physiological benefits related to breast milk.

c. You and your baby might feel reassured by the physical intimacy related to nursing.

Some of the more negative aspects of nursing and working include:

a. Special arrangements must be carried out, taking extra time and energy.

b. Initially, you may need to spend time at work pumping your breasts in the washroom.

c. The baby's caretaker(s) has to have a supportive attitude, necessitating more communication between the two of you. Look for someone who is familiar with the advantages and processes of breast-feeding, is open to your plans to work out this arrangement, and is willing to cooperate.

Your milk supply does not need to be reduced due to your times away from your baby. If you can postpone returning to work until after your baby is three months old, your milk supply will have been firmly established through frequent contact with your baby.

If you do decide to return to work before your baby is three months old, your milk supply may become diminished if you don't get enough rest, neglect to eat nutritional foods and drink plenty of liquids, and are tense or worried. You can help resolve these problems by napping on weekends, going to bed earlier, taking a nap after work, nursing while you rest, and getting extra help with household tasks.

You may find it important to work out sharing of household tasks (cooking, cleaning, laundry, shopping, child care, yard maintenance, etc.) with your husband. Some studies suggest that working women who share a household with a working mate are often saddled with an inordinate amount of the household tasks and child care. You can avoid this situation by talking about it with your spouse ahead of time, and also on an ongoing basis.

Keep in mind that even without returning to work, most mothers are busy with five jobs requiring a good deal of their time and energy: self-care, care of the household, mothering, supporting relationships, and milk production (if nursing). Commitments made beyond these responsibilities take away from the time and energy available for their management. All of the parts are affected by the whole. Management of these parts requires prioritizing and organization. Very often, working mothers are left with little time for themselves and for those outside of the home. This needn't be the case with careful planning.

How can you keep up milk production within this framework which is affected by time needed for the other parts? Several options are available.

COMPLETE BREAST-FEEDING
Keeping your baby on breast milk can be accomplished in the following ways:

1. *Work at home.* Do you have any skills you could use in the home for pay? Typing, art or music lessons, and research for a professor are examples of such work. This allows you time with your baby without child care expense.

2. *Establish a caretaker near your workplace.* If you can arrange for a caretaker who lives within a few miles from your workplace, you can arrange to be with your baby during the day. This is great for allowing you more contact with your child, and alleviates the necessity of hand-expressing milk.

3. *Work on a flexible work schedule or find a part-time job.* Broken shifts, short segments of work spaced at your convenience, and jobs that take up less than twenty hours per week will give you a greater amount of contact with your child by cutting down on the number of hours you'll need to be away in one stretch.

4. *Work full time, leaving your baby with the caretaker for the full period of time.* This arrangement provides the least amount of contact with your baby during the day, and requires the use of expression and storage of milk. You may find that your baby requires more attention from you after longer separation. (Usually, partial bottle-feeding is the only way to deal with this situation. Once your baby is on solid foods, he will require fewer bottles during the day. Keep in mind, though, that he might nurse just as often when with you for emotional support.)

FORMULA-FEEDING AND BREAST-FEEDING

Leaving Breast Milk. You can still give your baby the benefits of your milk even when you can't be with your baby during work hours. Before returning to work (two to three weeks ahead) begin expressing your milk. (Reread the section in this chapter entitled "Expression and Storage of Breast Milk.")

If you are able and wish to express milk at work, you will benefit from having access to a refrigerator. The milk can be expressed directly into nurser bags or a clean jar and kept chilled, then frozen at home. I know a woman who took a small ice chest to work for this purpose.

Supplementing with Formula. If you feel that expressing milk is too difficult, you may wish to have your baby's caretaker give bottles of formula while you are away. You can keep your milk supply stimulated by nursing your baby often when you're together. You may need to express some milk at work at first, but eventually your breasts will not be as full during long separations. Be sure the caretaker does not feed the baby close to when you'll be picking him up. Nurse your baby soon after your arrival, and nurse your baby before leaving so that your breasts will be empty at the beginning of your time away.

WET NURSE

Occasionally, a woman may find that her baby can accept a surrogate mother who is willing to nurse the baby during the day. Usually this woman is a close friend or relative of the baby's mother and has a child close in age to the baby. Such an arrangement obviously requires clear communication and genuine acceptance by all of the persons involved.

OTHER THINGS TO THINK ABOUT

Your baby may sleep more during the day and nurse more frequently during the evening when you are working. Even babies who were sleeping long periods at night may begin to nurse at night again. This need not be a problem if you sleep with your baby, either in your bed or on a bed in the baby's room. Extra snuggling from Mom is often what is being asked for and mothering at night can be a positive experience for both of you, especially when you consider the night hours are kind of a replacement for the hours you are away during the day.

Each baby reacts differently to having Mom work outside the home. Do each other a favor and evaluate it a step at a time, weighing the advantages and disadvantages, and the total effect the separation has on your family.

Attending school can be similar to working, but in many circumstances is a more flexible situation. Often there is child care available either on or near campus, so that nursing between classes becomes a possibility. Expressing milk between classes also works well if your schedule is well planned. A small baby often is permitted to come along to class if he is content nursing or in a cloth carrier, but always check this out with your instructor! Remember that you will need one hand free for note-taking.

It goes without saying that the father who can cook, shop, clean, and provide encouragement is invaluable. A supportive husband can make life easier for the family by simplifying the running of the household through his participation. If your husband can drive you to the sitter, it will also give you more time to nurse while he is driving.

Traveling can be easy with a breast-fed baby, but if you must be away from your baby for a day or more, you need not abruptly wean your baby. Purchase plastic breast shields to collect the milk that leaks and discard the extra milk. The greatest relief of engorgement can be obtained by using an electric breast pump (rent one and take it along), and using an oxytocic nasal spray. This will help ensure near complete emptying of your breasts. Upon your return, your baby may detect your diminished milk supply and will have missed you, so you can count on him nursing frequently and for long periods for a few days.

Some babies seem fine during their mother's absence, but others become disoriented and confused. If you realize that you are taking a chance as you leave your baby, then you will be better able to cope with the outcome. A few babies actually refuse the breast if Mother has been gone for an extended period, but you might be able to pick up where you left off if you display patience and perseverance in encouraging your baby to resume nursing.

Don't forget: people's life-styles differ. There are many ways to approach any desired outcome. Seek encouragement. Spend uninterrupted time with your baby. And, don't forget that all of this extra effort is for the very best of reasons: your baby!

IF BOTTLE-FEEDING IS YOUR CHOICE

Not every woman is comfortable with the idea of breast-feeding a baby. In our culture today it is possible to choose a feeding method that reflects personal preferences rather than biological necessity. The decision to bottle-feed, breast-feed, or do both in combination is a decision that is made by the infant's mother and father. Only in a limited number of situations does a baby absolutely require breast milk due to health reasons. In the majority of cases, bottle-feeding or supplemented breast-feeding provides an adequate diet for the young baby.

Many babies do fine on formula, but it is important to be careful when preparing bottles. Good hygiene is essential and manufacturer's directions for preparation must be followed exactly to insure that your baby will receive the right nutrients.

Although there are no formulas that match the composition of breast milk, there are products that attempt to approximate it. It is a good idea to discuss the choices available with the baby's physician or a nutritionist. You may have to try a few different brands before finding one that is compatible with your baby.

PREPARING A BOTTLE
Use the following list as a supplement to your guide for preparation until you become familiar with all the steps involved:

- Your kitchen area and all utensils used in preparation must be very clean.

- Bottles and nipples must be sterile before filling with formula. There are several types of bottle systems available on the market. Whether you use disposable, plastic, or glass bottles, you must follow manufacturer's directions for sterilization procedures.
- You can make up enough bottles for two days, but caps must be put on and the bottles must be placed directly into the refrigerator after you fix them.
- Never leave warm milk out for more than a few minutes since it is an ideal culture medium for bacteria to grow in.
- Always toss out milk that has been heated but not used. Make sure to clean out the bottle immediately if it is not the disposable type.
- Keep nipples in sterilized, covered containers.
- When you leave the house, take the prepared bottles with you straight from the refrigerator and heat just before using. Never keep prepared milk in a warm place, waiting for baby's use; you are taking the chance of introducing germs that can provoke gastrointestinal distress in your baby.
- It is okay to give an anxious baby a bottle that has not been warmed.
- Powdered mixes must be thoroughly dissolved so that lumps don't block the nipple. It helps to always add the powder to the liquid. Do not use extra powder for added nutritional value; it will cause an imbalance in the baby's body.
- Babies being fed formula can go longer between feedings than babies who are breast-fed since the formula is not digested as quickly. It is reassuring to many parents to know how much milk their baby is getting and can be a relief if you have switched from breast-feeding due to anxiety over whether your baby was receiving enough milk. Do not, however, force your baby to finish the bottle if he doesn't want to.
- Water and diluted fruit juices may be used in addition to formula to help avoid constipation.

ENJOYING FEEDING TIME

When feeding your baby take time to hold him close. It is important to avoid "bottle-propping" for several reasons: the baby can choke on milk flowing from the nipple, dental cavities are a problem with older babies who take their bottles to bed, and most of all, your baby needs his feeding times to be a source of skin-to-skin contact and physical comforting. The interaction that takes place at feeding time is one of the most special experiences of your baby's life.

One advantage of bottle-feeding is that the baby's father or other family members can participate in feeding time. This not only provides the mother with a break, but it draws others into being actively involved with the care and nurturing of the baby.

SUMMARY

Whatever method you use to feed your baby, it should be *your* choice. You must feel confident with your decision in order to feel competent about the job you are doing as a parent.

Rest, relax, and enjoy the time you spend feeding your baby. Before you know it, your child will be weaned and more independent; the early months of your baby's life are precious indeed! It will be only a matter of time until your son or daughter is anxious to toddle away from you instead of into your tender embrace. The hours you invest rocking and holding your baby will be an experience that you will never regret!

CHAPTER FIFTEEN
The Fifth Stage of Labor: A Word to Fathers and Labor Companions

"Give her the reward she has earned, and let her works bring her praise at the city gate." PROVERBS 31:31

The fifth stage of labor begins two hours after a baby is born and lasts six weeks. It is a time of tremendous physiological, anatomical, and emotional adjustment. Hormone levels shift and sway, the uterus sheds extra cells and shrinks in size, and the breasts swell with milk and other body fluids as lactation is established.

The days and weeks that immediately follow a baby's birth bring many changes. It is not a typical or routine time in one's life. Instead, it is a period of transition and moving from one physical and emotional state to another, of assuming new roles and responsibilities, and of learning to accommodate the shifts in usual schedules, normal body functions, and everyday habits. Normal routines are disrupted.

This forty-two-day period is a unique and demanding time. Activities must be adjusted and prioritized to accommodate the special needs associated with postpartum. The mother especially deserves to receive "the reward she has earned," and she will benefit from being given a break from her usual responsibilities.

A WEEK OF REST

As a "recuperation" vacation after returning from the hospital, I consider it mandatory for a new mother to refrain from the following activities for at least one or two weeks (no, I'm not kidding!): laundry, shopping, cooking, cleaning, primary care of older children, and church attendance.

The mother's first and foremost responsibility is to rest and relax while she gets to know her new baby. She deserves a complete break from her usual activities while her body adjusts to breast-feeding and a post-pregnant state. This is a time in a woman's life when she needs to be loved, supported, nurtured, and cared for; in short, to be treated like a queen! A hospital stay of two to five days simply is not a long enough period for a mother to adjust to her baby and her body.

Now comes the problem: Who will perform these tasks? Since fathers often are exhausted, too, it helps to have relatives and friends pitch in. Casseroles may be brought over and tasks given to those who wonder how to help. Sadly, our culture often does not offer new mothers the real support and help they need. We mistakenly think that we help a new mom by feeding, dressing, and bathing the baby. Emphatically not! We can help the mother much more by giving her good food, providing her with clean sheets and clothing, and watching over the baby while she gets time to herself in the bathroom. New mothers need assistance rather than direction!

FOR HUSBANDS ONLY

In a sense, new mothers need mothering. They do not need visitors (who drain their energy), or criticism (which drains their self-esteem), or outdated advice (which drains their patience).

Turn back to chapter 9 and read the section on "Working Together" (p. 82) to see what a woman needs in labor and ways labor companions can meet these needs. The fifth stage of labor requires the same kinds of support from loving labor companions. It is really no different, even though the contractions have subsided and the work does not seem to be as demanding. The fact of the matter is that many processes are taking place that require rest and a quiet environment if a mother is to adapt easily. Postpartum depression, or "the baby blues," usually is due more to fatigue and a sense of abandonment than a physical process.

New moms, even if they have borne eight children, benefit from time alone with their new baby and time for short rests at intervals throughout the day and night. Frequent snacks (see appendix A) and beverages for her thirst should be provided and served as needed. Since a nursing mother needs about 500 extra calories a day, her foods should be nutritious, yet appealing. A pitcher of juice or water should be kept available at all times.

Phone calls and visitors should be restricted. If someone wants to move in to help with the baby, your wife should feel completely at ease and comfortable with having that person around constantly. Your expectations of your guest should be made explicitly clear before her arrival; she is not coming to teach, but to support the mother's own learning and discovery. Such a guest must be willing to adapt to the role of a labor companion and perform household tasks with little direction. It is an honor to be included in the babymoon, not a right!

You might want to consider setting visiting hours for sixty to ninety minutes per evening or to refrain from accepting visitors during the first week at home. Don't feel bashful about restricting phone calls and visits—you didn't when you were first married! The transition period after a baby is born is not the time for extensive socializing.

If Mom seems like she needs a break from mothering, suggest a long shower or a walk outside if the weather is pleasant. Volunteer to watch the baby so she can have time to herself to be refreshed. She will need some rest that is uninterrupted by noises and she should be encouraged to sleep whenever the baby is sleeping. A back rub at least once a day can be a great help, as well as acceptance for being unable to make love for at least a month. Explore ways of soothing one another through touch that is not geared toward sexual arousal. This is a wonderful way to comfort and reassure her.

Your sexual needs as a husband may be met, without penetration, when she is rested, available, and willing to be with you. (Remember that Levitical law provided for a time away from sexual activity following childbirth, as well as a break from everyday routine.) Until the uterus recovers and the discharge called lochia stops (usually within three to four weeks), a woman's body is not healed sufficiently to resume intercourse. Your understanding and flexibility in this area will go a long way toward promoting her recovery.

Being sensitive and responsive to a new mother's need to be with her baby may help you overcome possible feelings of jealousy. It is important to keep in mind that most of her energy is being consumed by the tasks of the fifth stage of labor (physical recovery, psychological adjustment to the baby, and the onset of lactation). This is a temporary phase and she will learn to balance all of the needs of the family in time. Just as she seemed preoccupied and unable to respond fully to you during active labor, so will she be distracted now. If you wish, set up a special post-babymoon date and look forward to doing something romantic together, without the baby, for a couple of hours.

If you find yourself becoming critical or starting to complain, try not to direct it toward your wife. Either take it to the Lord in prayer or share your feelings with a fellow Christian you know well. Constructive direction is helpful, while unloving criticism only maims relationships. Be wise about how to communicate your concerns and feelings; be gentle and careful about what is said and how the words are spoken.

A WORD TO NEW MOTHERS

The first days at home with a new baby are exhausting. Forget about the clock and the world outside. This is a time to find out who your baby is and to avoid making the experience what you think it should be. Buy disposable diapers and paper plates and cups. Minimize distractions. Lie down and relax with your baby. Dismiss all those things you've heard about how long a baby should sleep and how often a baby needs to eat. Let others take care of you. Just respond lovingly to your baby's cues and be sensitive to your own need for rest and good food.

Enjoy this precious time, those tiny fingers, that delicate skin, the unique smell. Keep your baby close by if you are nursing him, for his presence will stimulate your body to release prolactin and will ensure a successful milk supply. Sleep when he sleeps, eat or drink while he eats. Take one day at a time, not worrying if you're doing it all "right." Some mothers make newborn care so complicated and organized they become unable to establish a milk supply or to enjoy the simple pleasure of holding a baby for hours on end. Your pants and blouses may not fit, and you may feel quite different from your usual self, but be patient. It will all come back to you soon enough.

Be kind to yourself and praise the Lord for the life he has entrusted to your care. Thank him for what he has given to you. Try not to complain; it only leads to unthankfulness and self-pity. If you are feeling angry, guilty, helpless, lonely, or generally depressed, get help and communicate what is on your mind.

All new mothers need companionship, reassurance, and encouragement. The fifth stage of labor has a way of making us feel vulnerable, like it or not! Being a Christian does not confer a super-humanity upon us, or exempt us from the effects of inevitable life changes. Instead, we can consider David's words in Psalm 103:1-19, reminding ourselves that God is indeed with us eternally as our example of what being a parent is all about:

Praise the Lord, O my soul; all my inmost being, praise his holy name. Praise the Lord, O my soul, and forget not all his benefits. He forgives all my sins and heals all my diseases; he redeems my life from the pit and crowns me with love and compassion. He satisfies my desires with good things, so that my youth is renewed like the eagle's.

The Lord works righteousness and justice for all the oppressed. He made known his ways to Moses, his deeds to the people of Israel: The Lord is compassionate and gracious, slow to anger, abounding in love. . . . He does not treat us as our sins deserve or repay us according to our iniquities. For as high as the heavens are above the earth, so great is his love for those who fear him; as far as the east is from the west, so far has he removed our transgressions from us.

As a father has compassion on his children, so the Lord has compassion on those who fear him; for he knows how we are formed, he remembers that we are dust. . . . But from everlasting to everlasting the Lord's love is with those who fear him, and his righteousness with their children's children—with those who keep his covenant and remember to obey his precepts. The Lord has established his throne in heaven, and his kingdom rules over all.

CHAPTER SIXTEEN

Sharing the Same Love

"May the words of my mouth and the meditation of my heart be pleasing in your sight, O Lord, my Rock and my Redeemer."
PSALM 19:14

*W*ords and actions, saying and doing . . . a marriage is made or broken on the basis of such things, and a family tree blossoms or withers in respect to what it is "fed."

Picture an action that conveys caring: a courteous gesture, the warmth of a gentle embrace, a cool cloth placed on a feverish brow, the sweetness of a genuine smile, a kind word spoken to provide reassurance, an offer to help. Compare these to what can happen when wills clash and tempers flare up: words are spoken that pierce the heart, eyes flash with malice, a hand shoves to push away, stony silence is the response to real need, a back turns to prove a point—a declaration that "I am not with you."

Our words and actions are simply the external reflections of what is going on inside our minds and hearts. We possess the ability to hurt and to heal, to tear down or build up those we claim to love. The ways we choose to express our inner thoughts and feelings matter. Our actions can bring peace, or battles, to the home front.

Jesus was born into a family as a firstborn son.

He experienced a family relationship, yet was without sin in the midst of imperfect family members. By the time he entered his brief period of ministry outside of his community he had had the opportunity to learn about human relationships firsthand. Because of God's willingness to send his own Son to be one of us, we can fully trust his Word to speak to us where we are.

Although God understands that there are no perfect people and no perfect relationships, he instructs us to follow Christ's example. He forgave, and so expects us to forgive; he served, and so expects us to serve. Jesus would not have said, "Go thou and do likewise" if he did not expect us to benefit from his instruction! We must learn to adjust our expectations to fit what is real in terms of who God created us to be.

Do you remember the key line in the movie "Love Story"? It declared that "love means never having to say you're sorry." This idealistic phrase does not fit who we really are. The relationships we share with other family members as sons and daughters, brothers and sisters, husbands and wives, and parents and children test us. Within the framework of the family our selfishness gets ground away by the friction of opposing needs, outlooks, desires, and personalities.

Learning to say we're sorry and to extend forgiveness to one another promotes harmony in a Christian home. No one is excluded! We all fall short every single day, but we can continually discover the value of compassion if we seek to follow what the Bible tells us about how we are to act "one to another." (See chapter 4.) Biblical standards for human relationships are true, for God's Word speaks to who we are and to what he created us to be.

BABIES BRING CHANGES

The appearance of a new baby in the family produces conflict and tension as well as joy and a sense of accomplishment. Roles must change. There is more work to do and more money to be earned and spent. Schedules are readjusted to accommodate the baby's needs for cuddling, food, and sleep. Decisions must be made and certain liberties restricted.

Children demand attention, space, protection, and guidance, among other things. The advent of parenthood brings about an explosion of responsibility. The "flesh" tends to get rubbed the wrong way at times and roars up in defiance, screaming, "What about ME?" Learning to balance the baby's needs with personal and marital needs takes time. There are no cookbook answers to spell out a recipe for "Adjusting to Parenthood." It takes time for a couple to develop a sense of balance and a state of equilibrium after becoming parents. Some couples never achieve it, but choose to give up instead. I am sure that you know families that were broken by extremes in behavior, never finding a balanced approach to the daily demands of life together.

Think of a family you know whose members are emotionally well-balanced and seem to have successfully adapted to one another. Such a family knows how to play together as well as work, worship, and live together. Unfortunately, our society is producing a minority of families that exhibit these traits. Emotional and physical neglect and abuse are becoming more common. Divorce is a likely outcome for many marriages.

Healthy families are not born with the arrival of a baby; they are carefully constructed by the individuals who are committed to creating them. As a mother and father, you each will bring your own separate histories to your children, as well as the history that you have shared as a couple. Your child's history and experiences will be closely woven with yours at first, but as the years go by, he will experience more on his own. These shared histories, and their resulting points of view, create a rich texture of ideas and perceptions that blend each life together to make a family.

Each person must learn to develop the capacity to see beyond his or her own point of view in order to understand where another family member is "coming from." When we limit ourselves to basing our relationships on our own histories and our own viewpoints, we make it impossible to "maintain the same love," as Paul exhorts believers to do in his letter to the Philippians, and thus fail to become "united in spirit, intent on one purpose."

Paul understood that relationships in the Lord cannot be built on a bedrock of "selfishness and empty conceit." Instead, in Philippians 2:1-4, he states that this can only result if "each one of you regard one another as more important than himself" (NASB). Without this foundation, marriages fail to fulfill who we are as men and women, and families dissolve into mere shadows of what the Lord intended them to be.

In her book *Lifelines: The Ten Commandments for Today*, Edith Schaeffer wrote: "God created people, male and female, with a capacity for oneness with each other, a fruitful physical oneness that would bring forth another generation of people. God created people with a capacity for oneness in working together, communicating verbally, exchanging ideas, doing creative works, eating together, and walking and talking with God in the cool of the evening. People were made in his image that they might have a three-way oneness, intellectually, spiritually, and physically on a horizontal level.

"People were made so that they could have a oneness with God spiritually, to love him, worship him, have communication with him, and to be able to seek his counsel and advice and help day by day. These two onenesses have been set forth to us in his Word, the Bible, and have to do with our knowing who we are and what will fulfill us. It is not a question of right and wrong, it is a question of what *is*. To act contrary to what *is* is to constantly bump one's head against a wall. We all do it in a variety of ways—and we all have bruises from the variety of walls we have hit!"

Enough has been said and written about roles and structure within the family, but it seems that speakers and authors often neglect that we need to be Christians first and foremost! As we draw closer to the Lord and follow him day by day, we learn how to behave toward others. His Word sets forth guidelines that we can use to direct our actions.

The style or manner in which we live out our interpretation of his Word varies from family to family. Yet the qualities that result from walking with the Lord are shared among all believers: honesty, humility, kindness, patience, gentleness, self-control, joy, peace, generosity, hospitality, and love are hallmarks of the Christian faith and can be expressed in an endless variety of ways. When we place too much emphasis on form, we can neglect substance. I have met many Christian families who have a "form of godliness" and yet lack many of these key qualities. We need to focus on caring for one another much more carefully!

The nitty-gritty of family life involves dividing up household tasks, learning to communicate effectively with one another, preparing meals, earning money, caring for children, and making decisions about how to spend time, money, and energy. While each family is unique, the Lord has provided a pattern for family life that gives us a framework to fill in with our individual talents and perspectives. We can never create a family structure as completely and perfectly as we might like, but if we hang in there, we will understand more and come closer to walking as Jesus walked.

Each day of family life involves countless opportunities for disagreement. Who will change this diaper? Do this load of dishes? Take out this bag of garbage? Are there male and female tasks? Should I work outside the home? What physician should we take the baby to? The possibilities are limitless!

The way that we cope with disappointments, disagreements, and everyday "disasters" influences our family relationships. The really big issues of our faith often are not as problematic as the little annoyances that distract us from our calling as wives and husbands, mothers and fathers. The way questions are asked and answered, such as, "How could you let this toast burn?" can be a key. We need to be careful that our questions don't become vehicles for expressing anger and hurtful put-downs to "get one's point across." Still, frequently we butt our heads up against walls and we get bruised. No matter how sincerely we attempt to live by God's Word, we cannot love perfectly.

What can we do about all those bumps and bruises then? First, we can accept them as inevitable. We can acknowledge our imperfection and be gracious about acknowledging it in others. Second, we can learn and practice the art of confession and repentance. We can say we're sorry and ask the Lord to enable us to change, even though many changes take place gradually! We can avoid some conflicts, and we can find ways to express anger fairly when situations arise faster than we can prevent them. Third, we can be faithful in forgiving others and refuse to nurture feelings of self-pity and dissatisfaction. The Lord gives us ways to live out his calling. We have concrete instructions that can work; the choice is ours.

As your family grows up, I hope you will find that the walls you run into come tumbling down when you call upon the Lord for help. I believe that if you make Jesus Christ your Lord and Master, as well as your Savior, you will find that growing closer to him will produce qualities in your life that will bring you meaning and ful-fillment in a world characterized by loneliness and alienation.

We serve an almighty, living God who has given us many promises upon which to base our faith and hope. What you say and do matter! We can directly affect the lives of others and, in so doing, demonstrate the truth of God's Word and the reality upon which it is based. Jesus has supplied us with a clearly marked map that shows us how to get to where we want to go. If we choose to follow him, we are on the side of life and freedom.

The next time you are tempted to "think small," try envisioning the larger picture instead. We need discernment to determine what really matters in respect to eternity, and thus avoid the pettiness that seems to burden so many families today. It makes it easier to do what the Lord requires of us when we keep in mind why we're here, where we're headed, and who we are as God's precious children.

The Lord loves each and every one of us as sons and daughters. Let us learn to better reflect what we've received from him within our own families while we are here.

"A new commandment I give unto you: Love one another. As I have loved you, so you must love one another. All men will know that you are my disciples if you love one another" (John 13:34, 35).

APPENDIX A
Family Nutrition Guide

Do you feel that your diet is healthful? You can find out whether it is or not by keeping a record of what you and your family eat for three days. You may then use the dietary guidelines and daily food guide included here to help you evaluate what was eaten and to determine the quality of your diet. (See page 44 for food amounts.)

SUGGESTIONS FOR HEALTHY EATING HABITS

1. Eat a variety of foods. Try to keep in mind that no single food contains all the nutrients in the amounts you need. Eat a variety of basic foods at each meal, using the daily food guide.

2. Maintain an ideal weight. While pregnant, do not go on a reducing diet. You may, however, increase physical activity through a program approved by your health care provider; eat less fat and fatty foods; eat less sugar and sweets; and omit the use of alcohol.

If you are within your normal weight range, eat and exercise to maintain your weight. Be sure you understand the growth curve of your de-

veloping baby, and accept the additional weight associated with your pregnancy. If you are 15 or 20 percent underweight when you become pregnant, increase your caloric intake beyond that recommended here and revise your exercise habits.

3. Avoid too much fat, saturated fat, and cholesterol. Moderation seems to be the key here. Choose lean meat, fish, poultry, dry beans, and peas as your protein sources. (While pregnant, eggs are an excellent source of protein that you don't need to restrict as much, since you are producing high amounts of estrogen.) Limit your intake of butter, cream, hydrogenated margarines, and coconut oil, as well as foods produced from these products. Trim excess fats from meats, skim the fat off stews and gravies. Broil, bake, boil, or grill your meats rather than frying them.

Cholesterol is one of the sterols (a lipid) manufactured in the body for a variety of purposes. It also is found in animal fats. Saturated fats are generally of animal origin and are solid at room temperature (exceptions: palm and coconut oils).

SATURATED/POLYUNSATURATED FAT CONTENTS*

Type of Fat/Oil	Calories in 1 Tbsp.	Total Fat Content (g)	Saturated Fat (g)	Polyunsaturated Fat (g)
Vegetable Fats				
Margarine, regular	100	12	2	3
Margarine, soft	100	12	2	4
Vegetable shortening	120	14	2	5
Whipped Topping	15	1	1	trace
Vegetable Oils				
Coconut	120	14	12	trace
Corn	120	14	2	8
Cottonseed	120	14	4	7
Olive	120	14	2	2
Palm	120	14	8	2
Peanut	120	14	2	5
Safflower	120	14	1	10
Soybean	120	14	2	8
Salad Dressing				
French, lo-cal	15	1	trace	trace
French, regular	65	6	1	3
Italian	85	9	2	5
Mayonnaise, light	65	6	1	3
Mayonnaise	100	11	2	6
Animal Fats				
Beef tallow	115	13	6	1
Butter	100	12	7	trace
Chicken	115	13	4	2
Half and half cream	20	2	1	trace
Heavy cream	80	6	4	trace
Lard	115	13	5	1
Sour cream	25	3	2	1

*Developed by Harriet Kohn, nutritionist

Substitutes for Saturated Fats

If the recipe calls for:	Use:
1 cup butter	1 cup margarine
1 cup evaporated whole milk	1 cup evaporated skim milk
1 egg (for thickening)	1 Tbsp. flour
1 cup sour cream	1 cup plain yogurt or mock sour cream (see recipe)
1 oz. baking chocolate	3 Tbsp. cocoa powder plus 2 tsp. margarine
1 Tbsp. cream cheese	1 Tbsp. mock cream cheese (see recipe)

Mock Sour Cream

2 Tbsp. skim milk or ⅓ cup buttermilk
1 Tbsp. lemon juice
1 cup lowfat cottage cheese

Mix all ingredients in blender or food processor until smooth.
Yield: 1¼ cups

Mock Cream Cheese

1 cup lowfat cottage cheese
4 Tbsp. margarine
1 Tbsp. skim milk

Mix all ingredients in blender or food processor until smooth.
Yield: 1¼ cups

High consumption of saturated fats may tend to raise blood cholesterol. Polyunsaturated fats are generally of vegetable origin and are liquid at room temperature. An increase in polyunsaturated fats over saturated fats tends to lower blood cholesterol. Monounsaturated fats have no effect on blood cholesterol. Two examples of monounsaturated fats are peanut and olive oils.

4. Eat foods with adequate starch and fiber. As you reduce your intake of caloric fats, you should increase your intake of calories from starches, called complex carbohydrates, in order to supply energy. Select those foods that are also good sources of fiber, such as whole grain breads and cereals, fruits and vegetables, beans, peas, and nuts.

5. Avoid too much sugar. Exposure to sugar on a frequent basis promotes dental decay. In addition, sugars are relatively high in calories compared to the nutrients they contain, making them low in "nutrient density." Limit your use of sugars and foods containing sugar. Select fruits that are fresh or canned without sugar.

6. Limit your use of sodium. Sodium is a factor associated with high blood pressure. It is estimated that about 20 percent of all Americans react unfavorably to sodium. At this time, there is no test to determine who is sodium sensitive and who isn't. Table salt consists of about 40 percent sodium, so it is prudent to not add salt at the table. Also, use little salt in cooking and limit your intake of salty foods.

HIDDEN SUGAR IN COMMON FOODS

FOOD	SERVING SIZE	TSP. OF SUGAR PER SERVING
Chocolate bar	1 average	15
Chocolate cake	1/12 cake (2 layers with icing)	7
Marshmallow	1 average	1½
Angel food cake	1/12 cake	6
Plain doughnut	3" diameter	4
Brownie	2" × 2" × ¾"	3
Ice cream	½ cup	5–6
Sherbet	½ cup	6–8
Apple pie	⅙ medium pie	12
Cherry pie	⅙ medium pie	14
Pumpkin pie	⅙ medium pie	10
Ginger ale	12 oz.	7
Sweetened soda pop	12 oz.	10

A Salt-Free Seasoning Alternative

2 Tbsp. onion powder
1 Tbsp. garlic powder
½ Tbsp. basil
1 Tbsp. paprika
2 Tbsp. parsley flakes

Combine spices together and blend well. You can use different proportions of ingredients depending on personal preference.

7. Drink alcohol only in moderation. Alcohol is very high in calories and low in nutrients. When pregnant, it is wise not to drink at all due to its link to birth defects. More than two drinks daily when you are not pregnant is inadvisable.

8. Limit caffeine intake during pregnancy and lactation. Caffeine is a mild stimulant. According to the FDA, it can cause insomnia, nervousness, irritability, anxiety, and disturbances in heart rate and circulation. While moderate amounts of caffeine can improve endurance, a U.S. Army study showed that the most beneficial amount was about two milligrams per pound of body weight. With an intake beyond this, the advantages of caffeine were nearly eliminated. A 150-pound person would need about twelve ounces of coffee to consume two milligrams per pound.

(NOTE: The first seven guidelines are based on those provided by the U.S. Dept. of Agriculture and the U.S. Dept. of Health.)

DAILY FOOD GUIDE

Food can serve a variety of purposes: to satisfy hunger, for distraction, a social activity's focus . . . but a woman who is pregnant or breast-feeding needs to eat! The nutritional requirements of pregnancy and lactation can draw one's energy reserves quickly and the fetus or baby who must rely on the mother for growth is affected by what she eats. Eating well is a vital component of a healthy life-style for both mothers and their children.

Keep in mind that in order for a meal or snack to produce satiety (the feeling of the absence of hunger), a meal should include:

—fiber (or bulk)
—carbohydrates
—protein and, not so surprisingly:
—fat.

The following list of foods can be considered as a "raw ingredients" chart. By combining these items creatively, you will find that mid-morning, mid-afternoon, and before-bed snacks, in addition to your meals, will keep your energy up without tipping the scales. Be sure to pay attention to the portion sizes and stock up on foods that appeal to both your appetite and your waistline.

Fruits. (All roughly equal 10 gm. carbohydrates and 45 calories.) Fruits contribute vitamins, min-

SOME FOODS AND DRUGS THAT CONTAIN CAFFEINE

FOODS AND DRUGS	MILLIGRAMS OF CAFFEINE PER SERVING
Coffee, 1 cup	250 mg.
Mountain Dew, 12 oz.	83 mg.
Cola, 12 oz.	65 mg.
Excedrin, 1 tablet	64 mg.
Tea, 1 cup	46 mg.
Midol, 1 tablet	32 mg.
Chocolate bar	25 mg.
Hot cocoa	10 mg.
Decaffeinated coffee	3 mg.

erals, fiber, and carbohydrates to the diet. Eat the washed skins of many fruits to increase your intake of fiber. Nearly all fruits are low in fat and none contain cholesterol. The body can make better use of the iron from food when it is eaten with a source of vitamin C at each meal.

Apple, 1 small
Apple juice, ⅓ cup
Applesauce (unsweetened) ½ cup
+Apricot halves, dried, 4
+Apricots, fresh, 2 medium
Banana, ½ small
Berries (unsweetened)
    Blackberries, ½ cup
    Blueberries, ½ cup
    *Raspberries, ½ cup
    *Strawberries, ¾ cup
Cherries, 10 large
Cider, ⅓ cup
Dates, 2
Figs, dried, 1
*Grapefruit, ½
*Grapefruit juice, ½ cup
Grapes, 12
Grape juice, ¼ cup
Melon
    + *Cantaloupe, ¼ small
    *Honeydew, ⅛ medium
    Watermelon, 1 cup
+ *Nectarine, 1 small
*Orange, 1 small
*Orange juice, ½ cup
*Papaya, ¾ cup
+ Peach, 1 medium
Pear, 1 medium
Pineapple, ½ cup
Pineapple juice, ⅓ cup
Plums, 2 medium
Prunes, 2 medium
Prune juice, ¼ cup
Raisins, 2 Tbsp.
*Tangerine, 1 medium

(* Vitamin C source)   (+ Vitamin A source)

Vegetables. (½ cup contains about 56 gm. carbohydrates, 2 gm. protein, and 25 calories.) Vegetables contribute vitamins, minerals, and fiber to the diet. Some vegetables are also a significant source of carbohydrates, classifying them as a bread exchange. Vegetables are very low in fat and none contain cholesterol.

*Asparagus	Green pepper	+ *Turnip
Bean sprouts	Greens	Mushrooms
Beets	+ *Beet	Okra
*Broccoli	Chard	Onions
*Brussel sprouts	+ *Collards	Sauerkraut
*Cabbage	Dandelion	String beans
Cauliflower	+ *Kale	*Tomatoes and juice
Celery	Mustard	V-8 juice
Eggplant	+ *Spinach	Zucchini

The following vegetables contain 15 calories or less per serving:

Chicory	Escarole	Radishes
Chinese cabbage	Lettuce	+ Watercress
Cucumber	Parsley	
Endive	Pickles, dill	

Breads and Cereals. (1 serving contains about 15 gm. carbohydrates, 2 gm. protein, and 70 calories.) Whole grain and enriched breads and cereals are important sources of B vitamins, iron, protein, and carbohydrates. Whole grain products also contribute magnesium, folacin, and fiber to the diet.

Bread, 1 slice:
White (including French and Italian)	Pumpernickel Raisin
Whole wheat	Bagel, small, ½
Rye	

Crackers
Arrowroot, 3	Pretzel Thins (sticks), 25
Graham, 2 squares	Ry-Krisp, 3
Matzo (4"×6"), ½	Saltines, 6
Oyster, 20	Soda (2½" square), 4

English muffin, ½
Plain bread roll, 1

Hot dog bun, ½
Hamburger bun, ½
Dried bread crumbs, 3 Tbsp.
Tortilla, 6"
Muffins, bran or corn, equal 1 bread and 1 fat
   (about 105 cal.)
Cereal
  Bran flakes, ½ cup
  Ready-to-eat cereal, unsweetened, ¾ cup
  Puffed cereal (unfrosted), 1 cup
  Cooked cereal, ½ cup
  Cooked pasta, ½ cup (spaghetti, macaroni,
    noodles)
  Popcorn, unbuttered, 3 cups
  Cornmeal, dry, 2 Tbsp.
  Flour, 2½ Tbsp.
  Wheat germ, ¼ cup

Meats, Cheeses, and Nuts. (1 oz. of any of these equals about 7 gm. protein, 3–5 gm. fat, and 55–75 calories.)

Protein. This group is high in protein, phosphorus, vitamins B_6, B_{12} and other vitamins and minerals. B_{12} is only found in foods of animal origins. Some of these foods are higher in certain nutrients: red meats and oysters, zinc; liver and eggs, vitamin A; dry beans, peas, and nuts, magnesium. Meats, fish, and poultry are all good sources of hemeiron, a type of iron well absorbed and utilized by the body.

Poultry cooked without skin, 1 oz.
Fish, fresh, frozen, or canned, 1 oz.
Lowfat cottage cheese, ¼ cup
Mozzarella or Farmer's cheese, 1 oz.

U.S. RECOMMENDED DAILY ALLOWANCES (U.S. RDA)

VITAMINS, MINERALS, AND PROTEIN	UNIT OF MEASUREMENT	ADULTS AND CHILDREN 4 OR MORE YEARS OF AGE	INFANTS UP TO ONE YEAR	CHILDREN 1–4 YEARS OF AGE	PREGNANT OR LACTATING WOMEN
Vitamin A	International Unit (I.U.)	5,000	1,500	2,500	8,000
Vitamin D	"	400	400	400	400
Vitamin E	"	30	5.0	10	30
Vitamin C	Milligrams (mg)	60	35	40	60
Folic Acid	"	0.4	0.1	0.2	0.8
Thiamin	"	1.5	0.5	0.7	1.7
Riboflavin	"	1.7	0.6	0.8	2.0
Niacin	"	20	8.0	9.0	20
Vitamin B_6	"	2.0	0.4	0.7	2.5
Vitamin B_{12}	Micrograms	6.0	2.0	3.0	8.0
Biotin	Milligrams (mg)	0.3	0.5	0.15	0.3
Pantothenic Acid	"	10	3.0	5.0	10
Calcium	Grams (g)	1.0	0.6	0.8	1.3
Phosphorus	"	1.0	0.5	0.8	1.3
Iodine	Micrograms	150	45	70	150
Iron	Milligrams (mg)	18	15	10	18
Magnesium	"	400	70	200	450
Copper	"	2.0	0.6	1.0	2.0
Zinc	"	15	5.0	8.0	15
Protein	Grams (g)	45	18	20	+30

Parmesan cheese, 3 Tbsp.
Egg, 1
Peanut butter, 1 Tbsp.

Milk and Dairy Products. (1 serving of milk equals about 12 gm. carbohydrates, 8 gm. protein, a trace of fat, and 80 calories.) Milk and most dairy products are high in calcium. They also contribute riboflavin, protein, and vitamins A, B_1, B_6 and B_{12}. Some dairy products are fortified with vitamin D. Choose lowfat or skim milk if you wish to reduce calories and cholesterol in your diet.

Skim or nonfat, reconstituted, 1 cup
Powdered, ⅓ cup
Yogurt, made from skim milk, unsweetened, 1 cup

Buttermilk, made from skim milk, 1 cup
Lowfat milk or yogurt—add 1 fat serving to each
    for accurate calorie count
Ice milk, ⅓ cup

Fats. (1 serving equals about 5 gm. fat and 40 calories.)

Avocado, 4" diameter, ⅛
Bacon, crispy-cooked, 1 slice
Butter or margarine, 1 tsp.
Cream, light, 2 Tbsp.
Cream, sour, 2 Tbsp.
Cream, heavy, 1 Tbsp.
Cream cheese, 1 Tbsp.
French dressing, 1 Tbsp.

CALORIES OF FAVORITE FAST FOODS

McDonald's:		Enchirito	391
Egg McMuffin	352	Bellbeefer	243
Hot cakes with butter and syrup	472	Supreme	480
Hash browns	130	Super Supreme	590
Hamburger	257		
Cheeseburger	306	*Wendy's:*	
Quarter-pounder	418	Hamburgers:	
Quarter-pounder with cheese	518	Single	472
Big Mac	541	Double	669
Filet-O-Fish	402	Triple	853
French fries (small)	211	Single with cheese	577
Vanilla shake	323	Double with cheese	797
Sundaes:		Triple with cheese	1,036
Caramel	282	Chili	229
Hot fudge	290	Frosty, regular	391
Strawberry	229		
Pineapple	230	*Pizza Hut:*	
		Thin and crispy (2 slices):	
Taco Bell:		Cheese	340
Taco	159	Pepperoni	370
Tostada	206	Super-style cheese	410
Bean burrito	345	Super-style pepperoni	430
Beefy tostada	291	Standard pork/mushroom	380
Burrito Supreme	387	Supreme	400
Pintos 'n' cheese	231	Super Supreme	520

Calories of Favorite Fast Foods (cont.)

Thick and chewy (2 slices):			Breast	286
Cheese	390		Thigh	343
Pepperoni	450		*Original recipe dinner:*	
Super-style pepperoni	490		All white meat	604
Standard pork/mushroom	430		White and dark meat	661
Super-style pork/mushroom	500		All dark meat	643
			Extra crispy dinner:	
Burger King:			All white meat	755
Hamburger	293		White and dark meat	828
Hamburger with cheese	347		All dark meat	765
Doublemeat hamburger	413		NOTE: All dinners include 2 pieces, roll, mashed potato/gravy, coleslaw. White meat includes wing and breast. Dark meat includes drumstick and thigh.	
Doublemeat hamburger with cheese	519			
Whopper Jr.	369			
Whopper Jr. with cheese	424		Roll (without butter)	61
Whopper Jr. doublemeat	488		Coleslaw	122
Whopper Jr. doublemeat with cheese	543		Kentucky Crisp Fries	156
Whopper	631			
Whopper with cheese	740		*Long John Silver's Seafood Shoppes:*	
Whopper doublemeat	843		*Fish with batter:*	
Whopper doublemeat with cheese	951		2 pieces	409
Apple pie	250		3 pieces	613
Onion rings:			Peg Legs (chicken wing meat with batter [5 pieces])	514
Regular	266			
Large	331		Ocean scallops (6 pieces)	257
Chocolate shake	337		Treasure Chest (1 piece of fish and 3 Peg Legs)	467
Vanilla shake	336			
French fries:			Breaded oysters (6 pieces)	460
Regular	209		Breaded clams (5 oz.)	465
Large	359		Super Ocean Sandwich	554
Ham & cheese specialty sandwich	573		Fries	275
Chicken specialty sandwich	620		Hush puppies (3)	153
Roast beef specialty sandwich	644			
			Arby's:	
Kentucky Fried Chicken:			Roast beef	350
Original recipe chicken:			Beef 'n' cheese	450
Wing	136		Super roast beef	620
Drumstick	117		Junior roast beef	220
Breast	199		Swiss King	660
Thigh	257		Ham 'n' cheese	380
Extra crispy chicken:			Turkey	410
Wing	201		Turkey deluxe	510
Drumstick	155		Club	560

1. ½ cup vanilla yogurt (protein)
   1 small apple, cored and chopped (carbohydrate)
   4 walnut halves, chopped (fat)
   Mix and sprinkle with cinnamon.
   Glass of homemade lemonade (12 oz. water, juice of ½ lemon, and sweetener to taste)
2. Orange-Protein Drink (3–4 servings)
   1 6-oz. can frozen orange juice (carbohydrate)
   1 6-oz. can water
   ⅓ cup nonfat dry milk powder (protein)
   1 egg, optional (fat)
   ½ tsp. vanilla
   Put all in blender with 4–6 ice cubes; cover and blend until ice is crushed.
3. Strawberry Frostie (1 serving)
   1 cup skim milk (protein)
   ½ cup unsweetened frozen strawberries partially thawed (carbohydrate)
   2 Tbsp. nonfat instant dry milk powder (protein)
   ½ tsp. sugar
   ½ tsp. vanilla
   1 egg, optional (fat)
   Put all in blender; cover and blend about 30 seconds until smooth.
4. 1 bran muffin with margarine and a little honey (carbohydrate/fat)
   Orange sections
   Glass of milk (protein)
5. 1 baked potato (carbohydrate) with sour cream (fat)
   Sprinkle with Bac-O's or other topping.
   Glass of milk (protein)
6. Pizza Muffin
   ½ English muffin, toasted (carbohydrate)
   ½ Tbsp. chunky-style Italian sauce
   1 oz. shredded mozzarella cheese (protein)
   Slices of salami or pepperoni (protein/fat)
   Place under broiler until cheese melts, or microwave on high for about 35 seconds.
   Iced or hot tea
7. Lettuce Salad
   Combine greens, carrots, celery, green peppers, cucumbers, etc. (fiber). Sprinkle with 1 crumbled hard-boiled egg (protein) or 1 oz. shredded cheese (protein). Add 1 Tbsp. dressing (fat), Ry-Krisp (carbohydrate), and/or ¼ cantaloupe (carbohydrate).
   Glass of club soda or water
8. Chicken strips (protein), white or dark, deboned, sliced for munching
   3 cups popcorn (carbohydrate) with 1 tsp. melted butter (fat)
   Iced or hot tea
9. Bagel and cream cheese (carbohydrate/fat)
   10 toasted almonds (protein)
10. ½ cup creamed cottage cheese (protein/fat)
    2 pineapple slices (carbohydrate) or 2 pear halves
    Glass of water
11. 4 wheat crackers (carbohydrate) with 1 Tbsp. peanut butter (protein/fat)
    ½ grapefruit or ¼ cantaloupe
    Cup of Postum or tea
12. Carrot and celery sticks (fiber)
    Sour cream dip (fat)
    1 hard-boiled egg (protein)
    Glass of orange juice (carbohydrate/vitamin C)
13. 1 slice raisin bread, toasted (carbohydrate)
    1 tsp. margarine (fat)
    1 cup strawberries (carbohydrate/vitamin C)
    Glass of milk (protein)
14. ½ cup vanilla, lemon, or coffee-flavored yogurt (protein)
    2 graham cracker squares (carbohydrate)
    Spanish peanuts (fat)
    Iced or hot tea
15. 1 slice angel food cake (protein/carbohydrate) frosted with 1 Tbsp. whipped cream (fat)
    Cup of Postum or decaffeinated coffee
16. ½ cup chocolate chip ice milk (protein)
    1 small brownie (95 calories) 1¾" × 1¾" (carbohydrate) topped with light cream (fat)
    Tea or decaffeinated coffee

QUICKIES

- Celery sticks with cream cheese or peanut butter
- Fruit salad: Chop up a combination of bananas, apples, grapes, oranges, melons, berries, etc. Toss with a little lime or lemon juice.
- Grape-Nuts and yogurt
- Eggnog: Blend milk with an egg, sweetener, vanilla, and nutmeg
- Toast and peanut butter
- Apricot halves or raisins for fast energy
- Baked custard (protein, carbohydrate, and fat, all in one) or rice pudding
- Pudding made with skim or nonfat milk
- Cheese and crackers
- Refried beans with cheese melted on top, sprinkled with chili, garlic, and/or onion powder
- Avocado slices sprinkled with lime juice, and crackers
- Tuna or chicken salad on crackers
- Cream of mushroom, chicken, or potato soup, made with milk

SUGGESTED BODY WEIGHTS

HEIGHT (feet—inches)	MEN (pounds)	NON-PREGNANT WOMEN (pounds)
4'10"		92-115
4'11"		94-119
5'0"		96-122
5'1"		99-128
5'2"	112-141	102-131
5'3"	115-144	105-134
5'4"	118-148	108-138
5'5"	121-152	111-142
5'6"	124-156	114-146
5'7"	128-161	118-150
5'8"	132-166	122-154
5'9"	136-170	126-158
5'10"	140-174	130-163
5'11"	144-179	134-168
6'0"	148-184	138-173
6'1"	152-189	
6'2"	156-194	
6'3"	160-199	
6'4"	164-204	

NOTE: Height without shoes; weight without clothes.
SOURCE: H.E.W. Conference on Obesity, 1973

The recommended weight gain for women during pregnancy is twenty-five to forty pounds, depending on your weight before you became pregnant and your frame size. Dieting during pregnancy that restricts caloric intake to under 2,500 calories per day will not allow you to follow the RDA for food. The time to lose weight is *after* you've given birth and weaned your baby.

APPENDIX B

Cardiovascular Fitness

*C*ardiovascular or aerobic fitness is brought about through large muscle activity that is done rhythmically and continuously for a period of twenty to thirty minutes every other day. The heart and lungs must work to bring blood and oxygen to the working muscles, which results in an increase in breathing and pulse rates. Initially, the heart rate will be quite high. As the cardiovascular system adapts to the stress of exercise, the heart and lungs become more efficient, so that, after six weeks of aerobic exercise, the heart rate is lower and the breathing calmer. Check with your health care provider before beginning any exercise program, especially while you are pregnant.

There are many benefits to cardiovascular exercise. (See figure 1.) Since this type of exercise spares blood sugar, the blood sugar level is maintained and hunger is not experienced following exercise. Also, the energy level is increased by avoiding blood sugar fluctuations. This can help fight tension, alleviate depression, and increase feelings of well-being.

When muscle tissue is developed during aerobic exercise, fatty deposits are used as energy, thereby exchanging "fatty weight" for lean muscle weight. The body becomes firmer, leaner, and healthier.

Cardiovascular fitness also results in increased stamina so that your body can perform under stress without undue fatigue. Stimulation of the heart and lungs makes them stronger, enabling them to work more efficiently throughout the day and hopefully making them less likely to succumb to illness. The stress of labor will not be as hard on your body if you have participated in a cardiovascular fitness program during pregnancy.

DETERMINING YOUR TARGET HEART RATE (T.H.R.) AND RANGE

1. Subtract your age from the number 220 ($220 - 20 = 200$).

2. Figure out what 70 percent ($.70 \times 200 = 140$) and 85 percent ($.85 \times 200 = 170$) of this

subtracted number are. These two numbers make up your T.H.R. range.

3. You should stay between the 70 percent and the 85 percent range, called your target zone, for twenty to thirty minutes to achieve the full benefits of aerobic exercise. Stay at the lower end of your range or below while you are pregnant.

MAINTAINING YOUR PULSE RATE IN YOUR TARGET ZONE

Your workout consists of three equally important and distinct parts:

1. The warm-up period: Five to ten minutes of less strenuous exercise, which should include stretching movements. This provides for a gradual buildup in heart rate so that your cardiovascular system is not suddenly taxed. It is designed to prevent injuries and soreness as well.

2. The stimulus period: Exercise that is rhythmical and continuous for a twenty- to thirty-minute period, designed to keep your heart rate in your target zone. Periodic self-monitoring of your pulse is advisable. Do this by placing your first and second finger upon the large artery on one side of your neck and counting the number of beats over a six-second period. Multiply this number by ten to obtain your heart rate per minute (16 beats for 6 seconds $\times$ 10 = 160).

3. The cool-down period: For five to ten minutes at the end of your workout, you simply lessen the intensity of activity to allow your heart rate to dip to 120 beats per minute or below. If you suddenly stop exercising you might inadvertently trap all the blood within the muscles that have been working. This may result in poor circulation to your brain, heart, or intestines, causing dizziness, extra heart beats, and nausea.

It's best to choose one type of exercise (see figure 2) and stay with it for at least six weeks to become trained in that particular activity. Begin slowly and work up to your target zone over the six-week period, exercising three or four times weekly. After two or three weeks of exercise, you

OBSERVED BENEFITS OF AN EFFECTIVE EXERCISE PROGRAM
FIGURE 1

1. Increased mental alertness.
2. Improved memory.
3. Ability to study effectively and efficiently.
4. Ability to cope effectively with problems of stress.
5. Ability to communicate effectively.
6. Self-discipline leading to a healthier life-style.
7. Increased ability to affirm others.
8. Goals clarified to achieve greater spiritual development.
9. Increase in overall level of energy.
10. Decrease in the severity, duration, and frequency of illnesses.
11. Affirmation by others.
12. Ability to recognize feelings and to express them constructively.
13. Positive outlook on life.
14. Sense of well-being.
15. Self-confidence.
16. Sense of accomplishment.
17. Nutritional awareness.
18. Ability to use the relaxation response effectively.
19. Decreased or eliminated periods of anxiety or depression.
20. Improved coordination.

should notice improved physical fitness; after five or six weeks, the improvement should be significant. Your body will be more efficient, you may sleep more soundly, and feel less tired. (During late pregnancy and for six weeks after giving birth, avoid exercise that involves bouncing, hopping, and jumping.)

As your fitness level improves, you'll need to exercise with vigor if you wish to make further progress. Always be sure to keep your heart rate in the 70 percent to 85 percent range. Evaluate your program monthly, updating it as needed. Use the heart-rate profile sheet to record your progress.

WARNINGS

Exercising in hot weather or at higher altitudes may increase your heart rate very quickly. Under such conditions, be especially careful to monitor your heart rate frequently. Drink extra fluids on warm days. Also, you may find that the "average" values for determining your target heart rate were too high for you. Evaluate and adjust your program if any of the following occur within a twenty-four-hour period following your workout:

1. Nausea and/or vomiting. Too little oxygen to digestive tract caused by too vigorous a workout or too quick a cool-down. Exercise less vigorously, cool down gradually and for a longer period.

2. Extreme breathlessness, lasting longer than ten minutes after workout. Exercise is too taxing for your heart and lungs. Keep your heart rate at the lower end of your target zone. If symptoms continue, keep heart rate even lower. While exercising, you should be able to talk.

3. Prolonged fatigue lasting longer than twenty-four hours. Exercise is too strenuous. Keep your heart rate at lower end of target zone or below, increasing level gradually.

4. Side stitch. Caused by too little oxygen. Take deep breaths, exhaling slowly. Lean forward to press pelvic organs up against your diaphragm.

5. Charley horse or muscle cramps. May be due to muscles unaccustomed to the activity reacting to strenuous exercise. Take a warm bath to eliminate waste products that build up on muscles and exercise less vigorously the next time.

6. Pain in calf muscles, which only occurs during periods of heavy exercise. Can be caused by exercising on hard surfaces, deconditioned muscles, or poor circulation to the legs. Use thick, solid shoes and heavy socks. Cool down slowly. Cramps should disappear after a couple of sessions. If not, then circulation is more likely to be the cause of this problem. Consider switching to another form of exercise, such as swimming rather than jogging.

7. Shin splints. This pain on the front and/or sides of your calves is caused by inflammation of connecting tissue, or muscle tears. Work out on softer surfaces, wear thicker, more solid shoes, or change to an activity that puts less demand on your lower legs.

8. Inability to sleep (which did not exist before you began working out). You are probably exercising too vigorously. Stay at lower end of target range or just below. Gradually work toward remaining in the target zone.

9. Flare up of gout or arthritic condition in joints (knees, ankles, hips, or toes). This is usually due to trauma in regions that are already vulnerable. You can apply remedies that may have helped in the past. Rest and delay returning to your program until the condition subsides, and wear adequate shoes. Begin at the lower end of your target range when you return to your program.

10. Dizziness, incoordination, confusion, light-headedness, cold sweats, pallor, glassy stare, blueness, or fainting. Your workout is too vigorous, resulting in a lack of oxygen to the brain. Rather than cool down, lie flat with your legs elevated, or put your head between your

knees while sitting until the problem passes. Talk to your doctor before resuming your activity.

11. Abnormal heart action. Sudden burst of rapid heart beats, persistent rapid beats five to ten minutes after exercising, irregular pulse, jumpy or fluttery pulse, or sudden slow pulse may or may not be dangerous and should be checked by your physician.

12. Pain or pressure in the center of your chest, arm, or throat due to exercise. If you experience this either during or after exercise, it may be a problem and you should see your doctor before resuming your program.

SELF-CHECK QUIZ

Ask yourself these questions periodically:

1. Am I including adequate warm-up and cool-down periods?
2. Do I exercise on at least three nonconsecutive days per week?
3. Do I spend at least twenty minutes in my target zone?
4. Do I avoid all warning symptoms?
5. Am I adjusting the rate and patterns of my exercise program to fit the special needs of pregnancy and postpartum?

FIGURE 2   THE CARDIOVASCULAR FITNESS TRAINING PATTERN

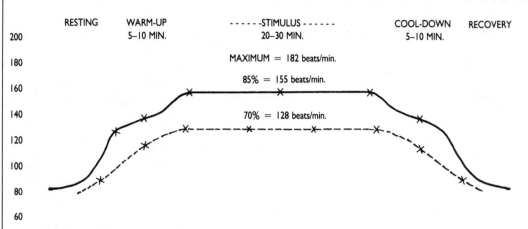

X = take pulse while slowly moving immediately following exercise
— = nonpregnant
--- = pregnant
Examples of aerobic activity to build up to:
 Cycling: 11–13 miles per hour (m.p.h.)
***Walking:** 5 m.p.h.
 Jogging: 5 m.p.h.
 Aerobic dancing
 Rope skipping: Work up to 70–80 steps per minute, alternating feet.
 Stair climbing: 10 steps—work up to 8 round trips per minute, using banister. May be done
                     for 11 minutes 5 times per week.
***Swimming:** 600 yards in 13 minutes.

*Ideal forms of aerobic exercise during pregnancy.

Summary of Obstetric Procedures and Medications

*I*t is always wise to review the more common obstetrical procedures and drugs as you prepare for your own obstetrical care. This will insure your ability to give your physician or health care provider "informed consent." This term, a legal medical concept, implies that the patient has been provided with understandable information that will enable her to decide whether or not to allow a health care provider to perform a certain procedure.

The following procedures and drugs are currently used throughout the United States. Each has its own indications for use, benefits, and risks. If you have any concerns or questions, your health care provider should be able to discuss them with you, and give you additional information.

DIAGNOSTIC PROCEDURES

AMNIOCENTESIS

This procedure involves the withdrawal of amniotic fluid from the uterus to gather any of the following information before the baby's birth:

Age of the fetus, detected from the examination of discarded skin cells in the fluid.

Sex of the fetus, determined from the presence of the sex chromosomes in discarded skin cells.

Fetal lung maturity, indicated by the ratio of the substances called lecithin and sphingomyelin present in the fluid. This ratio is a direct indication of fetal age and is especially important when planning an elective cesarean section.

A chromosome count can be made from examination of discarded skin cells, which can detect the absence or presence of a number of genetic syndromes.

The chromosome makeup can show disorders resulting from abnormal or missing enzymes.

Bilirubin content, important in determining whether an Rh-positive baby within an Rh-negative mother needs a blood transfusion while still in the uterus, or if labor should be induced because continued presence in the uterus has become too dangerous to the fetus.

Gas content of the amniotic fluid can be measured to tell whether the baby's oxygen supply is adequate.

Some benefits: It provides parents who are at risk of having a child with genetic abnormalities with means of determining whether certain abnormalities exist. However, abortion, or "pregnancy termination," is offered as a solution in the event of abnormalities. The National Institute of Health book *Antenatal Diagnosis* points this out clearly:

> *It is critical to note the pivotal "permissive role" played by the liberalization of abortion statutes in the late 1960s, which facilitated greatly the growth and utilization of amniocentesis and prenatal diagnosis services as a meaningful reproductive alternative. (U.S. Department of Health, Education, and Welfare, Bethesda, MD, April 1979.)*

Another benefit of amniocentesis is that it may determine the lung maturity of the fetus if medical reasons exist which require the baby to be born when gestational age is uncertain.

Possible risks: Theoretical possibility of risks to the mother include intrauterine bleeding and infection within the amniotic fluid. (This risk is about one percent.) Risk of injury to the fetus from the needle or from a resulting miscarriage is also around one percent.

The culture of fetal cells or analysis of the fluid may not be successful, and, in the case of undiagnosed twins, the results pertain to only one of the twin pair.

Many Christian parents who would not choose to abort after an amniocentesis may be exposing the pregnancy to unnecessary risks.

ULTRASOUND SCAN

Ultrasound is the use of sound waves beyond the range of hearing to display anatomical outlines. It provides diagnosis of early pregnancy; assessment of fetal growth and age; localization of the placenta; identification of multiple gestation; diagnosis of fetal death or confirmation of fetal life, attitude, and presentation; guidance for amniocentesis; detection of certain fetal abnormalities; fetal breathing effort and measurement of fetal heart tones (Doppler ultrasound).

Some benefits: To aid in the diagnosis of the above conditions, and to guide medical treatment and management of pregnancy and birth.

Possible risks: At this time, ultrasound diagnosis seems relatively safe, but this may be due to the fact that its long-term biological effects have yet to be adequately studied. The National Institute of Health has recommended that ultrasound be used only when medically indicated.

URINE ESTRIOL COLLECTION AND MEASUREMENT

Estriol is a form of the hormone estrogen, which is produced in high levels during late pregnancy. It is excreted in the urine, which can be collected for a twenty-four-hour period and measured for estriol levels. The production of estriol is an indicator of placental function and fetal well-being. Some common indications for urinary estriol monitoring include diabetes, high blood pressure (chronic or induced by pregnancy), poor previous obstetric history, postmaturity, eclampsia, and toxemia.

Some benefits: The ability to obtain information on the condition of the fetus and placenta, and direct obstetrical management when complications of pregnancy arise.

Possible risks: None are known, other than possible errors that could occur in testing procedures.

OXYTOCIN CHALLENGE TEST (OCT)

This test provides a way to assess how the mother and fetus would react to labor by conducting a "trial run." Labor is simulated through the administration of an intravenous drip of oxytocin, the hormone that contracts the uterus during birth. Uterine contractions and fetal heart rate patterns are recorded on an electronic fetal monitor (see following discussion). The fetal heart rate is studied as it responds to the contractions of the uterus. A negative test may indicate that the fetus would be adversely affected by the stress of actual labor, helping to determine whether a vaginal or surgical means of birth is in the best interest of the baby.

Common indications for administering the OCT include high blood pressure, diabetes, toxemia, low urinary estriol levels, possible postmaturity, and suspected intrauterine growth retardation.

Some benefits: It provides a controlled setting for determining whether the fetus and/or the mother might respond adversely to actual labor.

The mother can use her trial labor, if it was medically indicated, to practice her skills for coping with labor. (This, however, is not a reason in itself to attempt actual uterine stimulation!)

Possible risks: Slight possibility of a false positive OCT. There also is a theoretical possibility that the strength and length of induced contractions, with resulting shorter rest periods, create stress that the OCT records when actual labor may not create the same degree of stress.

NONSTRESS TESTING (NST)

The basis for the NST to evaluate fetal well-being is the assumption that the normal fetus produces characteristic fetal heart rate (FHR) patterns. One type of NST measures the FHR by using the external electronic fetal heart monitor without additional stimulation of the uterus or fetus. This provides a readout of the FHR over a period of time, which can be examined for unusual changes.

Another type of NST uses an auditory stimulus to arouse the fetus. Fetal activity is provoked with sound waves (2,000 cycles per second of pure tone), which are amplified and conducted by a small speaker attached to the mother's lower abdomen.

Some benefits: Use of either of the NSTs may eliminate the need for an OCT, which is more expensive and takes more time. Also, use of the NST can provide valuable information to guide medical management of the pregnancy, especially when the OCT is inadvisable.

Possible risks: Additional studies are needed to confirm the reliability of the second method of nonstress testing.

DAILY FETAL MOVEMENT COUNT (DFMC)

Some investigations have reported a significant decrease in fetal movement before an episode of fetal distress. The DFMC can be studied in various ways. Fetal movements may be counted by mothers for a twelve-hour period or during intervals throughout the day.

Some benefits: It's inexpensive, it's available outside of a clinical area, and it's easy for a woman to do herself.

Possible risks: Further studies are needed to confirm the value of this test in specific situations, and a mother may become overly anxious about the absence of fetal movements, which normally decrease in late pregnancy.

MATERNAL BLOOD STUDIES

A number of conditions pertaining to the well-being of the fetus can be detected by studying a variety of enzymes, hormones, and antibodies present in the mother's blood. There is no apparent risk associated with the procedures used for obtaining blood for these studies.

ELECTRONIC FETAL HEART MONITORING (EFM)

Continuous fetal heart monitoring before and/or during labor provides information on the condition of the fetus by tracing fetal heart patterns electronically. There are two modes of EFM. The "external mode" uses external transducers (leads), which are strapped on to the mother's abdominal wall. These measure the fetal heart rate (FHR) and the uterine activity. The "internal mode" uses a wire electrode that is inserted into the scalp of the fetus (just under the skin), which measures the FHR, and a catheter placed in the cervix or uterus measures intrauterine pressure.

In the case of the external mode, ultrasound or high frequency sound waves are emitted from the transducer, which measures the FHR. As the sound waves strike the moving surface of the fetal heart a signal is directed back to the transducer. The FHR is then printed out on a strip chart and a wave pattern is made visible on a screen (oscilliscope).

With the internal mode, an actual electrocardiogram of the baby is monitored. This is not subject to the many interferences that may limit the use of the external monitor.

Some benefits: A continuously recorded display of the fetal heart rate, variations between heartbeats can be seen and interpreted, and the quantity and quality of uterine activity is measured.

Possible risks: Accurate diagnosis of the fetal heart tracings requires skilled personnel. The skills of medical personnel in attendance are not always completely developed. Also, there may be a tendency on the part of some health care providers to "overdiagnose" when fetal distress is present. Normal fetal distress can be difficult to distinguish from fetal distress that is due to the poor condition of the fetus.

It is not fully known how normal labor is affected by physical restraint of the laboring woman and by her emotional responses to laboring while connected to a mechanical device.

Also, the use of the internal monitor can increase the risk of intrauterine infection.

FETAL BLOOD SAMPLING (FBS)
This measurement of the blood pH (acidity) when fetal distress is suspected, as depicted on the electronic fetal heart monitor, is not used alone in determining the condition of the fetus. In fact, this procedure is not routinely used since

many factors can influence the blood pH of the fetus. Also, it can be uncomfortable for the mother since she must lie on her back for several contractions while the sample is being taken.

Some benefits: When the EFM detects fetal distress, this test can provide further evidence that distress exists.

Possible risks: The maternal blood pH can influence the fetal blood pH. Laboratory errors in determining the pH level can occur. The pH can be a reflection of the stage of labor and the influence of the stress of intrauterine pressure. The sample can become contaminated with room air or amniotic fluid. The cause of the drop in pH may have been short-term in nature.

OBSTETRICAL PROCEDURES IN LABOR

ENEMA
Although this procedure certainly isn't confined to obstetrical use, it is a common practice as part of the obstetrical management of labor. An enema often is given to a mother upon admission to the hospital.

Some benefits: Empties the lower bowel so that the baby will have more room, and avoids the possibility of an involuntary bowel movement during the expulsion of the baby. Also helps to stimulate uterine activity.

Possible risks: Enemas may cause additional discomfort and anxiety for the mother. If you have already had several bowel movements in labor, an enema may cause some dehydration and can upset the electrolyte balance in your blood.

ROUTINE ADMINISTRATION OF INTRAVENOUS FLUIDS (IV)
An IV of glucose (basic sugar) and sterile water is routinely administered to a woman soon after admission to the hospital. Tubing is inserted into a vein, often at the back of the hand, to feed the liquid into the mother's circulatory system.

Some benefits: It provides energy and fluids

when food and liquid by mouth are not given. Other medications can be added readily to the fluid. An IV started early in labor may avoid additional discomfort when labor is more strenuous. Some physicians feel an IV is justified in case an emergency arises, at which time it might be difficult to properly start an IV.

Possible risks: An IV can be difficult to insert, and repeated attempts at insertion are irritating. Being hooked up to an IV influences mobility and can contribute to a feeling of illness rather than of wellness. (Note: It is possible to have a partial IV inserted, called a "Heparin lock," to "keep a vein open," but not be attached to IV tubes unless necessary.)

Some women are very anxious about needles; maternal anxiety can disrupt uterine activity in labor.

PARTIAL SHAVING OF THE MOTHER'S PUBIC HAIR

This procedure also is routine following admission to the hospital. It is not necessary since there is no clinical evidence to show that shaving reduces the chance of infection. If you arrange it ahead of time, you can simply clip the excess pubic hair from around the area of your vagina prior to going to the hospital if you wish. Any hair that remains is thoroughly washed with an antiseptic solution before the baby's birth.

Some benefits: To facilitate the repair of the episiotomy and to help with hygiene after the birth takes place.

Possible risks: Shaving the pubic hair may actually increase the possibility of infection in some cases.

AMNIOTOMY (ARTIFICIAL RUPTURE OF THE AMNIOTIC SAC)

During the first stage of labor, many physicians artificially rupture the membranes (amniotic sac) if they have not broken earlier. This is done by inserting a plastic, blunt-ended instrument into the vagina and through the opening of the cervix. The membranes are torn with the amnihook and fluid escapes from the uterus through the vagina. This procedure itself is normally painless. However, the uterus may be very irritable during the contractions that follow this procedure, creating a need for more strenuous application of pain-relief measures.

Some benefits: This procedure often changes the quality of uterine contractions, making them more intense. This can be of benefit when labor is progressing slowly. Amniotomy may be done to enhance the quality of the contractions if labor is to be started artificially. Also, if the internal EFM is to be used, the membranes must be ruptured.

Amniotomy may be performed to check for meconium staining, an indication of fetal distress.

Possible risks: The membranes provide a barrier to infection. Once they are broken, there is a greater possibility of infection occurring. The longer they have been broken, the greater the incidence of infection. Studies have shown that the amniotic fluid within intact membranes helps to evenly distribute the amount of pressure that the uterus applies to the baby's head. Consequently, the baby's head is more vulnerable once the membranes have broken. Further studies need to be done to evaluate what effects this has on the fetus. Rupturing the membranes can cause compression of the umbilical cord, which affects the fetal oxygen supply.

STIMULATION AND INDUCTION OF LABOR THROUGH PITOCIN-DRIP

Pitocin is the trade name given to a synthetic form of oxytocin, the hormone that causes uterine contractions in labor and during breast-feeding. Often the drip is metered through an "infusion pump," which measures the number of drips a mother receives per minute. Uterine contractions that are weak can be stimulated by

Pitocin. The uterus also can be provoked to contract through the administration of Pitocin.

Some benefits: If diagnostic tests reveal that a mature baby is overdue by three weeks or more, an induction can avoid complications associated with postmaturity of the baby and placenta.

If a medical problem exists for the mother, it is often important to begin labor before the problem becomes more hazardous to both the mother and her baby. If the membranes have ruptured spontaneously and labor doesn't begin within an optimal length of time, induction of labor can decrease the possibility of infection. (However, avoidance of vaginal exams can also help to decrease the risk of infection.) Pitocin can be used to stimulate contractions that are weak and are not opening the cervix.

Possible risks: Contractions can be longer and closer together under the influence of Pitocin. This can increase the risk of reduced oxygen supply to the baby. Because the contractions are often "harder" a mother may be more likely to request pain-relief medication, with resulting risks to the baby. Also, some studies have shown a slightly higher risk of jaundice in newborns born after Pitocin was given to the mother.

Pitocin can overstimulate the uterus if the dose is too great. This, in extreme cases, increases the risk of premature separation of the placenta, asphyxiation of the fetus, or uterine rupture.

Miscalculation of the baby's due date can lead to premature delivery of an infant, with a greater possibility of the baby having more medical problems than a full-term newborn.

EPISIOTOMY

An episiotomy is a surgical procedure a doctor or midwife may use to enlarge the vaginal outlet. It involves making an incision in the perineum, which is made up of body tissue located between the vagina and the rectum. An anesthetic may be administered to numb the area. The incision is sutured after the baby and placenta have been delivered.

Some benefits: If the perineum is inelastic or hasn't had time to stretch and distend gradually, an episiotomy will prevent uneven tearing of tissue. When a quick delivery is necessary due to fetal distress, an episiotomy can hasten the birth. Also, it is widely believed that the use of episiotomy helps to prevent relaxation of pelvic floor muscles since the baby's head may not be stretching the muscles for as long a period of time during the second stage of labor. If the baby's head is disproportionately large in comparison to the vaginal opening, an episiotomy will help to avoid accidental damage to the perineum.

Possible risks: Discomfort associated with the repair and healing of the episiotomy site can impair the comfort and ability of the mother to care for her newborn baby. Blood loss and infection are possible complications of this procedure.

All drugs used for anesthesia are potentially toxic. If injected into a blood vessel or given in too high a concentration, the medication will adversely affect the mother. (This is unlikely to happen if the anesthetic is administered by a competent health care professional.)

DORSAL/LITHOTOMY POSITION

In this position, a woman lies flat on her back with her legs propped up above her body in stirrups. It is a position that is used for several operative procedures other than childbirth. The dorsal/lithotomy position was adopted when women received general anesthesia during the second stage of childbirth and were asleep for the birth of their babies. Since all voluntary effort to enhance the baby's birth is impossible if a laboring woman is unconscious, her body had to be positioned to allow the physician to assume the active role in the baby's delivery. Forceps were commonly used to take the baby out of the mother's body.

If the mother is conscious and able to assume an active role in birthing her baby, she should use a position that allows her to utilize gravity and helps her to avoid the many negative effects of the dorsal/lithotomy position.

Some benefits: Gives the attending physician or midwife a clear view of the birth. Facilitates the use of forceps or vacuum extraction of the baby and the episiotomy procedure. If a spinal or epidural anesthetic has been administered and the legs cannot be voluntarily controlled, stirrups must be used.

Possible risks: Negatively affects the mother's urinary output, circulation, breathing, level of oxygen in the bloodstream, and alignment of bones in the pelvis. This position has been demonstrated to increase the length of labor and decrease the strength of uterine contractions. Also, there is a greater need to perform an episiotomy if the mother is flat on her back, since the baby is pressing down onto the lower part of the perineum and upon the rectum.

The mother cannot see what is happening and assumes a passive role in birthing her child. She cannot brace herself and use much voluntary effort to push during the second stage. There is an increased possibility that the placenta will be retained during the third stage of labor rather than spontaneously detaching from the uterine wall.

This position is not conducive to early breast-feeding and does not allow the mother to hold her baby comfortably after the birth has taken place.

LOW FORCEPS/VACUUM EXTRACTION

Obstetrical forceps are metal tongs used to rotate or deliver a baby if the mother is unable to birth the baby herself, or when the baby's condition requires a speedy delivery. Vacuum extraction is often used instead of forceps. It is a procedure used for the same reasons as forceps, but which involves applying suction through a disc placed upon the baby's head to bring the baby out of the mother's pelvis.

Some benefits: If there is fetal distress (fetal heart rate below 100 or over 160), obstetrical assistance can bring about a quicker delivery for

the baby. Also, when the mother is exhausted or unable to push because she has had a regional anesthetic, either of these procedures may be used to deliver the baby vaginally rather than by cesarean section.

Possible risks: These procedures establish a greater need for a larger episiotomy. (See page 192.) If forceps are used there may be reddish-colored bruise marks on the baby's temples or cheeks for a few days; rarely, temporary facial paralysis may result.

If vacuum extraction is used, it is common for the disc to leave a temporary bump on the baby's head where the disc was applied. Following vacuum extraction, there have been cases of fetal hemorrhage within the skull. Fortunately, this is rare.

OBSTETRICAL MEDICATION: A MEANS OF PREVENTION AND TREATMENT OF PAIN IN LABOR

Pain is not simply a sensory experience. It can become overwhelming, disrupting activity and leading to personality changes. Although the source of pain can be relatively the same from woman to woman, influences other than the actual stimulus modify pain perception. Reactions to a particular cause of pain not only vary among individuals, but vary in the same individual at different times. An individual's reaction is based on past experiences, present attitude, mood, emotions, judgment, the significance assigned to the stimulus, and the attitudes conveyed by the attendants.

There are many medications that can alter the experience of pain during childbirth. There is no single drug that is used routinely for all women. The methods used also vary between facilities. The use of medication during labor should be evaluated in terms of the mother's preference; the effects on the mother, baby, and labor process; the degree of pain relief desired; and the facility and the skill of the person administering the medication.

Each medication has its own specific indications and the limitations of a drug will vary under different conditions. Each has its own particular advantages and disadvantages. The medication used should cause the least degree of upset to the bodily functions of the mother, and should not pose unusual risk to her baby.

Since each woman reacts to the pain of labor in her own unique way, the need for medication varies from woman to woman. You should consider the effects and limitations of the drugs used during birth so that you can make a knowledgeable decision regarding their use when you are in labor.

Pain relief in labor is accomplished with the use of analgesia, which modifies the perception of pain, and anesthesia, which blocks sensation entirely. Analgesia may be psychological or chemical. Psychological modification of pain has been reviewed earlier. (See chapter 9.) Tranquilizers also are used in labor to relieve tension and anxiety.

Questions to ask your health care provider and childbirth instructor:

Comments by your health care provider:

DRUGS USED DURING CHILDBIRTH: BENEFITS AND POSSIBLE RISKS

Sedatives: Drugs that ease excitement by producing a restful feeling.

Barbituates: Phenobarbital (Luminal), amabarbital (Amytal), phentobarbital (Nembutal), butabarbital (Butisol), secobarbital (Seconal).

How they're administered: Orally or by IM (intramuscular) or IV (intravenous) injection.

Effect on mother: Reduces anxiety, possibly produces slowed heart rate, disorientation, lowered blood pressure (B.P.). Administration of one of these drugs may allow mother to sleep.

Effect on labor: In excessive doses given at too early a phase, labor may be slowed.

Effect on fetus/newborn: These drugs can accumulate in the baby's tissue. Lowered Apgar scores, poor sucking ability, slow respiration, decreased responsiveness, raised B.P., and/or poor muscle tone may be seen especially in infants whose mothers received one of these drugs within twenty-five minutes of the baby's birth.

Tranquilizers: Drugs that are capable of reducing anxiety and relieving tension. These drugs modify an individual's reaction to pain. They are frequently used along with narcotics.

Tranquilizers: hydroxyzine (Vistaril, Atarax), diazepam (Valium), promethazine (Phenergan), chlordiazepoxide (Librium), meprobamate (Equanil, Miltown), promazine (Sparine), prochlorperazine (Compazine), chlorpromazine (Thorazine).

How they're administered: Orally or by injection (IM or IV).

Effect on mother: Produces calm; may allow a mother to rest. Other effects may include dizziness, sleepiness, dry mouth, fluctuations in B.P., nausea, urine retention, disorientation.

Effect on labor: None known.

Effect on fetus/newborn: Effects may include possible impaired ability to maintain temperature and impaired behavior in the newborn lasting for several days. Since these drugs are usually used in combination with others, their effects are difficult to determine on an individual basis.

Analgesics: Agents that are capable of reducing, abolishing, or altering pain perception. They can benefit the fetus by stopping uncontrolled hyperventilation, which can be a mother's reaction to painful labor. They reduce the pain threshold so that an individual doesn't react to stimuli as being painful. When pain relief is inadequate, a mother may experience loss of confidence, fearfulness, anxiety and/or stress, which may affect her ability to cope with labor. Sensitivity to pain, rather than cervical dilation or the strength and frequency of contractions, is the cue for use of analgesics.

Narcotics: morphine, meperidine (Demerol, Mepergan), pentazocine (Talwin), alphaprodione (Nisentil).

How they're administered: By IV or IM injection. Nisentil may be given by subcutaneous injection.

Effect on mother: Feeling of separation between self and stimulus. Other effects may include depression, nausea, dry mouth, itchiness, dizziness, lowered breathing rate, raised B.P.

Effect on labor: Progress of labor may be slowed if given too early or it may become faster if given during the later part of the first stage (7 or 8 cm.).

Effect on fetus/newborn: Disorientation, less interested in mother's voice, lowered responsiveness, visual difficulties, bluish skin tone are all possible effects.

Anesthetics: Medications that completely block pain impulses by producing a loss of sensation. Can be given locally or regionally to numb a specific area, or if general anesthesia is used, it can cause a loss of consciousness. Effects on the mother, her baby, and the progress of labor vary greatly with the drug, the dosage, and the route of administration.

Anesthesia: procaine (Novocain), tetracaine (Pontocaine), chloroprocaine (Nesacaine), piperocaine (Metycaine), lidocaine (Xylocaine, L-caine, Seracaine), dibucaine (Nupercaine), mepivicaine (Carbocaine).

How they're administered:

Types:	Areas:
Pudendal block	Rectal/genital area
Paracervical block	Cervix
Caudal blocks	
Low spinal	Upper legs, lower pelvic area
Spinal block	Legs, lower pelvic area, may extend up to mid-chest
Saddle block	Area that would touch a saddle
Epidural block	Upper legs and pelvic area

Effect on mother: Possible drowsiness, restlessness, dizziness, lowered B.P., lowered heart rate, or toxic reaction.

Effect on labor: Possible stopping or slowing of labor if given too early. The most extensive blocks can interfere with the mother's ability to aid in the expulsion of the baby.

Effect on fetus/newborn: If fetal distress exists when drug is given, fetal depression may become complicated.

Other Anesthesia: prilocaine (Citantest), bupivicaine (Marcaine).

How they're administered: Local infiltration, perineum, lower vagina.

Inhalation Anesthesia: cyclopropane or trimethylene, ether, halothane (Fluothane), methoxyflurane, nitrous oxide, trichloroethylene (TCE, Trilene, Trimar).

How they're administered: By inhalation through nose and mouth. Results in loss of consciousness.

Effect on mother: May cause lowered breathing rate, changes in heart rate, changes in B.P., and irregular heartbeat. Can impair the functioning of digestive tract, liver, and/or uterus. Nausea, vomiting, depression, sleepiness, dizziness, disorientation, postpartum hemorrhage also are possible side effects of general anesthesia.

Effect on labor: Effect will vary with drug used. Contractions may be suppressed or may stop completely depending on the amount and the specific agent administered.

Effect on fetus/newborn: Baby must be delivered by cesarean section or forceps immediately following the administration of general anesthesia, thereby reducing the possibility of depression of the fetus and newborn.

Oxytocics: Agents that cause contraction of muscle fibers in mammary glands and uterine tissue used to stimulate or induce labor. Also used to prevent postpartum hemorrhage and to stimulate the let-down reflex when necessary for successful breast-feeding.

Oxytocics: synthetic oxytocin (Oxytocin, Pitocin, Syntocinon), ergonovine maleate (Ergotrate), methylergonovine (Methergine), sparteine sulfate (Spartocin, Tocosamine).

How they're administered: Through IV fluids, by IM injection, orally, or by nasal spray (for breast-feeding).

Effect on mother: Possible elevation or lowering of B.P., can cause strong contractions of longer duration, uterine rupture, nausea, headache, anxiety, swelling, vomiting, water intoxication.

Effect on labor: Quality labor can change dramatically with use of oxytocics, with contractions very quickly becoming stronger and longer. Oxytocics do not necessarily produce cervical dilation or progress of labor.

Effect on fetus/newborn: Can lead to lower oxygen in blood due to longer contractions and/or changes in heart rate.

APPENDIX D
What to Ask, Take, and Know

1. What to ask your physician or midwife about when she/he wishes to be contacted:
I am to call ＿＿＿＿＿＿＿at ＿＿＿＿＿ (phone no.) when my membranes rupture (yes or no), when contractions are lasting for ＿＿＿ seconds and are ＿＿＿ minutes apart. Other conditions about which I should notify my doctor/midwife:

2. What your health care provider will want to know:
This is ＿＿＿＿＿＿＿＿ . (I am in) (I think I am in) labor. The contractions I am having are ＿＿＿ seconds long, occurring about every ＿＿＿ minutes, and are (regular) (irregular). They started at ＿＿＿＿ (time). My membranes (are not) (may be) (are) leaking. I feel (describe how the contractions are affecting you): ＿＿＿＿＿＿＿＿＿ ＿＿＿＿＿＿＿＿＿＿＿＿ .

3. What to know about admission procedures:
(I am) (I am not) preregistered.
If not, I can get a preregistration form from
＿＿＿＿＿＿＿＿＿＿＿＿＿＿＿
＿＿＿＿＿＿＿＿＿＿＿＿＿＿＿ .
When in labor, I will go to＿＿＿＿＿＿
＿＿＿＿＿＿＿＿＿＿＿ hospital/center.
During business hours, I will go to ＿＿＿
＿＿＿＿＿＿＿＿＿＿＿＿＿＿＿ .
After ＿＿＿ P.M., I will go to ＿＿＿＿＿
＿＿＿＿＿＿＿＿＿＿＿＿＿＿＿ .
These areas are reached from ＿＿＿＿＿
＿＿＿＿＿＿＿＿＿＿ (street name).
Parking will be available ＿＿＿＿＿＿＿
＿＿＿＿＿＿＿＿＿＿＿＿ (location)
and costs ＿＿＿＿＿＿＿＿＿＿＿＿ .
I will be taken to labor and delivery on the ＿＿＿floor, in the ＿＿＿wing.

4. What labor aids to have with you (a possible list):
Your Bible; 2 pairs of clean, warm socks; sweet/sour lollipops for flavor; items for attention diversion; food for yourself and your labor partner; thermos with beverage; pocket

change; phone number list; corn oil or lotion for massage; tape recorder; cassette tapes of favorite music; hot water bottle for back. Also, breath spray or mouthwash; your own nightgown and pillows; Chapstick or lip gloss; camera; film; flash; birthday cake (freeze ahead) and candles. Also, clean seven-inch paint roller or two tennis balls for applying counterpressure to the lower back, and a watch with a second hand.

5. What to pack in your suitcase:
   Toothbrush, toothpaste, brush, comb, etc.; one clean nursing bra for each day you will be in the hospital (3) and nursing pads; reading materials, especially about breast-feeding and early parenting; birth announcements, stationery, pen; clean underwear, night clothes, robe, slippers (be sure to select garments that will facilitate nursing if you'll be breast-feeding); outfit and blanket in which to take your baby home (Baby will be dressed in hospital clothing during your stay, unless you desire otherwise); loose-fitting clothing for your return home; tape recorder and cassettes; packets of herbal teas, if desired; raisins and other dried fruits to help alleviate constipation.

6. What to ask about hospital procedures and alternatives (check those procedures that apply after discussing them with your physician or on your hospital tour):

   _____ Hospital gown/own nightgown
   _____ Check weight
   _____ Check blood pressure
   _____ Take temperature
   _____ Electronic fetal monitor/Amplified Stethoscope/Fetoscope
   _____ Blood specimen
   _____ Enema/Natural bowel movements
   _____ Mini-prep/No shaving of perineum
   _____ IV/Heparin lock
   _____ Vaginal exam (When? How often?).

7. As the labor companion, I:
   Will be able to remain with my wife/friend at all times; may be asked to leave (under what circumstances?); will be filling out admitting forms until asked to join my wife/friend.
   If I am asked to leave, a reasonable amount of time to complete the procedures is _____ minutes. If they do not call me by this time, I can check my partner's progress by speaking to _____ . The time to put on a gown will be _____ . I will ask _____ , if necessary, when to put on my scrub suit and mask for the birth.

8. What questions to ask about medications:
   If it becomes necessary for my health care provider to administer medication, what does she/he prefer to use and why? (Include your doctor's comments on what she/he prefers to use for vaginal and cesarean birth.):

   Record some of your feelings about using medication during labor and birth (What do you think will determine whether you use analgesia and/or anesthesia, if anything is used?):

   Medication Checklist—What to Ask:
   What is it?
   Why would I need it?
   How long will it affect me or my baby?
   What are the possible side effects?
   Is the dosage flexible?

9. Optional items to think about and discuss with health care provider:
   If available, what are the criteria for use of the birthing room? Birthing center? How does she/he feel about it? Is she/he comfortable with its philosophy?

Health care provider's comments:

Our preference:

Does your health care provider do episiotomies frequently? How often (percentage)? If not, is she/he familiar with the technique of perineal massage? When does she/he consider episiotomy to be useful? What anesthesia will she/he use?
Comments:

Preferences:

Does your health care provider practice gentle birth techniques?
Comments:

Preferences:

Would she/he deliver your baby in a position other than the lithotomy (reclining) position? Under what circumstances?
Comments:

Preferences:

Other questions, comments, and preferences: When do you hope to first breast-feed your baby?

Do you want uninterrupted contact with your baby?

What is the usual length of time for the baby to be in recovery before going to the nursery?

Will you be together as a family in the recovery room?
Comments:

Preferences:

Do you want rooming-in? Around the clock? When will it begin? What is the procedure? Can the father be with you overnight?
Comments:

Preferences:

Visiting hours at the hospital, and the people who may visit, are:

The typical length of stay after a vaginal birth is _____ . After a cesarean birth: _____ .
Comments:

Preferences:

APPENDIX E
Scriptural References

All Things Work Together for Good
Ecclesiastes 3:1-14
Romans 8:28

As a Woman in Travail
Psalm 48:6
Jeremiah 6:24; 13:21; 22:23; 30:6;
    49:24
Micah 4:9, 10

Attentiveness
Hebrews 2:1

Being One
Philippians 2:1, 2, 4

Blessings/Benediction
Hebrews 13:20, 21
James 1:17
1 Peter 4:6-11
2 Peter 1:5-9

The Body of Christ
1 Corinthians 12:18, 27

Breast-feeding
Isaiah 66:11

Childbirth
Genesis 3:16; 30:23, 24
Psalms 37:7a; 41:1, 2; 71:6; 125:1
Ecclesiastes 3:2
Isaiah 65:23; 66:9
John 16:21
1 Timothy 2:15

Children
Psalms 103:17; 112:1, 2; 115:13-15;
    127:3-5
Proverbs 10:1; 13:1; 17:6
Isaiah 44:2, 3
Matthew 19:14
Mark 9:36, 37
Ephesians 6:1
2 Timothy 3:14, 15

Children: Raising Them
Deuteronomy 6:6, 7
Psalm 78:1-8
Proverbs 1:8, 9; 2:1-5; 3:1-3, 11, 12;
    4:1-9; 6:20-22; 13:1; 22:6; 23:22-
    25; 29:15, 17
Colossians 3:21
Hebrews 12:9, 10

Comfort
Psalms 23:4; 119:76; 125:1; 145:18
Isaiah 61:2, 3; 66:13
Jeremiah 31:13
Romans 15:4
2 Corinthians 1:4, 5
2 Thessalonians 2:16, 17

Confidence
Psalm 27:3
Proverbs 3:26
Ephesians 3:12
Hebrews 4:16; 10:35
1 John 2:28; 3:21, 22; 5:14

Conscience-Cleansing
Hebrews 9:14

Creation
Psalms 8; 139:13-16
Isaiah 44:2

Discipleship: Its Cost
Matthew 13:44-46; 16:24-26

Encouragement
1 Thessalonians 4:18; 5:11
2 Thessalonians 2:16, 17
Hebrews 3:13; 10:25

Facing Trials
James 1:2-8
1 Peter 1:6, 7; 4:12-19

Faith
Matthew 17:20
Mark 11:22
Acts 3:16
1 Corinthians 16:13
2 Corinthians 5:7
2 Thessalonians 1:3-5
Hebrews 11:1

Family Relationships
Genesis 2:24
Psalm 128
Proverbs 5:18, 19; 14:1; 18:22; 31
Ephesians 5:31, 32; 6
1 Timothy 3:1-11
Titus 2:3-5
1 Peter 3:1-8

Friendship
Psalm 133
Proverbs 17:17
John 15:13, 15
1 John 4:7, 8

Gaining Aid
Psalms 5:1-3; 20:1, 2; 54:4; 77:1-6
Isaiah 41:10

Philippians 1:19
Hebrews 6:10
James 5:13

Gaining Power
Zechariah 4:6
Ephesians 3:16-19; 6:10

Giving Thanks
Psalms 30:12; 75:1; 116:17; 118:21;
   136:1-3, 26
1 Thessalonians 5:18

God's Greatness
Psalms 66; 71:14-24; 84; 92; 93; 95;
   96; 97; 99; 100; 101; 107; 111;
   113; 117; 118; 134; 135; 136;
   144; 145; 147

God's Love
Psalms 136; 145:8, 9
Jeremiah 31:3
Matthew 11:29, 30

God's Protection (See **Special Psalms**)

Good Gifts
Psalm 85:12
Matthew 7:11
James 1:17

Guidance
Psalms 25:5; 48:14; 73:21-28;
   119:105; 130; 143:10
Proverbs 3:6
Isaiah 45:3
John 16:13

Joy
Nehemiah 8:10
Psalms 5:11; 16:11; 20:5; 30:5, 11,
   12; 31:7; 40:16; 47:1, 6; 51:10-
   12; 52:9; 68:3; 70:4; 71:8, 14;
   81:1; 86:4; 89:16; 90:14; 91:4;
   100; 104:34; 118:24; 126:5;
   145:5
Proverbs 12:20
Ecclesiastes 2:26
Isaiah 35:10; 55:12; 61:10
Matthew 25:21
John 15:11; 16:24
Romans 5:11; 14:17; 15:13
Galatians 5:22
1 Thessalonians 5:16
James 1:2
1 Peter 1:8; 4:13

Labor (Work)
Psalms 127:1; 128:1, 2
Proverbs 10:16; 14:23

Isaiah 65:23
Matthew 11:28
1 Corinthians 3:8; 15:58
1 Thessalonians 1:3
Hebrews 6:10
Revelation 2:2

Making Plans
Proverbs 16:3, 9

Our Position in Christ
Romans 5:1-11
Hebrews 12:18-25

Peace
Psalms 4:8; 29:11; 34:14; 119:165
Proverbs 12:20
Isaiah 26:3; 54:10
John 14:27
Romans 5:1; 8:6; 14:17, 19
Galatians 5:22
Ephesians 2:14
Philippians 4:7
Colossians 3:15

Perseverance
Ephesians 6:11-18
1 Thessalonians 5:8
Hebrews 10:23-25; 12:1-12

Physical Training
1 Timothy 4:8

Prayer
Romans 12:12
Ephesians 6:18
Colossians 4:2
1 Thessalonians 5:17
James 5:16

Pregnancy
Psalms 51:5; 113:9; 138:8; 139:13-
   15
Ecclesiastes 11:5
Jeremiah 1:5

Protection
Deuteronomy 33:27
Psalms 91:9-15; 121:3, 5, 7; 145:20
Proverbs 12:21

Psalms to Highlight during Labor
Blessing — 67:1
Covering — 91
Creation — 8
Deliverance — 4; 142
Faithful Love — 117
God's Greatness — 145
Help — 63; 102:1, 2
Protection — 20; 121
Refuge — 16; 23
Rest — 62:1-4

Salvation — 18:1-6, 30
Savior — 27; 51:10-12; 61
Shelter — 61; 62 (esp. vv. 5-8);
   103:5

Purpose of Scripture
2 Timothy 3:16, 17

Responsibility (Parental)
Proverbs 13:22
Luke 11:17
2 Corinthians 12:14
Ephesians 6:4

Rest
Psalms 4:8; 63:6; 116:7; 131
Isaiah 30:15
Matthew 11:28

Sharing Our Worries
1 Peter 5:7

Special Psalms
Homage — 29
King of Glory — 24
Music — 33
Praise — 34; 47; 48; 56:10; 57:9;
   63:4; 64:10; 66:8; 67:3; 68:19,
   26, 32; 69:30, 34; 71:32; 72:19;
   79:13; 84:4; 92:1; 96:4; 103:20;
   106:5; 109:1, 30; 119:108, 175;
   145:3; 146:2; 147:1; 148; 150
Victory — 21; 47; 48

Strength
Psalms 29:11; 31:24; 73:26; 84:5;
   89:21
Isaiah 12:2; 30:15; 35:3; 40:30, 31
Jeremiah 16:19
2 Corinthians 12:9
Ephesians 3:16
Colossians 1:11
2 Timothy 4:17

Submission (to God's Will)
Luke 1:38

Thought Patterns
Philippians 4:6-8
Colossians 3:15-17

Trust
Psalm 37:3, 4

Two Together
Ecclesiastes 4:9-12
Song of Solomon 2:3-6; 8:7
Matthew 18:19, 20

Words
Proverbs 16:24
James 3

Worldly Philosophies
1 John 4:1-6

BIBLIOGRAPHY

BOOKS

Abouleish, E. *Pain Control in Obstetrics*. Philadelphia, PA: Lippincott, 1977.

Bean, C. A. *Methods of Childbirth*. New York, NY: Dolphin, 1973.

Billings, B. and Westmore, Ann. *The Billings Method: Controlling Fertility without Drugs or Devices*. New York, NY: Random House, 1980.

Blumenfeld, Samuel L. *The Retreat from Motherhood*. New Rochelle, NY: Arlington House, 1975.

Bonica, J., et al. *Advances in Pain Research and Therapy*. Vol. III. New York, NY: Raven, 1979.

Bonica, J. J. *Principles and Practices of Obstetrical Analgesia and Anesthesia*. Vols. I, II. Philadelphia, PA: Davis, 1967, 1969.

Bradley, R. *Husband-Coached Childbirth*. New York, NY: Harper & Row, 1965.

Brazelton, T. Berry. *On Becoming a Family: The Growth of Attachment*. New York, NY: Delacourte/Lawrence, 1981.

Brestin, Steve and Brestin, Dee. *Building Your House on the Lord: Marriage and Parenthood*. Wheaton, IL: Harold Shaw, 1980.

Brewer, Gail Sforza. *The Brewer Medical Diet for Normal and High-Risk Pregnancy*. New York, NY: Simon and Schuster, 1983.

Campbell, Ross. *How to Really Love Your Child*. Wheaton, IL: Victor Books, 1977.

Chard, T. and Richards, M., eds. *Benefits and Hazards of the New Obstetrics*. Lavenham, England: Lavenham Press, Ltd., 1977.

Cooper, Kenneth. *The Aerobics Program for Total Well-Being*. New York, NY: Evans, 1982.

Deutsch, Ronald M. *Realities of Nutrition*. Palo Alto, CA: Bull Publishing, 1976.

Dick-Read, G. *Childbirth without Fear*. New York, NY: Harper & Row, 1944.

Donovan, Bonnie. *The Cesarean Birth Experience*. Boston, MA: Beacon, 1978.

Ewy, Donna and Ewy, Roger. *Preparation for Breastfeeding*. New York, NY: Doubleday, 1975.

Ferguson, Marilyn. *The Aquarian Conspiracy: Personal and Social Transformation in the 1980's*. Los Angeles, CA: Tarcher, 1980.

Fraiberg, Selma. *Every Child's Birthright: In Defense of Mothering*. New York, NY: Bantam, 1977.

Gaskin, Ina May, et al. *Spiritual Midwifery*. Summertown, TN: Book, 1975.

Goldfarb, J. and Tibbetts, E. *Breastfeeding Handbook: A Practical Reference for Physicians, Nurses and Other Health Professionals*. Hillside, NJ: Enslow, 1980.

Gots, R. E. and Gots, B. A. *Caring for Your Unborn Child*. New York, NY: Bantam, 1979.

Gottschalk, W. *Problems and Risks of Obstetric Anesthesia*, in: *Risks in the Practice of Modern Obstetrics*. Aladjern S., ed., 2nd ed., St. Louis, MO: Mosby, 1975.

Graham, Harvey. *Eternal Eve—The History of Gynaecology and Obstetrics*. New York, NY: Doubleday, 1951.

Haire, D. *The Cultural Warping of Childbirth*. Milwaukee, WI: I.C.E.A., 1972.

Harrison, Helen. *The Premature Baby Book*. New York, NY: St. Martins, 1983.

Hazell, L. Dessez. *Common Sense Childbirth*. New York, NY: Berkley Medallion Books, 1976.

Hotchner, Tracy. *Pregnancy and Childbirth: The Complete Guide for a New Life*. New York, NY: Avon Books, 1976.

Howard, J. Grant. *The Trauma of Transparency*. Portland, OR: Multnomah, 1979.

Huggett, Joyce. *Two into One: Relating in Christian Marriage*. Downers Grove, IL: InterVarsity, 1981.

Jelliffe, D. and Jelliffe, E. F. P. *Human Milk in the Modern World*.

New York, NY: Oxford University, 1978.

Jones, Sandy. *Crying Baby, Sleepless Nights*. New York, NY: Warner, 1983.

Jordan, Brigitte. *Birth in Four Cultures: A Crosscultural Investigation of Childbirth in Yucatan, Holland, Sweden, and the United States*. Montreal: Eden, 1978.

Kippley, S. *Breastfeeding and Natural Child Spacing*. New York, NY: Penguin, 1975.

Kitzinger, S. and Davis, J. A., eds. *The Place of Birth*. New York, NY: Oxford University, 1978.

Klaus, M. H. and Kennell, J. H. *Maternal-Infant Bonding*. St. Louis, MO: Mosby, 1976.

La Leche League. *The Womanly Art of Breastfeeding*. 3rd ed., New York, NY: Plenum, 1981.

Lamaze, Fernand. *Painless Childbirth*. New York, NY: Pocket Books, 1965.

Lamott, K. *Escape from Stress*. New York, NY: Putnam, 1975.

Lawrence, R. *Breastfeeding—A Guide for the Medical Profession*. St. Louis, MO: Mosby, 1980.

Leboyer, Frederick. *Birth without Violence*. New York, NY: Knopf, 1975.

Leifer, M. *Psychological Effects of Motherhood—A Study of First Pregnancy*. New York, NY: Praeger, 1980.

Lewis, C. S. *The Problem of Pain*. New York, NY: Macmillan, 1962.

MacDonald, George. *At the Back of the North Wind*. Elgin, IL: David C. Cook, 1979.

McCaffrey, Margo. *Nursing Management of the Patient with Pain*. 2nd ed., Philadelphia, PA: Lippincott, 1979.

McNall, L. K. and Galeener, J. T., eds. *Current Practice in Obstetric and Gynecologic Nursing*. Vol. II. St. Louis, MO: Mosby, 1978.

Meichenbaum, D. *Cognitive Behavior Modification: An Integrative Approach*. New York, NY: Plenum, 1977.

Melzack, Ronald. *The Puzzle of Pain.* New York, NY: Basic, 1973.

Meyer, Linda D. *The Cesarean (R)evolution.* Edmonds, WA: Franklin, 1981.

Milburn, J. and Smith, L. *The Natural Childbirth Book.* Minneapolis, MN: Bethany, 1981.

Milinaire, Catherine. *Birth.* New York, NY: Crown, 1974.

Mills, Nancy. "The lay midwife," *Safe Alternatives in Childbirth.* David Stewart and Lee Stewart, eds., Chapel Hill, SC: NAPSAC, 1977.

Montagu, Ashley. *Touching.* New York, NY: Perinatal/Columbia University, 1971.

Myles, Margaret. *Textbook for Midwives.* 8th ed., New York, NY: Churchill-Livingston, 1975.

Narramore, Bruce. *An Ounce of Prevention.* Grand Rapids, MI: Zondervan, 1978.

_____ . *Parenting with Love and Limits.* Grand Rapids, MI: Zondervan, 1978.

_____ . *Help! I'm a Parent!* Grand Rapids, MI: Zondervan, 1972.

_____ . *You're Someone Special.* Grand Rapids, MI: Zondervan, 1978.

Navigator Studies. *God's Design for the Family.* Books 1-4. Colorado Springs, CO: NavPress, 1980.

Newton, Niles. *Maternal Emotions.* New York, NY: Hocher, 1955.

_____ . *The Family Book of Child Care.* New York, NY: Harper & Row, 1957.

Nilsson, Lennart. *A Child Is Born.* New York, NY: Delacourte/Lawrence, 1977.

Noble, Elizabeth. *Childbirth with Insight.* Boston, MA: Houghton-Mifflin, 1983.

_____ . *Having Twins.* Boston, MA: Houghton-Mifflin, 1980.

Oxorn, H. and Foote, W. *Human Labor and Birth.* New York, NY: Appleton-Century-Crofts, 1977.

Page, E., Villee, C., and Villee, D. *Human Reproduction.* Philadelphia, PA: Saunders, 1976, pp. 291-321.

Panuthos, Claudia. *Transformation Through Birth.* South Habley, MA: Bergin and Garvey, 1984.

Parfitt, Rebecca Rowe. *The Birth Primer.* Philadelphia, PA: Running, 1977.

Paul, B. *Health, Culture, and Community.* New York, NY: Sage, 1955.

Peterson, Gayle H. *Birthing Normally.* Berkeley, CA: Mindbody, 1981.

Phillipp, E. *Childbirth—A Complete Guide to Every Problem.* Glasgow: Fontana/Collins, 1978.

Powell, John. *Why Am I Afraid to Tell You Who I Am?* Allen, TX: Argus, 1969.

_____ . *The Secret of Staying in Love.* Allen, TX: Argus, 1974.

_____ . *Why Am I Afraid to Love?* Allen, TX: Argus, 1972.

Pritchard, Jack A. and MacDonald, Paul C. *Williams Obstetrics.* 15th ed., New York, NY: Appleton-Century-Crofts, 1976.

Pryor, K. *Nursing Your Baby.* New York, NY: Pocket, 1973.

Raphael, Dana. *The Tender Gift: Breastfeeding.* New York, NY: Shocken Books, 1978.

Reeder, S. J., Mastroianni, L., and Martin, L. L. *Maternity Nursing.* 14th ed., Philadelphia, PA: Lippincott, 1980.

Ribble, Margaret. *The Rights of Infants.* 2nd ed., New York, NY: Columbia University, 1965.

Richardson, Stephen A. *Childbearing—Its Social and Psychological Aspects.* Baltimore, MD: Williams and Wilkins, 1976.

Rokeach, M. *Beliefs, Attitudes, and Values—A Theory of Organization and Change.* San Francisco, CA: Tossey-Bass, 1970.

Romalis, Shelly, ed. *Childbirth: Alternatives to Medical Control.* Austin, TX: University of Texas, 1981.

Rothman, Barbara Katz. *In Labor—Woman and Power in the Birthplace.* New York, NY: Norton, 1982.

Sandberg, E. *Synopsis of Obstetrics,* 10th ed., St. Louis, MO: Mosby, 1978.

Schaeffer, Edith. *Commonsense Christian Living.* Nashville, TN: Nelson, 1983.

_____ . *Lifelines: The Ten Commandments for Today.* Westchester, IL: Crossway Books, 1983.

_____ . *Affliction.* Old Tappan, NJ: Revell, 1978.

_____ . *A Way of Seeing.* Old Tappan, NJ: Revell, 1977.

_____ . *What Is a Family?* Old Tappan, NJ: Revell, 1975.

Schaeffer, Francis. *Genesis in Space and Time.* Glendale, CA: Regal, 1972.

Schaeffer, Francis and Koop, C. Everett. *Whatever Happened to the Human Race?* Old Tappan, NJ: Revell, 1979.

Sears, William. *Creative Parenting.* New York, NY: Everest, 1982.

Smedes, Lewis B. *Sex for Christians.* Grand Rapids, MI: Eerdmans, 1976.

Stanway, P. and Stanway, A. *Breast Is Best—A Common Sense Approach to Breastfeeding.* London: Pan, 1978.

Sternbach, R. A. *Pain: A Psychophysiological Analysis.* New York, NY: Academic, 1968.

_____ . *The Psychology of Pain.* New York, NY: Raven, 1978.

Sumner, P. E. and Phillips, C. R. *Birthing Rooms—Concept and Reality.* St. Louis, MO: Mosby, 1981.

Trobisch, Ingrid and Roetzer, Elizabeth. *An Experience of Love—Understanding Natural Family Planning.* Old Tappan, NJ: Revell, 1981.

Trobisch, I. *The Joy of Being a Woman.* New York, NY: Harper & Row, 1975.

Trobisch, Walter. *I Married You.* New York, NY: Harper & Row, 1971.

_____ . *I Loved a Girl.* London: Lutterworth, 1970.

_____ . *Love Yourself: Self-Acceptance and Depression.* Downers Grove, IL: InterVarsity, 1976.

Vellay, P. *Childbirth without Pain.* New York, NY: Dutton, 1960.

Vitz, Paul C. *Psychology as Religion—The Cult of Self-Worship.* Grand Rapids, MI: Eerdmans, 1977.

Ward, Ted. *Values Begin at Home.* Wheaton, IL: Victor Books, 1979.

Welter, Paul. *The Family: Stronger after Crisis.* Wheaton, IL: Tyndale, 1982.

_____ . *How to Help a Friend.* Wheaton, IL: Tyndale, 1978.

Wertz, Richard and Wertz, Dorothy. *Lying-In: A History of Childbirth in America.* New York, NY: Free Press, 1977.

Wessel, Helen. *Natural Childbirth and*

the Christian Family. Rev. ed., New York, NY: Harper & Row, 1983.

_____. *Under the Apple Tree: Marrying-Birthing-Parenting.* Fresno, CA: Bookmates, 1981.

Wilson, C. Wilson and Hovey, W. Roe. *Cesarean Childbirth—A Handbook for Parents.* New York, NY: Doubleday, 1977.

Wolfensberger, Wolf. *Normalization.* National Institute of Mental Retardation. Toronto: York University, 1972.

Wolff, H. G. and Wolff, S. *Pain.* 2nd ed., Springfield, IL: 1958.

Worthington, B., Vermeersch, J., and Williams, S. R. *Nutrition in Pregnancy and Lactation.* St. Louis, MO: Mosby, 1977.

Wright, H. Norman. *The Pillars of Marriage.* Ventura, CA: Regal, 1979.

Wright, H. Norman and Inmon, Marvin N. *Preparing for Parenthood.* Ventura, CA: Regal, 1980.

Yancey, Philip. *Where Is God When It Hurts?* Grand Rapids, MI: Zondervan, 1977.

Young, Diony. *Bonding: How Parents Become Attached to Their Child.* Minneapolis, MN: 1978.

_____. *Changing Childbirth.* Rochester, NY: Childbirth Graphics, 1982.

Young, D., ed. *Obstetrical Intervention and Technology in the 80's.* New York, NY: Hawthorn, 1982.

MAGAZINES

Astbury, J. 1980. Labor pain: The role of childbirth education information and expectation. *Problems in Pain* W. C. Peck and M. Wallace, eds. London: Permagon.

Aubry, R. H., and J. C. Pennington. 1973. Identification and evaluation of high-risk pregnancy: The perinatal concept. *Clin. Obstet. Gynecol.* 161:3-27.

Beecher, H. K. 1956. Relationship of significance of wound to pain experienced. *JAMA* 161 (Aug):1609.

Blitz, B., and A. M. Dinnerstein. 1971. Role of attentional focus in pain perception. *Journ. Abnorm. Psych.* 77:42-45.

Brazelton, T. B. 1961. Psychophysiologic relations in the neonate: Effect of maternal medication. *J. Pediatr.* 58:513-18.

_____. 1970. Effect of prenatal drugs on the behavior of the neonate. *Am. J. Psychiat.* 126:95-100.

Burchell, R. C. and J. Gunn. 1980. The new birth experience. *JOGN Nurs.* July/Aug: 250-52.

Butani, P., and E. Hodnett. 1980. Mothers' perceptions of their labor experiences. *Mat. Child. Nurs.* J:72-82.

Butterfield, P. M., R. N. Emde, and B. B. Plate. 1978. Effects of silver nitrate on initial visual behavior. *Am. J. Dis. Child.* 132:426.

Caldeyro-Barcia, Roberto. 1975. Some consequences of obstetrical interference. *Birth and the Family* 2:34-38.

_____. 1979. The influence of maternal position on time of spontaneous rupture of the membranes, progress of labor and fetal head compression. *Birth and the Family* 6:7-15.

Campbell, A., and F. I. Worthington. 1982. Teaching expectant fathers to be better childbirth coaches. *Mat. Child. Nurs.* 7:28-32.

Cefalo, R. C. 1981. Improved analysis of monitoring can identify true fetal distress. *Ob. Gyn. News.* 16:3.

Cronenwett, L. 1974. Fathers' responses to childbirth. *Nurs. Res.* 3(May/June):210-17.

Davenport-Slack, B., and C. H. Boylan. 1974. Psychological correlates of childbirth pain. *Psychosom. Med.* 36:215-22.

Dick-Read, G. 1946. Correlations and emotional phenomena of natural labor. *Obstet. Gynaecol. Br. Empire.* 53:55-61.

Dobbs, K. B., and K. K. Shy. 1981. Alternative birth rooms and birth options. *Obstet. Gynecol.* 58:626-30.

Doering, S. G., and D. R. Entwisle. 1975. Preparation during pregnancy and ability to cope with labor and delivery. *Am. J. Orthopsychiatry* 45:825-37.

Flynn, A., et al. 1978. Ambulation in labor. *Br. Med. J.* 2:591-93.

Goodlin, R. C. 1980. Low-risk obstetric care for low-risk mothers. *Lancet* 1:1017-19.

Gulick, Elsie E. 1982. Informational correlates of successful breastfeeding. *MCN.* 7(Nov/Dec):370-75.

Highly, B., and R. Mercer. 1978. Safeguarding the laboring woman's sense of control. *MCN.* 3:39-41.

Hodnett, E. Patient control during labor: Effects of two types of fetal monitors. *JOGN Nurs.* 11:2, 94-99.

Holmes, T. H., and R. Rahe. 1967. Stress rating scale. *J. of Psychosom. Res.* 2:216.

Hughey, M. J., T. W. McElin, and T. Young. 1978. Maternal and fetal outcome of Lamaze-prepared patients. *Journ. of Ob. Gyn.* 6:643-47.

Huttel, F. A., et al. 1972. A quantitative evaluation of psychoprophylaxis in childbirth. *J. of Psychosom. Res.* 16:81-92.

International Childbirth Education Association. 1979. Amniotomy. *ICEA Review* 3:2.

_____. 1978. Maternal position during labor and birth. *ICEA Review* 2:3.

Johnson, J. 1973. Effects of accurate expectations about sensations on the sensory and distress components of pain. *Journ. of Personality and Social Psych.* 27:261-75.

Johnson, N. W. 1976. Breast-feeding at one hour of age. *MCN. Am. J. Mat. Child. Nurs.* Jan/Feb.

Klusman, L. 1975. Reduction of pain in childbirth by alleviation of anxiety during pregnancy. *Journ. of Consulting and Clinical Psych.* 42:162-65.

Kron, R. E. O., and K. E. Coddard. 1966. Newborn sucking behavior affected by obstetric sedation. *Pediatrics* 37:1012-17.

Livingston, J. C. 1979. Music for the childbearing family. *JOGN Nurs.* Nov/Dec:363-67.

Lubic, R. W. 1981. Alternative maternity care: Resistance and change. In *Childbirth Alternatives to Medical Control.* Shelley Romalis, ed. Austin, TX: University of Texas.

Magee, J. 1976. What the doctor learns about labor as a patient. *The Female Patient* 11(Dec):27-29.

Matthews, A. E. B. 1964. Reflections on the pain of labor. *Nurs. Mirror* 118:550-54.

Maynard, F. 1977. Home birth vs. hospital birth. *Woman's Day* June 28.

Meara, H. 1976. A way to successful breast-feeding in a nonsupportive culture. *J. Nurse-Midwifery* 21:20.

Mehl, L. 1976. Statistical outcomes of home birth in the United States: Current status. In *Safe Alternatives in Childbirth,* 1st ed. D. Stewart and L. Stewart, eds. Chapel Hill, SC: NAPSAC.

Melzack, R., and P. D. Wall. 1965. Pain mechanisms: A new theory. *Science* 150:971-79.

Mendez-Bauer, C., et al. 1975. Effects of standard position on spontaneous uterine contractility and other aspects of labor. *J. Perinat. Med.* 3:89.

Morris, N. 1960. Human relations in obstetric practice. *Lancet* 1:913.

Mulcahy, R. A., and N. Janz. 1973. Effectiveness of raising pain perception threshold in males and females using a psychoprophylactic childbirth technique during induced pain. *Nurs. Res.* 22:423-27.

Nettleblaat, P., C. F. Fagerstrom, and N. Uddenberg. 1976. The significance of reported childbirth pain. *J. of Psychosom. Res.* 20:212-21.

Pace, J. B. 1974. Psychophysiology of pain: Diagnostic and therapeutic implications. *J. Fam. Practice* 1(May):4.

Potter, H., and R. D. McDonald. 1971. Obstetric consequences of epidural anesthesia in multiparous patients. *Lancet* 1:1031-34.

Return of the Midwife. 1969. *Newsweek.* March 31:107.

Riordan, J., and B. A. Countryman. 1980. Basics of breast-feeding. *JOGN Nurs.* July/Aug:207-213; Sept/Oct:273-83.

Roberts, J. 1980. Alternative positions for childbirth. Part 1: First stage of labor. *J. Nurse-Midwifery* 25:11-18.

Roessler, R. 1973. Personality, physiology, and performance. *Psychophysiology* 10:315-27.

Rubin, R. 1968. Body image and self-esteem. *Nurs. Outlook* 16:20-23.

Sasmor, J. L., C. R. Castor, and P. Hassid. 1973. The childbirth team during labor. *Am. J. Nurs.* 73(March):444-47.

Scott, J. R., and N. B. Rose. 1976. Effect of psychoprophylaxis (Lamaze preparation) on labor and delivery in primiparas. *New England Journ. Med.* 22:1205-07.

Sosa, R., et al. 1980. The effect of a supportive labor companion on perinatal problems, length of labor, and mother-infant interaction. *New England Journ. Med.* 11:597-600.

Standley, K., et al. 1979. Dimensions of prenatal anxiety and its influence on pregnancy outcome. *Am. J. Obstet. Gynecol.* 135:22-26.

Stanton, M. E. 1979. The myth of natural childbirth. *J. Nurse-Midwifery* 24:25.

Stevens, R. J., and F. Heide. 1977. Analgesic characteristics of prepared childbirth techniques: Attention focusing and systematic relaxation. *J. Psychosom. Res.* 21:429-38.

Ulin, P. R. 1968. Changing techniques in psychoprophylactic preparation for childbirth. *Am. J. Nurs.* 68(Dec):2586-91.

Weisenberg, M. I. 1977. Pain and pain control. *Psychol. Bull.* 84:1008-44.

Willmurth, L. F. 1975. Prepared childbirth and the concept of control. *Nurs. Outlook*

Wolff, B. B., and S. Langley. 1968. Cultural factors and the response to pain: A review. *Amer. Anthropologist* 70:494-501.

Worthington, E., et al. Which prepared childbirth-coping techniques are effective? *JOGN Nurs.* 11:2, 45-51.

Yancey, P. 1984. Helping those in pain. *Leadership* 2(Spring):90-97.

Zax, M., et al. 1975. Childbirth education, maternal attitudes, and delivery. *Am. J. Obstet. Gynecol.* 123:185-90.

RECOMMENDED READING

PREGNANCY AND CHILDBIRTH

Debra Evans. *The Complete Book on Childbirth*. Wheaton, Ill.: Tyndale, 1986.

Tracy Hotchner. *Pregnancy & Childbirth: The Complete Guide for a New Life*. New York: Avon, 1984.

Sheila Kitzinger and Penny Simkin, eds. *Episiotomy and the Second Stage of Labor*. Seattle, Wash.: Pennypress, 1986.

Diana Korte and Roberta Scaer. *A Good Birth, A Safe Birth*, 2nd ed. New York: Bantam, 1984.

Gail Sforza Brewer and Janice Presser Greene. *Right from the Start*. Emmaus, Penn.: Rodale Press, 1981.

Penny Simkin, Janet Whaley, and Ann Keppler. *Pregnancy, Childbirth, and the Newborn*. Deephaven, Minn.: Meadowbrook Press, 1984.

David Stewart, ed. *The Five Standards for Safe Childbearing*. Marble Hill, Mo.: NAPSAC Reproductions, 1981.

Diony Young. *Changing Childbirth: Family Birth in the Hospital*. Rochester, N.Y.: Childbirth Graphics, 1982.

CURRENT ISSUES AND MOTHER-CHILD HEALTH

Yvonne Brackbill, June Rice, and Diony Young. *Birth Trap*. St. Louis, Mo.: C.V. Mosby, 1984.

Debra Evans. *Without Moral Limits: Women, Reproduction, and the New Medical Technology*. Westchester, Ill.: Crossway Books, 1989.

Alice Gilgoff. *Home Birth*, rev. ed. Granby, Mass.: Bergin & Garvey, 1989.

Doris Haire. *Cultural Warping of Childbirth*. Minneapolis, Minn.: ICEA, 1972.

Sally Inch. *Birthrights*. New York: Parthenon, 1984.

Brigitte Jordan. *Birth in Four Cultures*. Toronto: Eden Press, 1983.

Sheila Kitzinger and John A. Davis, eds. *The Place of Birth*. Oxford, England: Oxford University Press, 1978.

Rebecca Rowe Parfitt. *The Birth Primer*. Philadelphia: Running Press, 1977.

David and Lee Stewart, eds. *Compulsory Hospitalization: Freedom of Choice in Childbirth?* Marble Hill, Mo.: NAPSAC Reproductions, 1979.

—*Safe Alternatives in Childbirth*. Marble Hill, Mo.: NAPSAC Reproductions, 1976.

—*21st Century Obstetrics Now!* Vol. 1 and Vol. 2. Marble Hill, Mo.: NAPSAC Reproductions, 1977.

Charlotte and Fred Ward. *The Home Birth Book*. Garden City, N.Y.: Doubleday/Dolphin Books, 1977.

Richard and Dorothy Wertz. *Lying-In: A History of Childbirth in America*. New York: Free Press, 1977.

Excellent resources for information on maternity care alternatives are:

International Childbirth Education Association (ICEA), P.O. Box 20049, Minneapolis, MN 55420-0048.

International Association of Parents and Professionals for Safe Alternatives in Childbirth (NAPSAC), Rt. 1, P.O. Box 646, Marble Hill, MO 63764.

For cesarean prevention information write:

Cesarean Support, Education and Concern (C/SEC), 22 Forest Road, Framingham, MA 10701.

Cesarean Prevention Movement, P.O. Box 152, University Station, Syracuse, NY 13210.

BREASTFEEDING

Marvin Eiger and Sally Wendkos Olds. *The Complete Book of Breastfeeding*, 2nd ed. New York: Workman, 1987.

Kathleen Huggins. *The Nursing Mother's Companion*. Harvard, Mass.: Harvard Common Press, 1986.

La Leche League International. *The Womanly Art of Breastfeeding*, 4th ed. New York: Plume/New American Library, 1987.

Maureen Minchin. *Breastfeeding Matters*. N. Syndey, Australia: George Allen & Unwin, 1985.

Dana Raphael. *The Tender Gift: Breastfeeding*. Englewood Cliffs, N.J.: Prentice-Hall, 1973.

Jan Riordan. *A Practical Guide to Breastfeeding*. St. Louis, Mo.: C.V. Mosby, 1983.

Candace Woessner, Judith Lauwers, and Barbara Bernard. *Breastfeeding Today: The Mother's Companion*. Wayne, N.J.: Avery, 1987.

If you would like the name of a lactation consultant or breastfeeding center near you, contact:

International Lactation Consultant Association, P.O. Box 4031, University of Virginia Station, Charlottesville, VA 22903.

La Leche League International, 9616 Minneapolis Ave., Franklin Park, IL 60131.

NATURAL FAMILY PLANNING

Nona Aguilar. *The New, No-Pill, No-Risk Birth Control*. New York: Rawson, 1986.

Debra Evans. *The Mystery of Womanhood*. Westchester, Ill.: Crossway Books, 1987.

Sheila and John Kippley. *The Art of Natural Family Planning*, 3rd ed. Cincinnati: Couple to Couple League, 1984.

For more information on obtaining a natural family planning Home Study Kit, call or write: *The Couple to Couple League,* Dept. 43, P.O. Box 111184, Cincinnati, OH 45211, (513) 661-7612.

NOTE: Many of these books may be obtained through your local library or ordered through the International Childbirth Education Association at the address above or by calling the ICEA Bookcenter at 1-800-624-4934. ICEA offers a wide variety of educational materials and programs to assist expectant parents in obtaining high-quality, family-oriented maternity care.

GLOSSARY OF TERMS

Abdomen: The portion of the body containing the stomach, intestines, bowels, bladder, and uterus.

Abdominal wall: The muscles that form a corsetlike structure from the pubic bone to the ribs and breastbone, and from side to side across the abdomen.

Abruptio placentae: The premature separation of the placenta from the uterine wall.

Active labor: Regular uterine contractions that are associated with increasing dilation of the cervix and the descent of the baby.

Afterbirth: A term used for the placenta, amniotic sac, and umbilical cord.

Afterpains: Cramplike postpartum contractions usually lasting up to forty-eight hours, resulting from the efforts of the uterus to expel the afterbirth and prevent bleeding from the placental site.

Albumin: A simple protein in all animal tissues that may be present in maternal urine during pregnancy.

Alveoli: The milk glands in the breast that secrete milk when stimulated by the hormone prolactin.

Amniocentesis: The removal of amniotic fluid with a syringe for diagnostic or therapeutic purposes.

Amnion: A thin, transparent, tough sac which holds the baby in amniotic fluid. (Syn. with *amniotic sac, bag of waters*.)

Amniotic fluid: A clear to slightly cloudy fluid that protects the baby from injury in the uterus, helps to maintain an even temperature, and prevents the adhesion of the amniotic sac to the baby's skin.

Amniotomy: The artificial rupture of the amniotic sac performed by a physician.

Analgesia: The absence of a normal sense of pain, produced by chemical, psychological, or other means.

Analgesic: A drug that relieves pain but does not induce a loss of consciousness.

Anemia: A condition in which there is a reduction in the proportion of red corpuscles in the blood, thereby reducing the capacity of the blood to carry oxygen to body tissues.

Anesthesia: The partial or total loss of sensation, with or without a loss of consciousness.

Anesthetic: A drug or gas that produces partial or complete insensitivity to pain.

Antepartum: The time before the baby is born. This term is also applied to the labor and delivery functions and staff of a hospital.

Anterior position: The crown of the baby's head is facing toward the mother's abdomen as it descends into her pelvis.

Anus: The opening of the rectum between the buttocks.

Apgar score: A means of evaluating a newborn baby's breathing, heart rate, muscle tone, reflexes, and color at one, five, and ten minutes after birth. Each of the five categories is assigned a value of 0, 1, or 2. A score of 7–10 is normal; 6 or less means that the baby requires medical assistance.

Areola: The pigmented ring of skin on the breast around the nipple.

Back labor: The condition during labor that results from the pressure of the baby's presenting part against the back of the mother's pelvis.

Bag of waters: See *Amnion*.

Ballotement: A term used to refer to the rebounding of the baby's head away from the examining finger of the nurse or physician. This indicates that the baby has not yet settled into the pelvis.

Bearing down reflex: The involuntary pushing effort of the uterus during the second stage of labor.

Bilirubin: A waste product of broken-down red blood cells, normally converted into a nontoxic substance by the liver before being excreted from the body. A high bilirubin level in the newborn results in jaundice.

Birth: The process by which the baby is expelled or removed from the mother's uterus and begins life outside the mother. This takes place about nine months or 266 days after conception, or 280 days after the date of the last menstrual period.

Birth canal: The term applied to the structure formed by the vagina and uterus when the cervix is completely dilated in the second stage of labor.

Blastocyst: The ovum during its second week of development when it is a hollow ball of cells.

Bradycardia: A slow heart rate. In the unborn baby and newborn, this refers to a rate less than 120 beats per minute.

Braxton-Hicks contractions: Intermittent contractions of the uterus occurring throughout pregnancy that do not produce changes in the cervix and may not be noticeable until the last month.

Breast pump: A device that is used to draw milk from the breasts.

Breech presentation: The presentation of the buttocks instead of the head during childbirth.

Brow presentation: The presentation of the brow toward the cervix during labor, caused by the baby's chin being up rather than pressed toward the chest.

Caput: The baby's head.

Caput succedaneum: A temporary swelling on the baby's head.

Carpal tunnel syndrome: Loss of normal sensation and tingling of the fingers due to pressure on the inside of the wrist. During pregnancy, it is caused by fluid retention.

Catheter: A thin, plastic tube inserted into the bladder through the urethra to drain urine, or into the epidural space in order to inject an anesthetic.

Centimeters: The unit of measure used to describe cervical dilation.

Cephalic presentation: The presentation of the head during childbirth.

Cephalopelvic disproportion (C.P.D.): The condition in which the baby's head is larger than the space of the mother's pelvis.

Certified nurse-midwife: A registered nurse who is a graduate of an approved training program and who has passed a certification examination.

Cervix: The lower necklike segment of the uterus.

Cesarean birth/cesarean section: The birth of a baby

through an incision in the abdominal and uterine walls.

Chorion: The outermost membrane surrounding the baby and the placenta.

Chromosomes: Small, rodlike bodies found in the nucleus of every human cell. These structures normally occur in pairs of twenty-three and contain the genetic material of the cell.

Circumcision: The surgical removal of the foreskin of the penis.

Coccyx: The tailbone.

Codeine: An addictive painkilling substance derived from opium.

Colostrum: The substance that precedes the production of milk, rich in proteins and high in antibodies.

Conception: The fertilization of the egg by a sperm that initiates the growth of a human being and triggers the onset of pregnancy.

Congenital: Present at birth.

Contraction: A unit of work performed by a muscle over a period of time. In labor, uterine muscles contract to dilate the cervix and press the baby out of the mother's body.

Corpus luteum: A term meaning "yellow body" that describes the small secretory structure that develops within a ruptured ovarian follicle after an ovum is released.

Crowning: The time during the second stage of labor when the largest part of the baby's head appears in the vagina and does not recede between contractions.

Cystitis: Inflammation of the bladder and urinary tract.

Demerol: An analgesic drug.

Diaphragm: A rubber cup that fits over the cervix as a barrier method of contraception. Also, the muscular membrane that separates the lungs from the abdomen.

Dilation: The stretching open of the cervix brought about by uterine contractions during labor.

Doppler: A form of ultrasound used to listen and measure the baby's heart rate.

Eclampsia: A now rare condition of late pregnancy characterized by high blood pressure, severe headaches, visual interference, and convulsions.

Edema: The presence of an excessive amount of fluid in body tissues. Also referred to as fluid retention.

Effacement: The thinning and shortening of the cervix, measured in terms of a percentage.

Elective induction of labor: Induction of labor for convenience rather than due to medical indications.

Electrode: A small electrical conductor used to monitor the baby's heart rate directly during labor.

Electronic fetal monitoring (E.F.M.): The continuous monitoring of the baby's heart rate through a transducer positioned on the mother's abdomen, by telemetry, or via an electrode inserted through the cervix and attached to the baby's scalp.

Embryo: The term used to describe the baby between the second and twelfth week of its development.

Endometrium: The lining of the inner surface of the uterus.

Enema: The injection of fluids into the rectum to empty the lower intestine.

Engagement: The entrance of the presenting part of the baby into the midpelvis.

Engorgement: Distension of the breasts with milk.

Epidural: Regional anesthesia produced by injected medication through a catheter into the epidural space of the lower spine.

Episiotomy: The incision of the perineum at the end of the second stage of labor.

Estriol: A form of estrogen found in the urine or blood during late pregnancy.

Estrogen: A hormone secreted by the ovary and placenta throughout the menstrual cycle and pregnancy.

Face presentation: The presentation of the baby's face toward the cervix during labor.

Fallopian tube: The duct that conveys the ovum from the ovary to the uterus.

False labor: Braxton-Hicks contractions that mimic labor in their intensity.

Fertilization: See *Conception*.

Fetal distress: A term used to describe a shortage of oxygen to the baby resulting in a disrupted heart rate.

Fetus: The term applied to the baby after the twelfth week of pregnancy until birth.

Folic acid: A form of vitamin B that is vital to the production of blood cells and hemoglobin, especially during pregnancy.

Fontanels: The soft spots lying between the unjoined sections of the baby's skull.

Forceps: An instrument used to hold the presenting part and extract the baby from the vagina.

Foremilk: The milk that collects in the ducts behind the nipple between feedings and is lower in fat than the hindmilk.

Fundal massage: Massage of the uterus during the fourth stage of labor to assist the uterus in contracting and controlling bleeding.

Fundal palpation: Checking the height of the uterus by feeling it through the abdominal wall.

Fundus: The rounded portion of the uterus from which contractions originate.

Gene: The basic unit of heredity on a chromosome.

Gestation: The period between fertilization and birth.

Glucose: A sugar found in the blood that supplies energy to the baby.

Gravida: A pregnant woman.

Gynecologist: A physician who specializes in the problems of the female sexual and reproductive organs.

Hemoglobin: The iron-containing pigment of red blood cells where oxygen is stored.

Hemorrhage: Excessive bleeding.

Hemorrhoids: Swollen veins around the rectum.

Hormones: Chemical substances that stimulate various organs to act in specific ways.

Human chorionic gonadotropin (HCG): The hormone secreted by the chorion measured during a pregnancy test through urine.

Hypertension: High blood pressure; in pregnancy, a blood pressure above 140/90.

Hyperventilation: An imbalance between carbon dioxide and oxygen in the bloodstream created by overbreathing.

Implantation: Embedding of the developing baby into the lining of the uterus.

Induction of labor: The artificial production of labor.

Intravenous feeding (IV): The introduction of fluids, medications, or other substances into the body through a thin plastic tube inserted into a vein.

Intubation: Insertion of a tube into any hollow organ, as into the larynx or trachea.

Invasive techniques: Any medical procedure that invades the boundaries of the body.

Involution: The return of the uterus to its normal size after pregnancy.

Jaundice: A common condition of newborn infants in